Educational Opportunity Guide
A Directory of Programs for the Gifted

2003 Edition

Duke University
Talent Identification Program
1121 West Main Street, Suite 100
Durham, NC 27701
www.tip.duke.edu

Copyright © 2003/TIP—Duke University Talent Identification Program.
All rights reserved.

The *Educational Opportunity Guide: A Directory of Programs for the Gifted* is published annually by the Duke University Talent Identification Program (TIP), a non-profit organization dedicated to serving academically talented youth.

ISBN 0-9639756-9-2

Price: $15.00

For more information on TIP's programs and publications contact:
Duke University Talent Identification Program
1121 West Main Street, Suite 100
Durham, NC 27701
(919) 683-1400; Fax: (919) 683-1742
E-mail: info@tip.duke.edu
Web site: http://www.tip.duke.edu

INTRODUCTION

The *Educational Opportunity Guide: A Directory of Programs for the Gifted* is a directory of educational programs for academically talented students of all ages. It provides information on over 400 programs conducted at schools, colleges, and camps throughout the country and abroad. The guide is published annually by the Duke University Talent Identification Program (TIP), a nonprofit organization dedicated to serving academically talented youth.

Specific dates and costs for programs in this edition are for 2003. Except for minor editorial changes, the program descriptions appear as submitted by program directors. Because TIP has neither the staff nor the resources to evaluate the programs listed, **inclusion in the guide does not imply endorsement by the Duke University Talent Identification Program.** Students and parents are urged to carefully evaluate any program that interests them.

The Special Advertisement section at the beginning of the directory is intended to supplement, not replace, the basic information that is included in the main section. All programs listed in the main section were given the option to be included in the advertisements.

A Regional Talent Search section following the Special Advertisements describes the programs administered by TIP and three other regional talent searches. Also listed are Cooperative Programs administered by universities working cooperatively with TIP.

Listings in the guide are arranged alphabetically by the state and city where the program is offered. Contact information for the State Director and State Association are found at the beginning of each chapter. These contacts serve as an invaluable resource concerning services for gifted students.

It is our hope that the 2003 *Educational Opportunity Guide* will serve both gifted students and those committed to developing their potential. Special thanks to Joy Baldwin, Bailey Craft, Beth Cross, Kristen Stephens, and other members of the TIP staff for their assistance.

Elizabeth J. Simmons
Editor

Acknowledgments: *Duke University gratefully recognizes the following contributors* for their recent support of the Talent Identification Program:*

Dr. and Mrs. William Bevan (Bevan Scholars, The Robert N. and Katherine H. Sawyer Teaching Fellowship, The Elizabeth M. Bevan Memorial Scholarship, and The Hildegarde F. Chorpening Memorial Endowment Fund); Mr. and Mrs. M. Gregory Bostian; Harriette and Wiley Bourne, Sr.; Mr. and Mrs. Clyde F. Boyles; Doris B. Bryant (The Sunshine Lady Foundation); The E. Rhodes and Leona B. Carpenter Foundation; Jack Kent Cooke Foundation; Duke Club of North Texas; J. Patrick Emington Fund; The Mary Whiting Ewing Foundation; Mr. and Mrs. William A. Gilbert; The Glaxo Wellcome Foundation; Ramon Griffin Memorial Endowment; The Bruce J. Heim Foundation; Hillsdale Fund, Inc.; Hoechst Celanese Corporation; Mr. and Mrs. Glenn Infinger; Bernard A. and Roberta G. Lublin Endowment; John D. and Catherine T. MacArthur Foundation; Mr. and Mrs. Lew S. McGinnis; Barbara S. McHugh; MODEC International, LLC; Drs. Richard and Vinnie Morris; Jacqueline Anne Morris Endowment; Mrs. Sandy Myerson (The Paul J. Myerson, MD, Memorial Scholarship); Robert and Katherine Penn; Gordon E. Stanley; Robert J. Striffler; Mr. and Mrs. Steve Stroud; Joel F. Sussman; Ronald S. Temple Endowment; Alison Bracey von Brock Endowments; and Mr. S.M. Werner and Ms. A. Isaacson.

*This list represents donors who have made a contribution of $1,000 or more.

TABLE OF CONTENTS

Selecting the Right Prograam for your Child, iii

Special Advertisements, iv

Regional Talent Searches, 1
Duke University Talent Identification Program (TIP), 2
Center for Talent Development at Northwestern University, 3
Center for Talented Youth at The Johns Hopkins University, 4
Rocky Mountain Talent Search at the University of Denver, 5

Multiple Locations, 7
Alabama, 14
Alaska, 20
Arizona, 21
Arkansas, 24
California, 26
Colorado, 38
Connecticut, 42
Delaware, 52
District of Columbia, 54
Florida, 56
Georgia, 72
Hawaii, 81
Idaho, 81
Illinois, 82
Indiana, 88
Iowa, 91
Kansas, 95
Kentucky, 97
Louisiana, 102
Maine, 106
Maryland, 109
Massachusetts, 112
Michigan, 130
Minnesota, 136
Mississippi, 141
Missouri, 145
Montana, 150
Nebraska, 151
Nevada, 153
New Hampshire, 154
New Jersey, 157
New Mexico, 161
New York, 163
North Carolina, 170
North Dakota, 192
Ohio, 196
Oklahoma, 199
Oregon, 203
Pennsylvania, 207
Rhode Island, 214
South Carolina, 215
South Dakota, 224
Tennessee, 225
Texas, 233
Utah, 249
Vermont, 250
Virginia, 252
Washington, 263
West Virginia, 266
Wisconsin, 270
Wyoming, 272
Study Abroad, 273

Program Descriptions

Resources
National Associations for the Gifted, 291
National Scholarships for the Gifted, 291
Select Readings, 292
Directories of Educational Programs, 292
Internet Resources, 293
Independent Study Opportunities, 294
Academic Competitions and Activities, 295

Index, 297

SELECTING THE RIGHT PROGRAM FOR YOUR CHILD

With so many programs from which to choose, how do you find the perfect match for your child? While the task may seem at bit overwhelming initially, there are several factors to consider when reviewing potential programs.

1. What is the program's philosophy?
Be sure to select a program that has a philosophy consistent with your family values. For example, is the program competitive in nature or cooperative? Secular or affiliated with a religious organization?

2. Is the program residential or commuter?
Is your child mature enough to be away from home? What benefits would your child receive from participating in a residential program as opposed to a commuter program?

3. How is the program organized?
Does the program provide a balance between academic and social activities? Does the program have clearly stated goals and do they match the goals you and your child have? Are your child's interests and abilities reflected in the program? What is the teacher to student ratio in most classes?

4. What are the staff characteristics?
What are the qualifications of the teachers who will be working with your child? Are they familiar with the educational needs of students with special abilities and talents? What training have they received regarding the learning needs of gifted students?

5. What additional resources are available within the program?
Is there access to a library, computers, and other materials needed for a positive learning experience?

6. How are students evaluated?
How is student progress communicated? Are a variety of methods used? How often are students evaluated both formally and informally?

7. What are the rules?
Is adequate supervision provided? How are behavior problems addressed?

8. Is the program free from bias?
Are the special needs of girls, minorities, and students with disabilities addressed? Will there be staff that can serve as role models for my child?

It is suggested that you involve your child in seeking the answers to the above questions and selecting an appropriate program. A successful experience will more likely occur if your child finds the selected program engaging and rewarding.

Firespark!

The School for Gifted Students
"the best two weeks of your life"

Our 26th Year
July 20 – August 2, 2003

Firespark is
* A hands–on program taught by practicing professionals
* Outstanding facilities and equipment
* 120 hours of instructional time plus 15 hours of studio or rehearsal time during the two weeks
* Professional entertainment & student performances
* Studies in Art and Design, Music, Drama, Dance, Communication and Business

Learn more at www.firespark.org or phone us at
(800) 252-5119 or (770) 534-6741

Firespark is a coeducational program sponsored by
Brenau University, Gainesville, GA 30501

Please see listing on page 76 for complete information.

SPECIAL ADVERTISEMENTS

EXCEPTIONAL MINDS DESERVE CREDIT.

SMU COLLEGE EXPERIENCE PROGRAM
ACCELERATED LEARNING FOR 11TH & 12TH GRADERS

Exceptional students have the opportunity to get a head start on college. SMU's College Experience program offers qualified students the opportunity to expand their academic horizons and earn six hours of college credit. For five weeks, students live on campus, learn from experienced SMU faculty, and participate in a variety of social activities. Come see what college is all about – June 29-July 31, 2003.

To learn more and apply, contact us at
214.768.0123 *or* www.smu.edu/ce

SMU will not discriminate on the basis of race, color, religion, national origin, sex, age, disability, or veteran status.

Please see listing on page 238 for complete information.

SPECIAL ADVERTISEMENTS vii

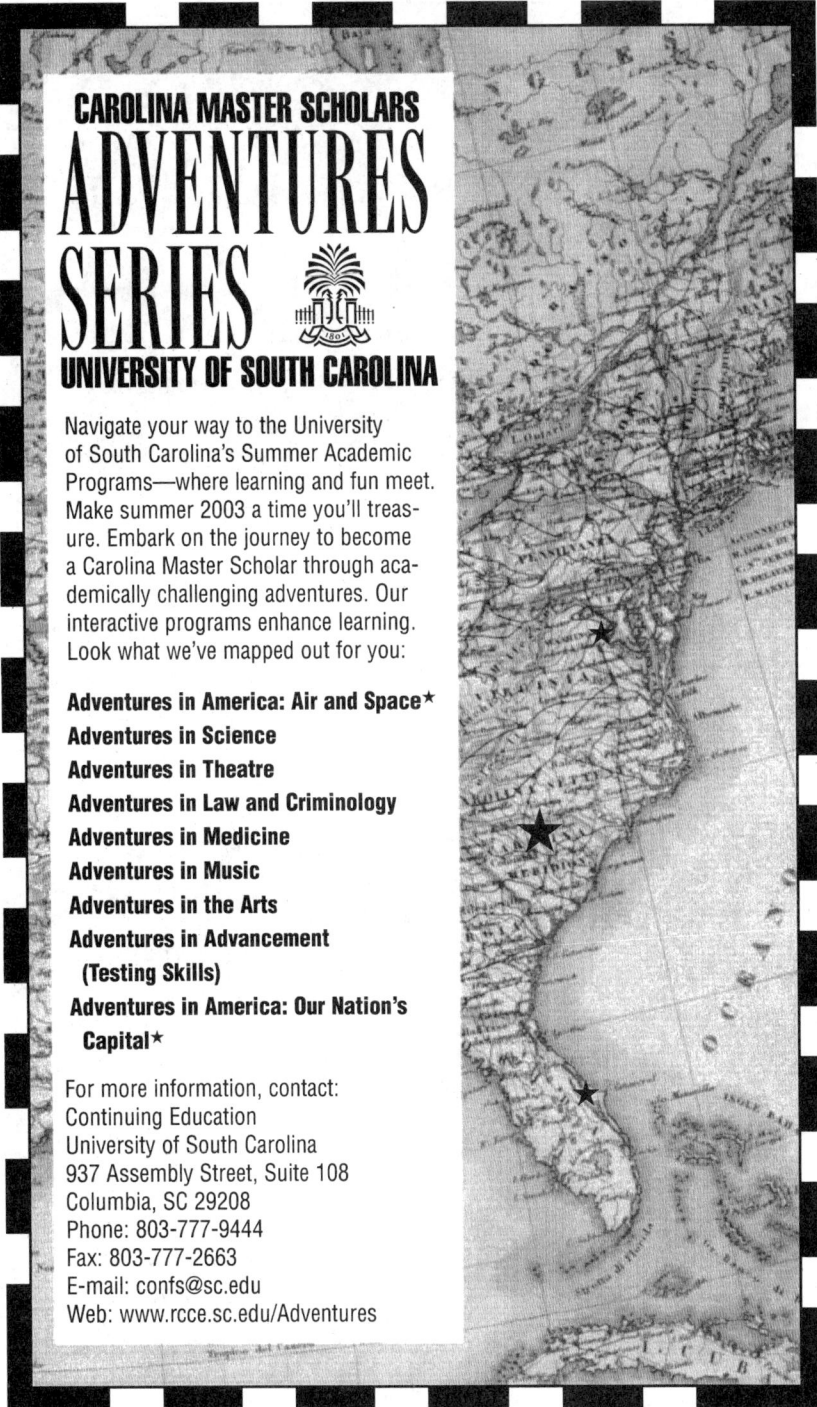

Please see listing on page 219 for complete information.

SPECIAL ADVERTISEMENTS

CHRIST SCHOOL
HEADMASTER'S SCHOLARSHIP

You know a boy with the natural gifts of leadership, character and intellect. All that boy needs to grow into his destiny is a chance…

Think about that boy you know.
Call or write for information today.

Do you know the boy we're looking for?

Christ School is an Episcopal affiliated, college preparatory, boarding and day school for boys, grades 8-12 with a 500 acre wooded campus near Asheville and the Blue Ridge Mountains.

Christ School
500 Christ School Road
Arden, NC 28704
828-684-6232 ext. 106
www.christschool.org

Please see listing on page 170 for complete information.

Parents of Gifted Students want the best in Educational Opportunities for their Children

The Advanced Academy of Georgia
at the State University of West Georgia

The Advanced Academy provides an early transition to college for carefully selected rising high school juniors and seniors who wish to enroll in an enriched residential college program while completing high school graduation requirements.

Advantages:
- Academic enrichment through challenging courses in the Honors College
- Live and learn with other similarly motivated young people from diverse backgrounds
- Enroll in regularly scheduled college classes and receive up to two years of college credit while completing high school graduation requirements
- Study from a broad curriculum taught by excellent university faculty
- Develop leadership skills and intellectual abilities through specialized programs and seminars

Requirements:
- SAT Verbal minimum of 580 (ACT English 25)
- SAT Math minimum of 530 (ACT Math 22)
- SAT Composite minimum of 1150 (ACT Composite 25)
- Minimum high school GPA of 3.5 (Academic Coursework only)
- Recommendations from high school teachers and counselor or principal

For information contact:
Ms. Susan Colgate, Director
The Advanced Academy of Georgia
Carrollton, GA 30118
770-836-4449
scolgate@westga.edu

Please see listing on page 74 for complete information.

SPECIAL ADVERTISEMENTS

The Cambridge at University
Cambridge, England

The Cambridge College Programme, which takes place at the oldest colleges of the University of Cambridge, situated on the River Cam in the historic centre of Cambridge, is the *oldest established teen program at the University*, and the *only* program at either Oxford or Cambridge where students are taught *only* by lecturers associated with the University. *Established in 1986.*

The Mathematical Bridge at Queens' College, attributed to Sir Isaac Newton.

Highlights of the 3-week July/August Programme:
- Certificate of attendance, and a written evaluation from each course professor for the student's high school or college file. Students may negotiate for credit at their high school or college.
- Morning choice of course in Archaeology, Astrophysics, Chemistry, 3 Law courses, Chivalry, Economics, Egyptology, Literary Villains, Art History, two Physics courses, International Relations, WW II, two Shakespeare courses, 3 Psychology courses, 2 Philosophy courses, Political Theory, Cambridge Scientific Discoveries, Biomedical Ethics, 2 Writing courses, Photography, Veterinary Medicine, or British Monarchy.
- Afternoon choice of course in Architecture, Austen, Marine Biology, British Espionage, Ice Age Art, 2 History courses, Criminal Law, Latin, Debate, 2 Math courses, Philosophy, Photography, Political Theory, 3 Physics courses, Religion, DNA, Evolution, Economics, Hitchcock, Studio Art, Churchill, Egyptology, Drama, Tibetan Buddhism, 2 Writing courses, Aarchaeology, or 3 Psychology courses.
- British History course for all students as a group, with lectures and excursions to historic sites in and around Cambridge.
- Three excursions to London for sites, museums and theatre, and day trips to the Roman city of Bath, Stonehenge, Warwick Castle, Stratford-upon-Avon.
- Theatre in London, including two plays in the West End, and a Shakespearen play in Stratford-Upon-Avon.
- Organized games of lawn tennis, quoits, basketball, rugby, cricket, lacrosse, soccer, croquet, ultimate frisbee, field hockey, football, squash, badminton, lacrosse, and volleyball, plus golf, rowing and punting on the River Cam, running, swimming, yoga, ice skating, and use of weights room and multigym.
- Ballroom, Irish, hip hop and salsa dancing; checkers, backgammon,

Professor Stephen Hawking meeting students at his office in Cambridge

Please see listing on page 274 for complete information.

SPECIAL ADVERTISEMENTS   xi

College Programme LLC of Cambridge
High School Students

Excursion to Stonehenge

"When such a program can be had at an academic legend the caliber of Queens' College... it's an experience one should consider without hesitation..."
—EXCELLENCE, A Magazine for Honor Students

"An adventure and life experience that will enrich each student's being forever."
—THE PHYSICIAN'S GUIDE TO QUALITY

bridge and chess games
- Evening movies, concerts, James Bond party, Shakespeare Festival of plays in college gardens, planetarium visits, polo matches, and bell-ringing demonstrations.
- Single or double rooms in dormitories with live-in Director and Deputy

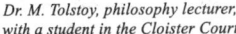

Dr. M. Tolstoy, philosophy lecturer, with a student in the Cloister Court

Directors.
- Optional theatre, orchestra or choir participation.
- Optional SAT review (5 classes).
- Optional one-week trip to Paris after the Programme.

The Daily Schedule:

7:30-8:45am	Self-service breakfast
9-10:30am	Elected class
11-11:30am	Announcements; sign-up for evening activity
11:30-12:30	British Cultural History lecture
12:30-2pm	Lunch, study time
2-3:30pm	Elected class
3:30-5:15pm	Study time
4-6pm	Optional SAT Review (first week), orchestra, choir or theatre, or golf lessons
4:30-7:15pm	Dinner
7:30pm	Supervised evening activities
9:30-11:30pm	Study hours

Fees:
The charge for students, including a room in a dormitory, breakfast and dinners while on campus, tuition, theatre, excursions, scheduled transportation to and from London airports, entrance fees, linen and daily maid service, is $5295. SAT course $450. Paris trip $1700. Golf instruction $250.

U.S. Office: Ms. Taryn Edwards, Director
Brochures and Inquiries
The John Hancock Building,
175 E. Delaware Pl., Chicago, IL 60611
(312) 787-7477, (800) 922-3552
Fax: (312) 988-7268

Please see listing on page 274 for complete information.

SPECIAL ADVERTISEMENTS

Please see listing on page 79 for complete information.

Please see listing on page 73 for complete information.

SPECIAL ADVERTISEMENTS

PLATO. SHAKESPEARE.
LEWIS & CLARK. VAN GOGH.
CLASSROOM REGULARS
SINCE 1900.

For each and every student, we have created a curriculum of core subjects highly valued by America's top colleges and universities.

For over a hundred years, Asheville School has offered high school students an education that prepares them for college, as well as all the years that follow. We offer each boarding and day student the chance to belong to a community built on a foundation of academic excellence, mutual respect, and shared values.

The only way to truly appreciate Asheville School is to experience it. Arrange a tour. Talk with our faculty, students, and alumni. We can't say with certainty whether Asheville School is right for you. But we invite you to find out for yourself what's best for your family, and your child's future.

360 Asheville School Road
Asheville, NC 28806

828.254.6345 • www.ashevilleschool.org • admission@ashevilleschool.org

Please see listing on page 171 for complete information.

SPECIAL ADVERTISEMENTS   xv

What do you get when you combine two parts hydrogen and one part oxygen then agitate? WHITE WATER.

For over 100 years Asheville School has provided exceptional education for high school students across the United States. It seemed natural to us that with 300 acres of forested mountains in Western North Carolina that we should create an equally exceptional summer program.

So we did.

Combining the spirit of summer camp with the rigors of the classroom, Asheville School's Summer Academic Adventures is the best of both worlds. It is a three-week program designed for academically talented students entering grades 7 through 10 who enjoy engaging classes and fantastic adventures. Mornings are spent studying the humanities, mathematics, science, art, and computer technology. Afternoons are spent playing games and sports, or whitewater rafting rafting, kayaking, rock climbing, and hiking in the great outdoors.

For more information, please contact us and we'll send you a catalogue with course and program information.

SUMMER ACADEMIC ADVENTURES
Asheville School

Call us at 828-254-6345.
Or reach us on the web at:
www.ashevilleschool.org.

Please see listing on page 172 for complete information.

Please see listing on page 175 for complete information.

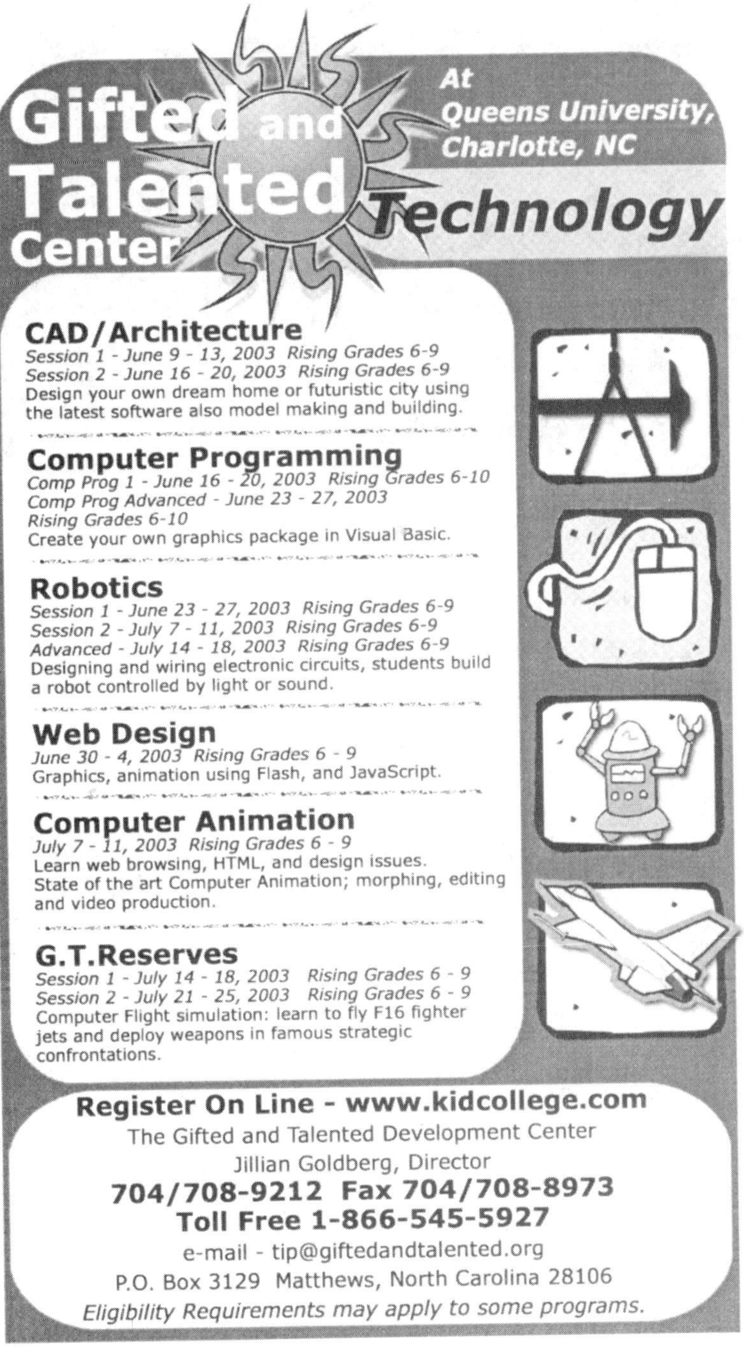

Gifted and Talented Center Technology
At Queens University, Charlotte, NC

CAD/Architecture
Session 1 - June 9 - 13, 2003 Rising Grades 6-9
Session 2 - June 16 - 20, 2003 Rising Grades 6-9
Design your own dream home or futuristic city using the latest software also model making and building.

Computer Programming
Comp Prog 1 - June 16 - 20, 2003 Rising Grades 6-10
Comp Prog Advanced - June 23 - 27, 2003 Rising Grades 6-10
Create your own graphics package in Visual Basic.

Robotics
Session 1 - June 23 - 27, 2003 Rising Grades 6-9
Session 2 - July 7 - 11, 2003 Rising Grades 6-9
Advanced - July 14 - 18, 2003 Rising Grades 6-9
Designing and wiring electronic circuits, students build a robot controlled by light or sound.

Web Design
June 30 - 4, 2003 Rising Grades 6 - 9
Graphics, animation using Flash, and JavaScript.

Computer Animation
July 7 - 11, 2003 Rising Grades 6 - 9
Learn web browsing, HTML, and design issues. State of the art Computer Animation; morphing, editing and video production.

G.T. Reserves
Session 1 - July 14 - 18, 2003 Rising Grades 6 - 9
Session 2 - July 21 - 25, 2003 Rising Grades 6 - 9
Computer Flight simulation: learn to fly F16 fighter jets and deploy weapons in famous strategic confrontations.

Register On Line - www.kidcollege.com
The Gifted and Talented Development Center
Jillian Goldberg, Director
704/708-9212 Fax 704/708-8973
Toll Free 1-866-545-5927
e-mail - tip@giftedandtalented.org
P.O. Box 3129 Matthews, North Carolina 28106
Eligibility Requirements may apply to some programs.

Please see listing on page 175 for complete information.

Gifted and Talented Center

At Queens University, Charlotte, NC

Arts

Writers Workshop
June 9 - 13, 2003 2 Sessions Rising Grades 6-8 & 9-12
Creative writing, visiting authors, seminars, and polished work.

Fine Arts Portfolio
June 9 - 13, 2003 Rising Grades 8-9 & 10-12
Build a college-bound portfolio: life-drawing, oil painting, and design.

Actor's Studio
June 15 - 22, 2003 Rising Grades 9-12
Resumes, headshots, film and stage acting, auditioned monologues. End of week sharing.

Young Actor's Workshop
June 22 - 28, 2003 Rising Grades 6-9
Variety of theater workshops and final performance.

Playwriting
June 16 - 20, 2003 Rising Grades 9-12
Weaving words for the stage and the cinema: hands-on tutorials, seminars, open mike night.

Fashion Design
June 16 - 20, 2003 Rising Grades 9-12
Drawing techniques, fabric, cut and construction: create designs for production

Musical Theater
July 14 - 19, 2003 Rising Grades 6 - 9
Excerpts from the best of Broadway and gems from the opera; final performance on Saturday.

Register On Line - www.kidcollege.com
The Gifted and Talented Development Center
Jillian Goldberg, Director
704/708-9212 Fax 704/708-8973
Toll Free 1-866-545-5927
e-mail - tip@giftedandtalented.org
P.O. Box 3129 Matthews, North Carolina 28106
Eligibility Requirements may apply to some programs.

Please see listing on page 174 for complete information.

SPECIAL ADVERTISEMENTS xix

Gifted and Talented Center
At Queens University, Charlotte, NC
Arts & Science

Film Studies
June 23 - 27, 2003 Rising Grades 9-12
Seminal works, trend setting directors, producers and actors, hands-on camera work

Gt Law
June 30 - 4, 2003 Rising Grades 6-9
Aspiring lawyers study the legal system and stage a mock trial.

Animation
June 30 - 4, 2003 Rising Grades 6-9
Traditional techniques, story boarding, cel painting, claymation.

Serious Law
July 7 - 11, 2003 Rising Grades 6-9
Finally a sequel for law enthusiasts! Indepth study and role play.

Forensics
July 14 - 18, 2003 Rising Grades 8-10
Unravel the mysteries of crime.

Pre Med
Session 1 - July 14 - 18, 2003 Rising Grades 6-8
Session 2 - July 21 - 25, 2003 Rising Grades 9-12
Physiology, anatomy, hands-on dissection and bioethics.

Psychology
July 21 - 25, 2003 Rising Grades 9-12
What makes us tick? Personalities, norms, disorders, human development.

Register On Line - www.kidcollege.com
The Gifted and Talented Development Center
Jillian Goldberg, Director
704/708-9212 Fax 704/708-8973
Toll Free 1-866-545-5927
e-mail - tip@giftedandtalented.org
P.O. Box 3129 Matthews, North Carolina 28106
Eligibility Requirements may apply to some programs.

Please see listing on page 174 for complete information.

Please see listing on page 25 for complete information.

Please see listing on page 30 for complete information.

ADVENTURE TREKS

Adventures in the North American West for young people beginning at age 13

- Outstanding safety record
- Focus on fun and community
- Multi-activity adventures
- Investment in education
- All equipment included
- 1:4 instructor to student ratio
- Average instructor age: 28
- Staff return rate: 75%
- References available

For the most rewarding summer of your life, please call or email for a free brochure and video.

ADVENTURE TREKS
John Dockendorf, Director
www.adventuretreks.com
advtreks@aol.com
888.954.5555

Please see listing on page 8 for complete information.

xxiv SPECIAL ADVERTISEMENTS

Please see listing on page 224 for complete information.

"COLLEGE WAS A BLAST. NOW I'M READY FOR HIGH SCHOOL."

SMU TALENTED AND GIFTED PROGRAM
ACCELERATED LEARNING FOR RISING 8TH, 9TH, & 10TH GRADERS

Academic talent is not dictated by age. That's why SMU offers the TAG program for qualified students who have completed grades seven through nine. For three weeks, students participate in two advanced-level courses designed to stretch thinking and learning. Many students even earn three hours of college credit. Join us in July, 2003 and enter high school with a college transcript.

To learn more and apply, contact us at
214.768.0123 *or* www.smu.edu/tag

SMU will not discriminate on the basis of race, color, religion, national origin, sex, age, disability, or veteran status.

Please see listing on page 234 for complete information.

Baylor School

DISTINGUISHED SCHOLARS PROGRAM

The Baylor School Distinguished Scholars Program rewards exemplary 9th and 10th grade boarding students with full and partial scholarships, based soley on merit, to one of the finest college preparatory schools in the South.

- Nominees should demonstrate academic excellence, breadth of interest, and extracurricular involvement.

- They must have a GPA of 3.7 or higher and place among the top ten percent in a Baylor approved national test.

- They should exhibit leadership skills and show the promise of remaining committed to these personal standards.

- As recipients of this scholarship, they will join other student leaders at a school highly regarded for its rigorous academics and college preparation.

Founded in 1893, Baylor School is an independent, coeducational day and boarding school enrolling students in grades six through twelve.

For more information about this exciting opportunity, please contact the Baylor Admission Office at **1-800-2 BAYLOR**, or visit us at **www.baylorschool.org**

Please see listing on page 226 for complete information.

SPECIAL ADVERTISEMENTS xxvii

Find your way to Webb.

It is a place of values–
A school where trust and honor form the heart of daily life,

where independence and responsibility reinforce one another,

where diversity and tradition stand together.

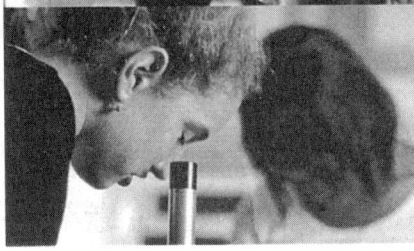

It is a place of discovery–
A community where you realize the value of individual expression,

where you are recognized for your talents,

where you learn about the world while finding your place in it.

It is a place of achievement–
An environment where students know that success comes with effort,

where they see that excellence has many forms,

where they are challenged by teachers they know as friends.

Webb is the place where you belong.

The Webb School
Bell Buckle, Tennessee
(931) 389-6003
admissions@webbschool.com
www.thewebbschool.com

The Webb School is a co-educational college preparatory day/boarding school for grades 6 – 12.

Webb School welcomes applicants of all races, religion, creed, or ethnic origin.

Please see listing on page 226 for complete information.

RMA sets standards that enable young men to achieve extraordinary excellence for a lifetime of accomplishment.

- Individualized college placement program
- Grades 7-12, fully SACS accredited
- 100% college acceptance, past 4 years
- Character Development Program
- Exclusive Student Success Program
- HomePass – new family weekend program

RIVERSIDE MILITARY ACADEMY

Building Excellence in Young Men Since 1907

Gainesville, Georgia
1-800-GO-CADET · 1-800-462-2338
770-532-6251 · www.cadet.com

Please see listing on page 176 for complete information.

Please see listing on page 109-for complete information.

SPECIAL ADVERTISEMENTS xxxi

OXFORD
CAMBRIDGE
PARIS

- Acclaimed intensive summer study programs for high school students at Oxford and Cambridge Universities and in Paris.

- Two unique academic enrichment programs for 8th and 9th Graders at Cambridge University and in the heart of Paris.

- Outstanding advanced courses covering all areas of the curriculum, from Medical and Natural Sciences to the Humanities and Social Sciences to the Visual and Performing Arts.

- Superb faculties, including Rhodes, Marshall and Fulbright Scholars, drawn from Oxford and Cambridge Universities, the Sorbonne and other leading institutions.

For further information please contact:
OXBRIDGE ACADEMIC PROGRAMS
1-800-828-8349 • 212-932-3049
info@oxbridgeprograms.com • www.oxbridgeprograms.com
In cooperation with The Foundation for International Education

Please see listing on page 281 for complete information.

Please see listing on pages 66 and 68 for complete information.

The Green River Preserve
For Rising 4th through 8th graders
Expedition Programs for 9th – 12th graders

Imagine your child with a peer group of motivated learners exploring a 3400 acre private wildlife preserve. Our unique program features:

- A coed, non-profit natural science program for gifted and motivated learners. 1, 2 & 3 week sessions.

- A five square mile mountain preserve near Brevard, NC — considered one of the finest private wildlife preserves in Western North Carolina.

- Excellent facilities, carefully selected staff, enrollment limited to 98 children; 3 to 1 child-to-staff ratio, insuring a nurturing family atmosphere and individualized attention.

- Non-competitive recreational programs — fly fishing, archery, swimming, climbing tower, BB skeet and camping.

- Special enrichment programs — art, drawing, pottery and sculpture, skits and drama, creative writing, fly tying, hand crafts and outdoor cooking.

- Daily field trips to caves, waterfalls, forest trails and mountain overlooks — new friends and fun hands-on learning.

- Nighttime music and storytelling.

- Expedition Programs for 9th – 12th graders in backpacking, kayaking and wilderness arts. Visit our website for more information.

For more information please contact:
Missy & Sandy Schenck, directors
The Green River Preserve
301 Green River Road, Cedar Mountain, NC 28718
Phone: (828) 698-8828 • Fax: (828) 698-9201
Email: grpreserve@citcom.net
Website: www.greenriverpreserve.com

Please see listing on page 174 for complete information.

Please see listing on page 36 for complete information.

SPECIAL ADVERTISEMENTS xxxv

$\mathcal{D}uke$ Gifted Letter
A quarterly newsletter for parents of gifted and talented children

The *Duke Gifted Letter* provides timely and authoritative information for enriching the lives of gifted children and their families. The newsletter presents an unparalleled collection of articles, interviews, forums, and guides on topics of interest to parents of gifted children and youth. Within its pages parents will find the best information in an engaging and accessible format.

Recent and forthcoming articles

"What Does It Mean to be Gifted?" • "Musical Talent: Innate or Learned?" • "Understanding Children's Reactions to Trauma" • "Minority Children in Gifted Education: A Problem and a Solution" • "Finding Scholarship Money for College" • "Stress Management" • "Review of Literary Magazines for Children" • "Home Schooling the Gifted" • "Developing an Educational Plan for Your Child"

Regular features

Product Tips • The Emotional Edge • Parent's Platform • The Top Shelf • Research Briefs • Consultant's Corner • Technology Matters • Magna Cum Laude • Expert's Forum • The Editor's View

---

Yes! I want to subscribe to the *Duke Gifted Letter!* Please enter my subscription.
☐ One-year (four informative issues) subscription at $24
☐ **Two-year subscription at $36 (normally $48)**

Name

Address   E-mail address

City   State   Zip

Daytime phone number   TP3M1

Send payment (checks should be made payable to Duke University) to the Journals Fulfillment Department, Duke University Press, Box 90660, Durham, NC 27708-0660; or call 888-387-5765, toll-free within the U.S. and Canada. www.dukeupress.edu/DGL/

xxxvi   SPECIAL ADVERTISEMENTS

What's the excitement about?

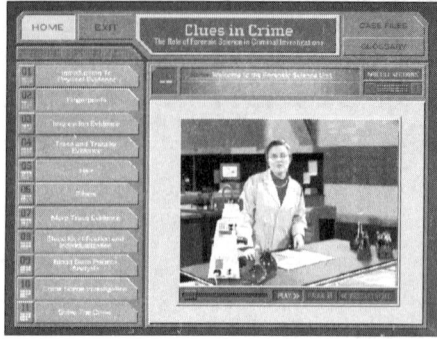

With new Duke TIP interactive CD-ROM courses, the fun and challenges of our best summer programs can be experienced at home. Using video, sound and interactive exercises, Duke TIP instructors lead multimedia adventures in forensic science (*Clues in Crime*), 20th century music (*Switched on Sound*), and 1960s history (*Peace and Protest*). To learn more, visit www.tip.duke.edu today.

www.tip.duke.edu
919-683-1400

Duke University TIP

Please see listing on page 183 for complete information.

One step ahead...

With Duke TIP Learn On Your Own and MAP courses, students in grades 4-11 can move ahead by studying outside of the classroom and at their own pace in courses like *Algebra I &II, Discovering King Arthur, Reflective and Persuasive Writing, MathPack: Quest,* and *Word Power*.

To learn more, visit
www.tip.duke.edu
919-683-1400

Duke University TIP

Please see listing on page 183 for complete information.

SPECIAL ADVERTISEMENTS xxxvii

ℒEARN-to-ℒIVE Together
Honors Leadership Academy for Young Women

Be a part of this unique, residential program for young women (grades 7-12). Utilizing the theme of **LEARN** (Lead, Explore, Achieve, Research, and Nurture) to **LIVE** (Love, Initiate, Visualize, Energize), experiential activities provide the opportunity for each participant to refine her leadership potential in a supportive environment "**Together.**"

ℒEARN-to-ℒIVE

Together

Held on the campus of:
University of West Georgia
Carrollton, Georgia
July 6-11, 2003

For information...
e-mail: L2L@charter.net
www.learn-to-live.org

A Program of...LEARN to LIVE, Inc. A 501(c)(3) Non-Profit Organization

Please see listing on page 74 for complete information.

UNIVERSITY OF SOUTH CAROLINA
LEARNING & FUN

SUMMER ACADEMIC PROGRAMS • WHERE LEARNING AND FUN MEET!

Our Summer Academic Programs offer an array of educational opportunities in a fun, safe environment. Our programs are designed for students ages 11 through 17. Whether you want to become a journalist, a lawyer, or an artist, you can gear up for it at USC.

Criteria: Application; some programs require recommendation letters
Grades: 7–12   **Cost:** Varies
Contact: Continuing Education, University of South Carolina, Columbia, SC 29208
Phone: 803-777-9444 **Fax:** 803-777-2663 **E-mail:** confs@gwm.sc.edu
Web: www.rcce.sc.edu/sap

Please see listing on page 220 for complete information.

Make this summer amazing with Duke TIP!

Duke PreCollege Program
Students get a taste of Duke University life before graduating from high school. Participants live on West Campus and join undergraduates in a wide variety of college courses, earning credit while meeting people from around the world. It's an unforgettable summer and a great way for students to learn about Duke!

International and Domestic Field Studies
Greece, France, Costa Rica, California and New Mexico are among the many sites where students explore diverse topics including filmmaking, astronomy, creative writing, tropical medicine, ecology, astronomy and mythology. Duke TIP Field Studies offer students hands-on experiences in amazing places.

Global Dialogues & Leadership Institutes
At the Leadership Institute, students challenge themselves in and out of the classroom and develop important skills to discover the leader within. International diplomacy and law are the themes of the Global Dialogues Institute, where students meet exciting guest speakers, examine different perspectives and discuss and debate critical world events.

www.tip.duke.edu
919-684-3847
Financial aid available

Duke University TIP

Please see listing on page 184 for complete information.

Texas A&M University at Galveston

SESSION I	June 14-22
	June 14-24 (Distinguished Achievement Program)
Courses	Marine Biology, Veterinary Medicine, Scuba/Research Diving
Ages	13-18
SESSION II	July 5-13
	July 5-15 (Distinguished Achievement Program)
Courses	Marine Biology, Advanced Skills Scuba, Computer Technology
Ages	15-18

www.tamug.edu/tag

Please see listing on page 241 for complete information.

SPECIAL ADVERTISEMENTS   xxxix

A BOY'S SCHOOL FOR MEN

Recognized as one of the leading college preparatory schools in the nation, McCallie School is now accepting nominations for the McCallie Honors Scholarships for 2002-03. These scholarships provide tuition, room, and board for outstanding students to study and grow at McCallie. For information, call McCallie School at 1-800-234-2163, visit our web site at www.mccallie.org, or contact us at info@mccallie.org.

MCCALLIE
HONOR TRUTH DUTY

McCallie School
Chattanooga, Tennessee
800-234-2163

Please see listing on page 228 for complete information.

SEA CAMP

Texas A&M University at Galveston

A hands-on Marine Adventure for 10-18 year-olds.

Sea Camp 1 – Ecology/Marine Biology
Sea Camp 2 – Continuation of Sea Camp 1
Sea Camp 3 – Fish Camp
Sea Camp 4 – Marine Mammal Workshop

Sea Camp 5 – Coastal Camping
Sea Camp 6 – Study in Belize
Sea Camp 7 – Ecotourism Adventure
– Quintana Roo Peninsula, Mexico

P.O. Box 1675, Galveston, Texas 77553
409-740-4525 office   409-740-4894 fax
seacamp@tamug.tamu.edu
www.tamug.tamu.edu/~seacamp

Please see listing on page 240 for complete information.

ADVANCE
Program for Young Scholars

The ADVANCE Program for Young Scholars combines rigorous academic instruction with a cornucopia of fun activities designed to stretch each students' physical capabilities and cultural awareness. Our students work hard, play hard, and go home happy. Then they come back.

Dr. David Wood, Director
ADVANCE Program for Young Scholars
Northwestern State University
PO Box 5671   Natchitoches, LA 71457
(800) 259-4438 (in LA only); otherwise (318) 357-4500
e-mail: palmerh@alpha.nsula.edu
www.advanceprogram.org

Please see listing on page 102 for complete information.

Phillips Exeter Academy Summer Session
July 6-August 9, 2003

Five weeks of exploration and discovery.

For the summer of 2003, we invite you to become an Exonian. Join us as we welcome to campus some 590 students, who come to us from nearly every state and from over three dozen foreign nations. Participate in innovative, challenging academic programs and in Harkness (seminar) classes that place you at the center of the learning process. Become part of a richly diverse community of students and faculty.

Enjoy full access to our campus with its state-of-the-art Phelps Science Center, the world's largest secondary school library, unrivaled performing arts facilities, and expansive athletic arenas.

For more detailed information and an application packet, please contact the Summer School Office.

Phillips Exeter Academy Summer School
20 Main Street, Exeter, NH 03833-2460
Tel (603) 777-3488 | **Fax** (603) 777-4385
email summer@exeter.edu | www.exeter.edu/summer

Please see listing on page 156 for complete information.

SPECIAL ADVERTISEMENTS   xli

DEER HILL expeditions

Please see listing on page 38 for complete information.

The University *of* Chicago
Summer Session

3–9 week intellectual adventures for high school and undergraduate students
June 24–August 30, 2003

Take college courses, go on a paleontologic dig, work in a cutting-edge biological lab, produce and direct films, and much more!

The University *of* Chicago
Office of Summer Studies
1427 E. 60th Street
Chicago, IL 60637
773 782 6033
uc-summer@uchicago.edu
www.grahamschool.uchicago.edu/summer

Please see listing on page 84 for complete information.

ST. TIMOTHY'S SCHOOL
Educating Girls Since 1882

Share in the Tradition

Located just outside of Baltimore, Maryland

- Average Class Size 7-10 Students •
- Faculty:Student ratio 1:4 •
- AP Courses in 10 Subjects •
- Excellent College Placement •

8400 Greenspring Avenue • Stevenson, MD 21153
410.486.7200 • admis@sttimothyschool.com
WWW.STTIMOTHYSSCHOOL.COM

Please see listing on page 111 for complete information.

BRADLEY
U N I V E R S I T Y

WOW!

World of Wonder
Institute for Gifted and Talented Youth
June 2-27, 2003 (4 - 1 wk, day sessions)
Bradley University offers the best in high-interest instruction. Over 90 courses offer challenging instruction in small classes.

Class selections may include:
Mini-veterinary, medical, or law school, news journalism, movie production, scuba, rocketry, Math Masters, literature photography, biology, planetarium visits, space missions, performing arts.

College of Education & Health Sciences
Cathy Sherlock (309) 677-3181
Dr. Mary Ann Manos, Director (309) 677-2614
206 Westlake Hall
Bradley University, Peoria IL 61625
Fax (309) 677-2952

Please see listing on page 86 for complete information.

SPECIAL ADVERTISEMENTS

SAINT ANDREW'S SEWANEE SCHOOL
Sewanee, Tennessee

A first-rate college preparatory education in a caring community of 250 day and boarding students.

A chance to take college classes for credit at the adjacent University of the South.

A great place to start your future.

http:\\sasweb.org
Tel. (toll free) 866-513-8290

Please see listing on page 32 for complete information.

BIKE TRIPS
USA CANADA EUROPE

Easy, moderate, long distance, and off-road trips. 1 to 9 weeks. Coed. Separate groups for junior high, 9th, 10th, or 11th-12th graders. ACA accredited. Pick-up & return to NY/NJ/Boston areas. 34th year.

FREE BROCHURE 800 343-6132
STUDENT HOSTELING PROGRAM
PO BOX 419, CONWAY, MA 01341

bicycletrips.com

Please see listing on page 12 for complete information.

MarineQuest

One-Week Summer Sessions
- Coast Trek
- Biology of the Sea
- OceanLab
- Ocean Chemotion

Special Events
- Real Hawaii – Oahu
- Marine Biology Camp for Teens – Florida

E-mail: marinequest@uncw.edu
910-962-2386

UNCW
UNIVERSITY OF NORTH CAROLINA AT WILMINGTON
Public Service and Continuing Studies
An EEO/AA Institution

Please see listing on page 189 for complete information.

TELL US ABOUT IT!

Please send any questions, comments, or suggestions regarding this publication to eog@tip.duke.edu

REGIONAL TALENT SEARCHES AND COOPERATIVE PROGRAMS

The Duke University Talent Identification Program, which publishes this guide, is one of four major regional Talent Search programs in the United States. The other three are located at The Johns Hopkins University, Northwestern University, and the University of Denver. Each Talent Search conducts an annual search for academically talented middle school and junior high school students using the SAT or ACT as an out-of-level test. In an effort to serve every state and avoid duplication of effort, each program incorporates a particular group of states as its Talent Search region.

Talent Searches also administer summer and, in some cases, academic year programs for gifted students. These programs are independent of one another, however, admission to all is based on SAT or ACT scores, and Talent Search participants from one region may apply to programs offered by another. Descriptions of some of these programs are found on the following pages and in the chapter for the state where the Talent Search is located.

Also included in this guide are the programs offered by Western Kentucky University, the University of Southern Mississippi, Northwestern State University and Southern Methodist University. These specialized academic programs are offered in cooperation with the Duke University Talent Identification Program. Information on these Duke TIP Cooperative programs can be found at the beginning of the chapter for the state in which they are located.

Duke University Talent Identification Program
Durham, NC

The Duke University Talent Identification Program (TIP) is a nonprofit educational organization founded in 1980. TIP is a national leader in identifying academically talented students and providing innovative opportunities for the fullest development of their educational potential.

TIP Talent Searches

4th and 5th Grade Talent Search identifies academically talented students, offers above-level testing and provides the *Navigator* newsletter and *Guide to Academic Resources* to motivate younger students toward continued high academic achievement.

7th Grade Talent Search identifies academically talented 7th graders and measures their performance on the SAT or ACT against similarly talented peers. Participants also receive the *Educational Opportunity Guide*, *Insights* newsletter, and *The College Guide*, a magazine about college selection and application.

Educational Programs

Duke TIP provides fun and challenging educational opportunities for advanced students of many age groups. Summer programs give students in grades 7-10 the opportunity to learn challenging material at an accelerated pace. The three-week programs are offered on a variety of college campuses, providing young scholars the unique opportunity to experience residence hall life and college classroom instruction. For future leaders, TIP Leadership Institute guides a select group of participants in the academic study of leadership and the development of skills that will enhance the students' ability to impact their communities. Students seeking to visit exotic locations in the United States, Europe, and Latin America that also feature ideal research environments can choose from the two- or three- week Field Studies courses. Through the PreCollege Program, rising twelfth-grade high school students attend classes with Duke undergraduates during the summer session and receive university credit.

Publications: *Educational Opportunity Guide: A Directory of Programs for the Gifted*, *Duke Gifted Letter* (quarterly parent newsletter), *Advanced Placement (AP) Teacher Manuals* (available in nine subject areas), and TIP Independent Learning enrichment courses in booklet form and on CDs.

Other Duke TIP Events and Activities: Scholar Weekends, the Family Conference, and Advanced Placement (AP) Teacher Workshops.

Criteria: Varies. Consult Web site for details.

Grade: 4-12.

Cost: Varies. Consult Web site for complete information.

Contact: Duke University Talent Identification Program
Box 90747
Durham, NC 27701
(919) 684-3847
E-mail: info@tip.duke.edu
Web site: http://www.tip.duke.edu

Center For Talent Development
Northwestern University
Evanston, Illinois

Apogee/Spectrum/Equinox Summer Programs
June 29-July 19, 2003 (Session I); July 28-August 17, 2003 (Session II)

The Apogee Program develops the academic potential of talented young students (completing grades 4-6). Offering residential and commuter options, the program achieves a balance of academics and social activities. All students take one course during one of two three-week sessions. Class size is 14-18 students. Courses offered in 2003 include Creative Writing, Novel Ideas, Science Fiction and Fantasy, Playwriting and Drama, Writing from All Angles, Journalism, Community Action, Middle Ages, Order in the Courtroom, Time and Design, Philosophy, Prealgebra, Chances Are, Algebra I, World Around Us, Engineering and Physics, Aerodynamics, Forensics, and Bits and Blocks.

The Spectrum Program develops the academic potential of students (completing grades 7-9). It offers students an opportunity to study advanced courses in a supportive setting. Students study one course intensively for a three-week period. Classes meet five days a week. Each day involves five hours of instruction in class plus several hours of additional study and homework. Enrichment activities supplement students' academic program. Courses offered in 2003 include Creative Writing, Nonfiction Writing, Literary Analysis, Latin I, Latin II, Persuasion and Debate, International Relations, Introduction to Philosophy, Logic and Critical Thinking, Youth and Society, Algebra I and II, Math Modeling, Geometry, Biology, Ecology, Chemistry, Physics, and C++.

The Equinox Program offers an invigorating mix of challenging course work, social activities, and cultural enrichment. Students (grades 10-12) study one course intensively for a three-week period. Classes meet five days a week, 5-7 hours per day, with 2-3 hours of homework. Courses in 2003 include AP English, Creative Writing, Film Studies, AP U.S. History, AP European History, AP Macroeconomics, AP Psychology, Philosophy, Precalculus, Topics in Calculus, Advanced Math Topics, Ecology Field Studies, Ethics, Law and Advocacy, Physics Honors, Modern Physics, Human Biology, and Research Methods. Successfully completed courses carry high school credit of one or two semesters.

Criteria:	Application (deadline: May 7); test scores; EXPLORE or PLUS (Apogee); SAT or ACT (Spectrum, Equinox); personal essay.
Grade:	4-6 (Apogee); 7-9 (Spectrum); 10-12 (Equinox).
Cost:	$2,200 (residential); $1,200 (commuter). Financial aid is available.
Contact:	Joe Salvatore, Summer Program Director Center for Talent Development Northwestern University 617 Dartmouth Place Evanston, IL 60208 (847) 491-3782; Fax: (847) 467-4283 E-mail: ctdsummer@yahoo.com Web site: http://www.ctd.northwestern.edu

Center for Talented Youth
The Johns Hopkins University
Baltimore, Maryland

Center for Talented Youth Programs
Year-round

The Johns Hopkins University developed the first integrated program that identified, challenged, and rewarded academically talented young people. The first academic Talent Search was conducted at Hopkins in 1972 by Dr. Julian Stanley. Since then the program has expanded to serve students from kindergarten through 12th grade in a variety of programs starting with three Talent Searches: Elementary (grades 2-4), Young (grades 5-6), and Older (grades 7-8). The Center for Talented Youth (CTY) offers a range of summer programs for students in all three searches. Programs for 7th to 10th grade students are offered at the following locations:

- Franklin and Marshall College in Lancaster, Pennsylvania
- Dickinson College in Carlisle, Pennsylvania
- Roger Williams College in Bristol, Rhode Island
- Skidmore College in Saratoga Springs, New York
- Loyola Marymount University in Los Angeles, California
- Washington College in Chestertown, Maryland
- Hood College in Frederick, Maryland
- Moravian College in Bethlehem, Pennsylvania
- University of California at Santa Cruz in Santa Cruz, CA
- The Johns Hopkins University in Baltimore, Maryland

In addition, CTY has Distance Education courses in math, science, and writing for students from kindergarten through 12th grade; weekend day and overnight conferences for students and parents held at colleges, universities, museums, zoos, and science centers around the country; a diagnostic and counseling center for assisting families and schools with assessment, planning, and counseling; and *Imagine,* a magazine for gifted students.

Criteria:	Each program has different test score requirements. Consult Web site for details.
Grade:	K-10 (on-line); rising 3-10 (three-week summer residential and day programs).
Cost:	$590-$2,450 (three-week session).
Contact:	Center for Talented Youth The Johns Hopkins University 3400 N. Charles Street Baltimore, MD 21218 (410) 516-0278 E-mail: ctyinfo@jhu.edu Web site: http://www.cty.jhu.edu

Rocky Mountain Talent Search
University of Denver
Denver, Colorado

Rocky Mountain Talent Search Summer Institute
June 9-20 (Session 1); July 6-26 (Session 2)

Now in its twenty-first year, the University of Denver Summer Institute offers high-ability students the opportunity to select from a variety of courses for intensive summer study in a supervised campus setting. Set against the beauty of the Rocky Mountains, the program offers rigorous high school and college-level courses in physics, chemistry, biology, geometry, advanced mathematics, creative writing, humanities, and social sciences. Classes are small, and the curriculum is fast-paced. Courses include lab work, field trips, and guest lectures. Instructors are university faculty, outstanding secondary school teachers, and content experts. Students select a three-hour morning and a three-hour afternoon course. Daily, organized recreational/social activities, weekend trips, special events, and dormitory life promote friendships and social interaction. The University of Denver, one of the four regional talent search universities, sponsors the Rocky Mountain Talent Search program. Tentative courses include Geometry, Psychology, Introduction to Philosophy, Drama/Theater, International Relations, Physics/Astrophysics, Cell Biology, Mock Trial, Chemistry, Robotics, Creative Writing, Literature, Statistics, Optoelectronics, Anatomy, Latin, Ecology, and Mythology.

Criteria:	Application; recommendations; test scores: SAT, ACT, PLUS (score criteria vary).
Grade:	Rising 7-10 (ages 12-15).
Cost:	$295-$1,830 (2002 prices). Limited financial aid is available (deadline: May 1).
Contact:	Rocky Mountain Talent Search University of Denver 1981 South University Boulevard Denver, CO 80208 (303) 871-2983; Fax: (303) 871-2566 E-mail: krigby@du.edu Web site: http://www.du.edu/education/ces/si.html

MULTIPLE LOCATIONS

These programs offer exciting opportunities in more than one location. Be sure to visit each program's Web site for additional information.

Academic Study Associates
June-August

Academic Study Associates (ASA) offers pre-college enrichment programs at the University of Massachusetts, Emory University, UC Berkeley, and Oxford University. High school students are given the opportunity to sample the academic, social, and recreational aspects of college life, while at the same time learning how to balance all three. Enrichment courses are offered in the sciences, arts, and humanities. SAT Prep by The Princeton Review, English as a Second Language, and professional tennis, soccer, and golf instruction are available. Afternoon, evening, and weekend excursion/activity programs are included. For middle school students the Pathways at Amherst program balances academics and summer fun. ASA also offers language and culture programs in France, Spain, and China, where language instruction is combined with family or residential living and excursion/activity programs.

Criteria: Application; teacher recommendation.

Grade: Rising 7-12.

Cost: $3,895-$6,395 (varies with program). Limited financial aid is available.

Contact: David Evans
Academic Study Associates
10 New King Street
White Plains, NY 10604
(800) 752-2250; Fax:(914) 686-7740
E-mail: summer@asaprograms.com
Web site: http://www.asaprograms.com

Adventure Treks
June 15-August 18

Adventure Treks offers fun, exciting, 16-28 day multi-activity adventure programs in North America for young people (age 13-18). Adventure destinations include Northern California, Alaska, Montana, the Pacific Northwest, the Canadian Rockies, and Idaho. Participants camp out each night and do a variety of adventure activities such as backpacking, whitewater rafting, sea kayaking, mountain climbing, rock climbing, canoeing, and mountain biking. In addition to an immeasurable amount of fun, these adventures are designed to teach teamwork, self-responsibility, community living, and outdoor skills while building self-confidence. A 1:4 instructor-to-student ratio guarantees individual attention and instruction from excellent role models.

Criteria: Personal essay; recommendations.

Grade: 7-12.

Cost: $1,995-$3,795. Limited financial aid is available.

Contact: John Dockendorf
Adventure Treks
P.O. Box 1321
Flat Rock, NC 28731
(888) 954-5555; Fax: (828) 696-1663
E-mail: advtreks@aol.com
Web site: http://www.adventuretreks.com

Congressional Student Leadership Conference
March-April (six-day programs); June-August (six- and ten-day programs)

The Congressional Student Leadership Conference (CSLC) empowers and guides its students to develop their skills, gifts, and energies to become the leaders they are capable of becoming. CSLC leadership curriculum is offered in three areas: democracy in action, business and entrepreneurship, and defense and intelligence. Through these programs students are given opportunities to learn leadership and are encouraged to discuss and debate ideas and perspectives. Students are exposed to fields of study and opportunity and are taught to think critically and analytically—to see all sides of an issue—to make better and more informed decisions. Distinguished faculty, prominent guest speakers, simulations, and field experiences give CSLC students unparalleled opportunities for growth and advancement. Participants return to their homes, schools, and communities better prepared to serve and lead. Programs are also offered for middle school students; see National Junior Leaders Conference listing for additional information.

Criteria: Recommendations; GPA; nomination; application.

Grade: Rising 10-12, college freshman.

Cost: $1,095-$1,795. Limited financial aid and need-based scholarships are available.

Contact: Congressional Student Leadership Conference
Admissions Office
7040 W. Palmetto Park Road, #4-293
Boca Raton, FL 33433
(866) 394-5323; Fax: (561) 417-9996
E-mail: info@lead-america.org
Web site: http://www.lead-america.org

Excel (Putney Student Travel)
June-August (Three-, four-, and seven-week programs)

Excel invites students to broaden their minds, refine their artistic and athletic abilities, and contribute to a dynamic community at one of our eight distinctive pre-college programs: Amherst College, Williams College, Bennington College, UC Santa Cruz, Oxford/Tuscany, Madrid/Barcelona, Prague/Krakow, and Cuba. With unparalleled access to the academic and cultural resources these campuses have to offer, Excel's active, small group seminars emphasize field-based study and collaborative learning. Students from around the world with initiative, a love for learning, and willingness to stretch academically and personally are encouraged to apply. Excel's vibrant teaching staff fully commit their academic expertise and enthusiasm to the students living on campus and lead after-class activities and weekend excursions. Arts, humanities, and sciences are offered, as well as SAT preparation and sports clinics.

Criteria: Application (and fee); personal essay; recommendations.

Grade: 9-12.

Cost: $3,990-$6,390. Limited need-based financial aid is available.

Contact: Tim Weed, Executive Director
Excel Programs
345 Hickory Ridge Road
Putney, VT 05346
(802) 387-5885; Fax: (802) 387-4276
E-mail: excel@goputney.com
Web site: http://www.goputney.com

Interlocken Center for Experiential Learning
July-August

Since 1961, more than 10,000 young people have explored the world Interlocken style. The Interlocken Center for Experiential Learning offers summer travel adventures that encourage students to learn through experience, active involvement, and discovery. Traveling with Interlocken is a creative process in which students are actively involved in shaping their summer experience; they are not bound by a rigid itinerary. Three to six weeks in length, Interlocken's summer programs include Traveling Theatre in New England and Europe; Wilderness Adventure in Alaska, California, New England, and Colorado; Cycling in Europe and Quebec; Leadership Training in New Hampshire; and Community Service in the United States, Central and South America, Africa, and Asia. Interlocken also runs an International Summer Camp in New Hampshire; a caring, creative community of 180 boys and girls and 60 staff members from around the world. Campers take an active part in choosing their own activity programs from a wide array of offerings, both traditional and eclectic.

Criteria: Application (and fee); recommendations; interview.

Grade: Rising 8-12, PG (travel programs); 3-8 (summer camp).

Cost: $3,200-$5,200. Financial aid is available. A 5% discount is offered to *Educational Opportunity Guide* readers. Details at http://www.interlocken.org/discounteog.

Contact: Tom Herman, Director of Marketing
Interlocken Center for Experiential Learning
19 Interlocken Way
Hillsboro, NH 03244
(603) 478-3166; Fax: (603) 478-5260
E-mail: mail@interlocken.org
Web site: http://www.interlocken.org

National Computer Camps
June-August

National Computer Camps—America's original computer camp, now in its 26th season—offers educational and recreational computing classes for students with all levels of experience from beginner to super-advanced. PC and Mac computers are used. Students may study Basic, Visual Basic, C++, HTML, Java, JavaScript, or assembler languages. Application software taught includes Photoshop, 3-D graphics, Web animation, Flash, networking, PowerPoint, Excel, music, and more. There is an optional sports and recreation program. One-week and multi-week sessions are offered. Camps are located in Atlanta, Georgia; Cleveland, Ohio; San Francisco, California; Los Angeles, California; Pittsburgh, Pennsylvania; and Fairfield, Connecticut. Write or call for a free illustrated brochure; also visit the National Computer Camps Web site.

Criteria: Interest in program.

Grade: Age 8-18 (coed).

Cost: $575-$740 (per week).

Contact: Dr. Michael P. Zabinski, Director
National Computer Camps, Inc.
P.O. Box 585
Orange, CT 06477
(203) 795-9667
E-mail: info@NCCamp.com
Web site: http://www.NCCamp.com

National Junior Leaders Conference (LeadAmerica Foundation)
June-August (six- and ten-day programs)

The National Junior Leaders Conference (NJLC) empowers and guides its students to develop their skills, gifts, and energies to become the leaders they are capable of becoming. NJLC leadership curriculum is offered in three areas: law and justice; business and entrepreneurship; and defense, intelligence, and diplomacy. Through these programs students are given opportunities to learn leadership and are encouraged to discuss and debate ideas and perspectives. Participants are exposed to fields of study and opportunity and are taught to think critically and analytically—to see all sides of an issue —to make better and more informed decisions. Distinguished faculty, prominent guest speakers, simulations, and field experiences give NJLC students unparalleled opportunities for growth and advancement. Students return to their homes, schools, and communities better prepared to serve and lead. Programs are also offered for high school students; see the Congressional Student Leadership Conference listing for additional information.

Criteria: Recommendations; GPA; nomination; application.

Grade: Rising 7-9.

Cost: $1,095-$1,795. Limited financial aid and need-based scholarships are available.

Contact: National Junior Leaders Conference
Admissions Office
7040 W. Palmetto Park Road, #4-293
Boca Raton, FL 33433
(866) 394-5323; Fax: (561) 417-9996
E-mail: info@lead-america.org
Web site: http://www.lead-america.org

The Road Less Traveled
Summer (one- to six-week sessions)

The Road Less Traveled offers a wide variety of wilderness expeditions and community service programs for both experienced and novice outdoor travelers age 13-19 and families with children 10 and over. Programs range from one to six weeks in length. Expeditions include high adventure wilderness trips, leadership programs, and sessions specifically designed for young people age 13-14. The unique expeditions are designed to mix the benefits and fun of pure adventure with the life-enhancing virtues of knowledge. The lessons learned on a windswept bluff are often as important as those conveyed in a high school classroom. Mind, muscles, and heart are engaged in a process of discovery and investigation. The programs reach beyond the wilderness to the fascinating people, and cultures of the western and New England states and abroad. Participants stretch beyond guidebook highlights to the most compelling areas and experience the true heart of the American West, the New England states, Australia, Costa Rica, and Nepal. All expeditions are geared to responsible young people who welcome unusual, exciting experiences, and who want to learn and be challenged.

Criteria: Application (and fee); interview.

Grade: Age 13-19; families with children age 10 and over.

Cost: $1,395-$5,595.

Contact: Jim and Donna Stein, Directors
The Road Less Traveled
2331 N. Elston Avenue
Chicago, IL 60614-2907
(800) 939-9839, (773) 342-5200; Fax: (773) 342-5703
E-mail: info@theroadlesstraveled.com
Web site: http://www.theroadlesstraveled.com

Student Hosteling Program
June-August

The Student Hosteling Program (SHP), is the outstanding teenage bicycling program in the United States, offering bicycle touring trips through the countrysides and cultural centers of the world. SHP trips provide adventure, fun, outdoor education, and the opportunity for emotional growth while at the same time providing one of the safest and most wholesome youth environments available. Groups are small—usually 8 to 12 trippers and 2-3 leaders—making possible a close and rewarding group experience. They travel by bicycle, at their own pace and close to the land, using public and private transportation when necessary. SHP groups live simply, using campsites, hostels, and other modest facilities. In the countryside, groups buy food at local markets and cook their own meals. In cities, restaurants are often used. The Student Hosteling Program, in its 34th year, is accredited by the American Camping Association.

Criteria: Application (and $50 fee); written contract agreeing to program principles.

Grade: 7-12.

Cost: $800-$5,500.

Contact: Student Hosteling Program
           Box 419
           Ashfield Road
           Conway, MA 01341
           (800) 343 6132, (413) 369-4275; Fax: (413)369-4257
           E-mail: shpbike@aol.com
           Web site: http://www.bicycletrips.com

Summer Discovery Pre-College Enrichment Programs
June-August (three- to six-week programs)

Summer Discovery is a personalized, academic, and co-curricular program for high school students at either UCLA, Los Angeles; UCSB, Santa Barbara; University of Michigan, Ann Arbor; University of Vermont, Burlington; Georgetown University, Washington, D.C.; or Cambridge University, England. Classes for college credit and academic enrichment are augmented with a wide array of sponsored activities and academic and recreational services. Included are study-skills workshops, SAT prep by The Princeton Review, community service, ESL, TOEFL prep, academic counseling and support, sports instruction, organized recreational activities, evening programs, tours of Disneyland, Universal Studios, major league baseball games, Montreal, Lake Placid, The Smithsonian Institute, tours of the White House, London, Stratford, and other area attractions. Visits to other college campuses are also provided. Summer Discovery students live together on campus in their own residence hall with dedicated, experienced, and supportive resident counselors from America's leading universities and secondary schools. The staff-to-student ratio is approximately 1:9. Staff are on duty 24 hours per day to provide for students' personal, academic, and social welfare.

Criteria: Application (and fee); transcript; counselor recommendation; CSIET accredited.

Grade: Rising 9-12.

Cost: $3,500-$6,500. Limited financial aid is available.

Contact: Neal Waldman, Director
           Summer Discovery Educational Programs
           1326 Old Northern Boulevard
           Roslyn, NY 11576
           (800) 645-6611; (516) 621-3939 (in NY)
           E-mail: discovery@summerfun.com
           Web site: http://www.summerfun.com

SuperCamp®
July-August

Making Great Kids Greater! Gain the academic edge along with lifelong learning skills at a fun 10-day summer residential program held on prestigious college campuses worldwide. **Life skills** courses such as Effective Communication, Building Relationships, Listening Skills, Problem Solving, and an Outdoor Adventure Day improve self-esteem, develop confidence and increase motivation. Students gain **"learning-to-learn" tools** that increase comprehension, retention, and improve grades. Students can benefit from skills courses such as Memory, Quantum Reading, Note Taking, Test Preparation, and Power Writing. More than 73% of graduates improve their grade point averages, 68% increase their motivation, and 98% say they continue to use their skills long after the program has ended. Be a part of their 22nd year and discover what 35,000 SuperCamp graduates worldwide already know.

Criteria: Application (and fee); GPA; ACT; deposit.

Grade: Rising 4-12 and college (age 9-24).

Cost: $1,795 (grades 4-5); $2,095-$2,295 (grades 6-12 and college). Limited scholarships, early payment, and group savings are available.

Contact: Enrollment Department, Extension 1
SuperCamp
1725 South Coast Highway
Oceanside, CA 92054
(800) 285-3276, (760) 722-0072; Fax: (760) 722-3507
E-mail: info@supercamp.com
Web site: http://www.supercamp.com

Yunasa Summer Institute for the Gifted (The Institute for Educational Advancement)
Dates and locations to be announced

Inspired by the Lakota Indian word for balance, the Yunasa Summer Institute for the Gifted (Yunasa) provides highly gifted middle school students with techniques and skills to integrate the intellectual, emotional, social, and physical aspects of their lives, so that they may find balance within themselves. This weeklong experience affords campers a physically and emotionally safe enviroment in which each participant gains new confidence and skills and is challenged to achieve their personal best while having fun. In addition to camp activities such as swimming, canoeing, and ropes courses, campers participate in small group workshops led by an exceptional faculty made of up of nationally known experts in the field of gifted education, including Patricia Gatto-Walden, Betty Mechstroth, Michael Piechowski, Elizabeth Jones Stork, and Stephanie Tolan.

Criteria: Application (and fee); educator's recommendation; sample of work; transcripts; standardized test scores; highly gifted.

Grade: Rising 6-8.

Cost: $950. Need-based financial aid is available.

Contact: The Institute for Educational Advancement
625 Fair Oaks Avenue, Suite 285
South Pasedena, CA 91030
(626) 403-8900; Fax: (626) 403-8905
E-mail: mail@educationaladvancement.org
Web site: http://www.educationaladvancement.org

ALABAMA

STATE DIRECTOR

Dr. Nina Pearson, Education Specialist
Special Education Services
Alabama Department of Education
P.O. Box 302101
Montgomery, AL 36130-2101
(334) 242-8114; Fax: (334) 242-9192
E-mail: npearson@alsde.edu

STATE ASSOCIATION

Alabama Association for Gifted Children

AAGC is committed to sensitizing Alabama to the nature and importance of appropriate education for gifted students by serving as a public advocate concerning the needs of gifted young people, facilitating the exchange of information concerning gifted students, encouraging research on the best ways of effectively addressing the cognitive and affective needs of gifted youth, and on the social significance of properly educating them, facilitating and assisting the development of local organizations to support gifted education.

Nancy Johnson, President
7950 Highway 72 West, #G196
Madison, AL 35758
E-mail: nanjjohn@mchsi.com

REGIONAL TALENT SEARCH

Duke University Talent Identification Program
See listing on page 2 for complete information.

BIRMINGHAM

The Altamont School
Academic Year and Summer (June 10-July 19)

Altamont is a coeducational, college-preparatory day school for grades 5-12. Altamont's purpose is, first, the thorough preparation of students for college; second, the development of community consciousness and conscience; and finally, the development of a personal sense of worth and dignity. The academic year includes several programs for gifted and talented students: Advanced Placement preparation in all major subject areas; acceleration opportunities in math and foreign language; a college credit Advanced Studies Program with the University of Alabama at Birmingham; intensive computer, art, music, writing, drama, and foreign language studies. The college tour every October highlights the personal College Search Program. Altamont's Summer Study Program includes acceleration, enrichment, and credit courses, as well as drama, art, computer, writing, orchestra, and sports camps. Highlights of school life include the Big Brother/Big Sister Program for new students, a faculty advisor system, active community service, and an Honor Code.

Criteria: Application (and $50 fee); transcript; test scores; GPA; ISEE; interview.

Grade: 5-12 (academic year; 3-12 (summer).

Cost: $8,988 (grades 5-6); $10,476 (grade 7); $10,656 (grade 8); $11,184 (grades 9-12). Does not include books (approximately $300) and additional fees for field trips, music lessons, and tutoring. All prices for 2002-2003 school year.

Contact: James M. Wiygul, Associate Headmaster
          The Altamont School
          4801 Altamont Road
          Birmingham, AL 35222
          (205) 879-2006; Fax: (205) 871-5666
          E-mail: sstevens@altamontschool.org
          Web site: http://www.altamontschool.org

Indian Springs School
Academic Year

"Learning through living," the motto of Indian Springs, is at the heart of our program. Operating like a small town, the school involves students at every level. A student mayor presides at weekly town meetings. Typically, one-quarter of our senior classes are named National Merit Semifinalists. Most students leave with college credit earned through the Advanced Placement program. The student-to-teacher ratio is 9:1, and most teachers hold advanced degrees. There are abundant extracurricular opportunities, including drama, choir, instrumental music, fencing, Scholar's Bowl, and a whole host of athletic teams. With a large, wooded campus and classrooms open to the outdoors, the atmosphere at Indian Springs is informal. The dress code is relaxed and a comfortable feeling comes from students' being involved in the formulation and enforcement of rules. Grade 8 is open only to day students, with boarding students in grades 9-PG.

Criteria: Application (and $50 fee); transcript; test scores; recommendations; SSAT; interview.

Grade: 8 (day students); 9-12, PG (boarding students).

Cost: $21,500 (full boarding); $19,750 (five-day boarding); $11,850 (day). Need-based scholarships are available.

Contact: Charles H. Ellis, Director of Admission
           Indian Springs School
           190 Woodward Drive
           Indian Springs, AL 35124
           (888) 843-9477, (205) 988-3350; Fax: (205) 988-3797
           E-mail: cellis@indiansprings.org
           Web site: http://www.indiansprings.org

Dauphin Island

**The Discovery Hall Summer High School Program
(Dauphin Island Sea Lab)**
June 6-August 1

The oceans offer a unique fascination that stimulates the understanding of science by doing science at the ocean's edge. Located on Dauphin Island at the mouth of Mobile Bay, seven miles off the mainland in the Gulf of Mexico, this program offers students a course in marine science that includes biology, geology, geography, chemistry, and much more. Students live on campus and participate in over 150 contact hours of lectures, lab work, and field experiences. Every week students board a research vessel and do scientific collections in the Bay and Gulf of Mexico. This academic course offers students an appreciation and awareness of the ocean and its inhabitants and problems that must be solved as the coastal zone grows in population. This course has been approved by the Alabama Department of Education, and recommends that students receive one-year high school science credit or science elective upon successful completion of the program.

Criteria: Application (and $50 fee); transcript; personal essay; recommendations.

Grade: Rising 10-12. Financial aid is not available

Cost: $1,200.

Contact: Denise Keaton, DHP Registrar
The Discovery Hall Program
Dauphin Island Sea Lab
101 Bienville Boulevard
Dauphin Island, AL 36528
(251) 861-7515; Fax: (251) 861-7421
E-mail: dkeaton@disl.org
Web site: http://www.disl.org

Mobile

Alabama School of Mathematics and Science
Academic Year and Summer Session

The **Alabama School of Mathematics and Science** is a public, residential, coeducational, institution for high school sophomores, juniors, and seniors with special intellectual ability and a commitment to scholarship in mathematics and science. The advanced academic program is designed to ensure a thorough grounding in mathematics and science; to develop verbal and writing skills; to provide learning opportunities in language, culture, history, and wellness; and to stress the impact of technology on society. All students live in residence halls under the supervision of a professional staff of residential advisors. The comprehensive residential life program includes student government, athletics, clubs, and student publications. There are opportunities for tutorials, guest lectures, field trips, and visits to cultural events, as well as to educational and scientific institutions. The **Alabama Institute of Math and Science (AIMS)**, the summer program arm of the Alabama School, offers courses during the summer for students (rising 7-10 graders) from all states.

Criteria: Application; transcript; personal essay; recommendations; teacher report; GPA; ACT; interview; Alabama resident (academic year only).

Grade: 10-12 (academic year); rising 7-10 (summer session).

Cost: Tuition, room, and board are provided. $1,000 activity fee (academic year). Cost for AIMS Summer Program to be determined.

Contact: Office of Admissions
Alabama School of Mathematics and Science
1255 Dauphin Street
Mobile, AL 36604-2519
(251) 441-3250; Fax: (251) 441-3251
E-mail: admissions@asms.net
Web site: http://www.asms.net

MONTGOMERY

The Montgomery Academy
Academic Year

The Montgomery Academy is an independent, nonsectarian, college-preparatory school offering a superior education within a challenging, supportive environment. Through the "Pursuit of Excellence" in scholarship, extracurricular activities, and character development, students will undertake a program of intellectual and personal development reaching far beyond classrooms and playing fields. Together with parents, the faculty will seek to cultivate in students a lifelong love of learning and habits of independent thought, fair play, responsible citizenship, and personal integrity. The Montgomery Academy graduates will speak, write and think clearly; will demonstrate interest and proficiency in mathematics and science; will work toward fluency in a second language; and will have knowledge of the human experience through art, music, history, and literature. They will be able to use technology to obtain knowledge; to work independently and in teams; to value and develop physical health; and to participate constructively in their community and their world.

Criteria: Application; transcript; writing sample; admissions testing.

Grade: K-12.

Cost: $4,840-$9,240. Need-based financial aid is available (for academic year only).

Contact: Rhea C. Kirk, Director of Admissions and Marketing
The Montgomery Academy
3240 Vaughn Road
Montgomery, AL 36106
(888) 345-8210, (334) 272-8210; Fax: (334) 277-3240
E-mail: kirk.r@montgomeryacademy.org
Web site: http://www.montgomeryacademy.org

Tuscaloosa

Capstone Summer Honors Program (University of Alabama)
June-July

The University of Alabama's Capstone Summer Honors Program offers rising high school seniors the opportunity to sample university life, earn college credit, and compete for scholarships. The program coincides with the university's first term of summer school. Participants enroll in two regularly scheduled freshman-level courses and an exploratory seminar, which exposes the rich array of resources, ideas, and experiences a university offers. Students earn seven semester hours of college credit upon successful completion of course work. They have access to all university recreational facilities and enjoy many planned social and cultural activities. Capstone students compete for eight $4,000 scholarships to attend the University of Alabama after graduation. Awards are based on performance during the program, high school grades, recommendations, test scores, resumé, and essay.

Criteria:	Application (and fee); transcript; recommendations; GPA; test scores (PSAT, SAT, or ACT); resumé; personal essay.
Grade:	Rising 12.
Cost:	$800 (2002 cost).
Contact:	Director Capstone Summer Honors Program University of Alabama Box 870132 Tuscaloosa, AL 35487-0132 (800) 933-BAMA, (205) 348-5666; Fax: (205) 348-9046 TDD: (205) 348-2921 E-mail: admissions@ua.edu Web site: http://www.ua.edu

TUSCALOOSA

SITE—Student Introduction to Engineering
(The University of Alabama College of Engineering)
July

The University of Alabama's College of Engineering will host three sessions of a weeklong residential program for rising high school juniors and seniors. The Student Introduction to Engineering (SITE) Summer Program is designed to give participants early exposure and appreciation for coursework required to major and excel in engineering. Approximately 40 students are selected to participate in each session. The academic emphasis of the program centers on collaborative learning concepts, computer skills and usage, along with a general overview of pre-calculus and English. Some other activities include an industrial plant tour, hands-on laboratory demonstrations, seminars by engineering faculty, and seminars on college life.

Criteria: Recommendations.

Grade: Rising 11-12.

Cost: $200 (2002 cost).

Contact: SITE
The University of Alabama
Box 870200
Tuscaloosa, AL 35487-0200
(205) 348-4267; Fax: (205) 348-3241
E-mail: mcarlisle@coe.eng.ua.edu
Web site: http://www.eng.ua.edu

ALASKA

STATE DIRECTOR

Greg Maloney
Education Specialist II
Gifted and Talented Education
Alaska Department of Education & Early Development
801 W. 10th Street, Suite 200
Juneau, AK 99801-1894
(907) 465-2972; Fax: (907) 465-2806
E-mail: greg_maloney@eed.state.ak.us

STATE ASSOCIATION

AGATE
P.O. Box 97
Haines, AK 99827

REGIONAL TALENT SEARCH

Center for Talented Youth (The Johns Hopkins University)
See listing on page 4 for complete information.

LOCTIONS THROUGHOUT ALASKA

Adventure Treks
June 15-August 18

See listing on page 8 for complete information.

ARIZONA

STATE DIRECTOR

Gifted Program Specialist
Exceptional Student Services
Arizona Department of Education
1535 West Jefferson
Phoenix, AZ 85007
(602) 542-3852; Fax: (602) 542-5404

STATE ASSOCIATION

Arizona Association for Gifted and Talented

AAGT was formed in 1974 by a dedicated group of parents and teachers who saw the need for a unified voice to represent Arizona's gifted children. Our continuing challenge is to meet the needs of Arizona's gifted children with limited funds for their education and development. AAGT provides the only voice in Arizona dedicated to providing the information and guidance necessary for parents, teachers, administrators, and legislators to develop and support gifted education in our state. Our advocacy takes many forms including an annual conference for parents and educators, a quarterly newsletter, scholarships for gifted students, and the most comprehensive resource guide for gifted children in Arizona. These benefits, and more, are available to members of AAGT. The mission of the Arizona Association for Gifted and Talented (AAGT) is to advocate for the diverse population of gifted children in the state of Arizona. We strive to accomplish that mission by disseminating information, supporting local parent groups, and encouraging the growth of quality programs for gifted children among other things.

Melanie Richards, President
P.O. Box 31088
Phoenix, AZ 85046-1088
(602) 482-8415
E-mail: melanie1richards@earthlink.net

REGIONAL TALENT SEARCH

Center for Talented Youth (The Johns Hopkins University)
See listing on page 4 for complete information.

Tucson

A Summer of Excellence (The University of Arizona Honors College)
June 9-July 10 (Session 1); July 14-August 13 (Session 2)

A Summer of Excellence (SOE) is the University of Arizona's premier pre-college program for academically talented students. Sponsored by The Honors College, A Summer of Excellence provides juniors and sophomores with a fun and intellectually challenging summer on the beautiful University of Arizona campus. Students come from Arizona and across the nation. Through SOE, students will gain independence, learn about themselves, and confidently set goals for their future in higher education. The course(s) taken will begin their University of Arizona transcript and are transferable nearly anywhere. Full details (including admission and scholarship application forms, policies, important dates, and more) are available on the SOE Web site.

Criteria: Application (deadline: May 1); $25 application fee ($35 after May 1); transcript; recommendations; GPA; ACT; gifted and talented.

Grade: Rising 11-12.

Cost: $1,250 (approximate cost). Need-based financial aid is available.

Contact: Stephanie Adamson, Director
A Summer of Excellence
University of Arizona
P.O. Box 210006
Tucson, AZ 85721-0006
(520) 621-6901; Fax: (520) 621-8655
E-mail: soe@honors.arizona.edu
Web site: http://www.honors.arizona.edu/soe.html

Astronomy Camps (The University of Arizona Alumni Association)
June 4-11 (Session 1: Beginning Camp); June 17-25 (Session 2: Advanced Camp)

Astronomy Camps are weeklong adventures in "DOING" science using astronomy as a teaching and discovery tool. Students become astronomers operating research telescopes, keeping nighttime hours, interacting with leading scientists, and interpreting their own observations. By operating the large telescopes (40-60 inch diameter) and electronic instruments at Mt. Lemmon Observatory (9,200 feet altitude) north of Tucson, students are able to observe, record, and monitor a wide variety of celestial objects. In addition, demonstrations, field trips, and guest lectures about modern topics in space exploration help demonstrate what scientists and engineers really do and show the importance of research in society. Professional astronomers, graduate students, and undergraduate astronomy/physics majors serve as counselors and role models and are in contact with the students full time. No prior knowledge of astronomy is required. Both beginning and advanced camps are available depending on age and mathematics background.

Criteria: Application; personal essay; recommendations.

Grade: Rising 7-12.

Cost: $550 (Session 1); $600 (Session 2). Financial aid is available.

Contact: Dr. Donald McCarthy, Jr.
Steward Observatory
University of Arizona
933 N. Cherry Avenue
Tucson, AZ 85721-0065
(520) 621-4079; Fax: (520) 621-9843
E-mail: dmccarthy@as.arizona.edu
Web site: http://www.astronomycamp.org

TUCSON

St. Gregory College Preparatory School
Academic Year

St. Gregory College Preparatory School is a coeducational, nonsectarian, independent school offering college-bound students a stimulating environment, small class sizes, highly skilled and motivated teachers, a wide variety of fine arts and extracurricular activities, and a demonstrated commitment to excellence in education. The principal purpose of the school is to provide a rigorous and superior education in the humanities, sciences, and the arts for students from all social, ethnic, and economic backgrounds. St. Gregory offers a learning environment in which students (grades 6-12) have the opportunity to grow to their fullest potential. St. Gregory seeks out and accepts students based on academic ability without regard to race, religion, or gender. Need-based scholarship assistance is available. St. Gregory is looking for academically capable, highly motivated students who are interested in both scholarship and a wide variety of extracurricular pursuits. Above all, St. Gregory strives to attract each year an interesting and diverse group of individuals.

Criteria: Application (and fee); transcript; personal essay; teacher report; recommendations; standardized test scores; interview.

Grade: 6-12.

Cost: $10,720 (grades 6-8); $11,800 (grades 9-12). Need-based financial aid is available.

Contact: Debby R. Kennedy, Admissions Director
St. Gregory College Preparatory School
3231 North Craycroft
Tucson, AZ 85712
(520) 327-6395; Fax: (520) 327-8276
E-mail: admissions@stgregoryschool.org
Web site: http://www.stgregoryschool.org

ARKANSAS

STATE DIRECTOR

Ann M. Biggers, Administrator
Gifted and Talented Programs
Arkansas Department of Education
Education Building, Room 203-B
4 State Capitol Mall
Little Rock, AR 72201
(501) 682-4224; Fax: (501) 682-4220
E-mail: abiggers@arkedu.k12.ar.us

STATE ASSOCIATION

Arkansans for Gifted and Talented
Dr. Marcia Imbeau, President
101 Bulldog Drive
Plumerville, AR 72127
(501) 354-2269
E-mail: mimbeau@comp.uark.edu

REGIONAL TALENT SEARCH

Center for Talented Youth (The Johns Hopkins University)
See listing on page 4 for complete information.

CONWAY

Arkansas Governor's School (Arkansas Department of Education)
June 15-July 26

The Governor's School is a six-week residential program, administered by the Arkansas Department of Education, on the Hendrix College campus for approximately 400 Arkansas rising high school seniors. The purpose of this school is to give gifted students a challenging opportunity to experience 20th century theories about the interpretation of facts. The emphasis is placed on conceptual or abstract, rather than concrete knowledge. The curriculum is designed to focus on contemporary issues and to provoke curiosity and inquiry from the students. The school offers curriculum in the following areas: academics and arts (in the field of special interest in which the student was selected); general conceptual development; and personal and social development.

Criteria: Application (deadline: January 31); transcript; personal essay; recommendations; test scores; ACT or SAT; GPA; nomination; audition (visual and performing arts); Arkansas resident.

Grade:	Rising 12.
Cost:	None.
Contact:	Ann M. Biggers, Administrator Arkansas Governor's School Arkansas Department of Education Room 203 B, #4 Capitol Mall Little Rock, AR 72201 (501) 682-4224; Fax: (501) 682-5010 E-mail: abiggers@arkedu.k12.ar.us Web site: http://www.hendrix.edu/ags/agshome.htm

SEARCY

Honors Symposium (Harding University)
June 27-July 25 (two-week sessions)

The Harding University Honors Symposium is a residential, two-week academic enrichment program designed to challenge, encourage, and uplift motivated high school students who have completed their junior year. The academic content appeals to students of both the humanities and sciences and includes a study of world religions. Those accepted attend class, participate in chapel services, engage in community service projects, and enjoy recreational activities. In preparation for the transition to college, students experience campus life while residing in a university residence hall supervised by counselors. Eight professors from various academic disciplines instruct the students in classroom and outdoor learning experiences. Now in its eleventh year, the Symposium strives to build relationships with faculty and fellow students; therefore, enrollment is strictly limited to fifty students per session. Participants invariably form lasting relationships with other junior scholars. Three hours of transferable university credit are awarded to all those who successfully complete the Symposium.

Criteria:	Application (deadline: May 15); $150 application fee; transcripts; GPA; recommendations; standardized test scores; nominations.
Grade:	Rising 12.
Cost:	$635.00.
Contact:	Jeffrey T. Hopper, Director Harding Honors Symposium 10838 Harding University Searcy, AR 72149 (501) 279-4478; Fax (501) 279-4184 E-mail: hopper@harding.edu Web site: http://www.harding.edu/symposium

CALIFORNIA

STATE DIRECTOR

LaDona Hein, Consultant
Gifted & Talented Education
California Department of Education
1430 "N" Street
Sacramento, CA 95814
(916) 323-5831; Fax: (916) 323-2833
E-mail: LHein@cde.ca.gov

STATE ASSOCIATION

California Association for the Gifted

The members of CAG are parents, educators, and community members—anyone interested in the education of gifted and talented young people. Mini-conferences and meetings throughout California are planned and sponsored by the two elected representatives in each of the eleven CAG regions, often in conjunction with an affiliated organization active in that region. Local organizations are encouraged to become affiliates of CAG to provide networking throughout the state. The May V. Seagoe Memorial Scholarship is CAG's grant to educators and is intended to foster excellence within gifted education, encourage commitment to serve gifted students, and promote an understanding of giftedness through research.

Dana Reupert, President
15141 East Whittier Boulevard, Suite 510
Whittier, CA 90603
(562) 789-9933; Fax: (562) 789-9833
E-mail: cagoffice1@aol.com

REGIONAL TALENT SEARCH

Center for Talented Youth (The Johns Hopkins University)
See listing on page 4 for complete information.

LOCATIONS THROUGHOUT CALIFORNIA

Adventure Treks
June 15-August 18

See listing on page 8 for complete information.

LOCATIONS THROUGHOUT CALIFORNIA

Education Unlimited Summer Learning Adventures
June-August

Since 1993, Education Unlimited has conducted a variety of world-class summer academic enrichment programs for students entering grades 4-12. Camps include the Public Speaking Institute, American Legal Experience, Computer Camp, College Admission Prep Camp, Actor's Workshop, and a six-week summer study program at UC Berkeley. All camps are residential with an option for day students. In addition to the outstanding curriculum offered at each camp, recreational activities keep the summer FUN! Videos about the camps are available. Call or visit the Education Unlimited Web site for more information.

Criteria:	Application (and fee). Some camps require transcript; GPA; SAT; personal statement; recommendations.
Grade:	Rising 4-12.
Cost:	$700-$4,495. Partial need-based financial aid is available.
Contact:	Education Unlimited 1678 Shattuck Avenue, #305 Berkeley, CA 94709 (800) 548-6612; Fax: (510) 548-0212 E-mail: camps@educationunlimited.com Web site: http://www.academicsummercamps.com

BERKELEY

Academic Study Associates
June-August

See listing on page 7 for complete information.

Carpinteria

Cate School
Academic Year

Cate School, established in 1920, is a four-year, college preparatory, coeducational boarding school. Located on a mesa, 12 miles east of Santa Barbara, in the foothills of the Santa Ynez Mountains, the campus overlooks the Pacific Ocean, the Channel Islands, and the Carpinteria Valley. The 265 students come from more than twenty-five states and ten foreign countries. Approximately 17 percent are day students. Class size averages between ten and twelve students. In addition to a rigorous academic curriculum, all students participate in an extracurricular program, which includes sports, drama, art, music, dance, community service, and an extensive outdoor program. Cate seeks students with maturity, curiosity, and a willingness to assume increasing responsibility and independence. An ability to communicate comfortably and well with peers and adults is important in a community where students and faculty live closely together.

Criteria: Application (and fee); transcript; personal essay; recommendations; SSAT; interview.

Grade: 9-12.

Cost: $29,900 (boarding); $21,500 (day). Over $1.5 million financial aid is offered to approximately 70 students each year.

Contact: Peter J. Mack, Director of Admission
Cate School
1960 Cate Mesa Road
Carpinteria, CA 93013
(805) 684-4127, ext. 217; Fax: (805) 684-2279
E-mail: admission@cate.org
Web site: http://www.cate.org

Claremont

Astrocamp (Guided Discoveries)
June 15-August 2 (one- and two-week sessions)

Astrocamp students explore the wonders of the universe with qualified instructors of the physical and earth sciences. The activities include hands-on labs in astronomy, rocketry, physics, light and lasers, weather and atmosphere, geology, the solar system, space technology, and adventure activities such as high and low ropes courses, climbing wall, bouldering, the Human Gyroscope, Space Ball, and Newton's Chair. The Mission Lab guides students on a simulated exploration of a newly discovered moon in the solar system and leads them on a search for extraterrestrial life.

Criteria: Application.

Grade: Age 8-14 (one-week session); age 10-15 (two-week session).

Cost: $750-$1,500. Limited scholarships are available.

Contact: Stacy Garrett, Camp Secretary
Astrocamp
Guided Discoveries
P. O. Box 1360
Claremont, CA 91711
(800) 645-1423, (909) 625-6194; Fax: (909) 625-7305
E-mail: sgarrett@guideddiscoveries.org
Web site: http://www.guideddiscoveries.org

Claremont

Catalina Sea Camp (Guided Discoveries)
June 15-August 2 (one-week sessions)

Catalina Sea Camp students explore the wonders of Catalina Island with qualified instructors of marine science and island ecology. Campers participate in hands-on labs and adventure activities including: scuba diving certifications, snorkeling, ocean kayaking, underwater video and photography, fish, sharks, marine invertebrates, plankton, algae, marine mammals, and island terrestrial biology.

Criteria: Application.

Grade: Age 12-17.

Cost: $875-$2,600. Limited scholarships are available.

Contact: Stacy Garrett, Camp Secretary
Catalina Sea Camp
Guided Discoveries
P. O. Box 1360
Claremont, CA 91711
(800) 645-1423, (909) 625-6194; Fax: (909) 625-7305
E-mail: sgarrett@guideddiscoveries.org
Web site: http://www.guideddiscoveries.org

IDYLLWILD

Idyllwild Arts Academy
Academic Year and Summer (one-, two-, and three-week sessions)

The **Idyllwild Arts Academy** is one of the finest boarding arts high schools in the country for pre-professional training in creative writing, dance, music, theatre, moving pictures (film, video, and multimedia), and visual arts in conjunction with a demanding academic program. Graduates of the Academy are sought by the most prestigious colleges, universities, and conservatories in the nation. Small classes, a caring faculty, and individualized attention provide an education that is unique and stimulating. The **Summer Program** offers intensive workshops designed for students of all ages and abilities. Ensembles, classes, and workshops vary in duration from 1-3 days to 1-6 weeks. Courses include Dance: ballet, jazz, tap, and modern; Music: band, chamber music, choir, jazz, orchestra, and piano; Theatre and Song and Dance: acting, movement, musical theatre, technical theatre, and voice; Visual arts: ceramics, jewelry, painting and drawing, photography, 3-D art, and computer graphics; Creative writing: fiction, playwriting, and poetry.

Criteria: Application (deadline for the Academy: April 1); application fee; transcript; interview; personal essay; teacher recommendation; audition or portfolio; sample of work; test scores; TOEFL; SSAT.

Grade: 8-12, PG (academic year); age 5-adult (summer).

Cost: $31,900 (boarding); $17,800 (day). Summer program cost varies. Financial aid is available.

Contact: Anne E. Behnke
52500 Temecula Road
Idyllwild, CA 92549-0038
Academy Admission: (909) 659-2171, ext. 223; Fax: (909) 659-2058
Summer Program: (909) 659-2171, ext. 365; Fax: (909) 659-5463
E-mail: admission@idyllwildarts.org (Academy); iasumcat@aol.com (Summer)
Web site: http://www.idyllwildarts.org

LOS ANGELES

The Mirman School for Gifted Children
Academic Year

The school provides a supportive environment in which gifted children can develop divergent and critical thinking skills, take intellectual risks, progress at their own speed, and share their unlimited curiosity and love of learning with other bright children. The teachers seek to address the social, emotional, and personal needs of each individual child. Strong emphasis is placed on the values of personal integrity, respect, community, and caring. Every class, beginning with the five-year-olds, participates in community service projects. The **Lower School** program (age 5-9) includes Spanish, computers, physical education, art, music, and science. **Upper School** students (age 10-14) study math, science, English, history, foreign language (Spanish or Latin), art, theatre, and physical education. Electives are offered in advanced computers, advanced science, speech, Shakespeare, poetry, ethics in film, and choir. Older students also create their own schedule once a week during the Learning Enhancement and Achievement Program.

Criteria:	Application (and fee); transcript; teacher recommendation; test scores; GPA; interview; Stanford-Binet Form L-M or 4th Edition (minimum score of 145), WISC III-R (minimum score of 133), or WPPSI-R (minimum score of 133).
Grade:	1-9.
Cost:	$13,550 (Lower School); $14,500 (Upper School). Financial aid is available.
Contact:	Dr. John Adelsheim The Mirman School for the Gifted 16180 Mulholland Drive Los Angeles, CA 90049 (310) 476-2868; Fax: (310) 471-1532 Web site: http://www.mirman.org

LOS ANGELES

National Computer Camps
June-August

See listing on page 10 for complete information.

Oceanology at Occidental College (Occidental College)
June 29-August 2

This five-week program provides a hands-on introduction to physical oceanography and marine biology. Students are introduced to studying the ocean by using everything from fishing poles and snorkeling gear to the Vantuna, an 85-foot vessel outfitted for oceanographic research. Monday through Thursday there are lectures and labs; Friday is spent aboard the Vantuna. Topics covered include chemical and physical oceanography; classification and natural history of plankton, algae, invertebrates, fish, and mammals; and marine ecology and the effects of pollution. Visiting researchers may discuss topics such as wastewater treatment and deep-sea vent communities. Students live in a residence hall under the guidance of four Occidental students who help plan social activities, such as trips to the beach and Disneyland. This summer program provides a sound background in marine science, a taste of college life, and an introduction to the Los Angeles area. Students receive college credit for four semester units.

Criteria:	Application (deadline: May 31); transcript; recommendations.
Grade:	Rising 12, PG.
Cost:	$4,700 (tuition, room, board, lab fees, and books); approximate costs.
Contact:	Dr. Gary Martin Occidental College Department of Biology 1600 Campus Road Los Angeles, CA 90041 (323) 259-2890; Fax: (323) 341-4974 E-mail: gmartin@oxy.edu Web site: http://www.oxy.edu/oxy/marinebiology

Los Angeles

Summer Discovery Pre-College Enrichment Programs
June-August (three- to six-week programs)

See listing on page 12 for complete information.

Monterey

Santa Catalina School
Academic Year

"At my dinner table sit girls from Mexico, Saudi Arabia, Germany, New Jersey, and California. We're from different cultures yet here with a common goal: to achieve our best." Santa Catalina School offers girls the beauty of the Monterey Peninsula with its world famous aquarium and the cultural and intellectual stimulation of nearby San Francisco museums, theaters, and universities. Dedicated faculty are the cornerstone of Santa Catalina's superior college-preparatory program. Honors and Advanced Placement courses are offered in all disciplines, and opportunities in community service, student government, clubs, and publications enhance the rigorous academic curriculum. The Performing Arts and Music Centers encourage participation in drama, music, and dance and the Bedford Athletic Complex provides space for strong athletic teams to practice and compete. In 2002, Santa Catalina welcomed the addition of a 25-yard by 30-meter pool, a 150-seat recital hall, and wireless Internet access in the dormitories. The mission of Santa Catalina is to foster intellectual growth, moral values, individualism, and leadership.

Criteria:	Application (and fee); transcript; personal essay; recommendations; test scores; interview; GPA; SSAT.
Grade:	9-12.
Cost:	$30,100 (residential); $17,800 (day). Need-based financial aid is available, plus a Merit Scholarship for entering freshmen and sophomores.
Contact:	Heather Daly, Director of Admission Santa Catalina School 1500 Mark Thomas Drive Monterey, CA 93940-5291 (831) 655-9356; Fax: (831) 655-7535 E-mail: admissions@santacatalina.org Web site: http://www.santacatalina.org

Ojai

The Thacher School
Academic Year

Since 1889, Thacher has prepared talented students for top colleges and lives of leadership and service. The traditional and rigorous curriculum (which includes 19 Advanced Placement courses) culminates in a Senior Research and Exhibition project. In a community renowned for its warmth, students live by an Honor Code: doors are unlocked, and many exams for juniors and seniors are unproctored. Challenges of outdoor life, community work, and peer leadership encourage resourcefulness, judgment, and integrity. The school offers extensive outdoor opportunities including horse programs, rock climbing, kayaking, gymkhana, plus 30 competitive athletic teams. Twenty-five percent of the student body receives financial aid. Each dorm room provides Internet access.

Criteria: Application (and fee); transcript; personal essay; recommendations; test scores; GPA; ISSE; SSAT; interview.

Grade: 9-12.

Cost: $29,450 (boarding); $19,500 (day). Financial aid is available.

Contact: Monique L. DeVane, Director of Admission
The Thacher School
5025 Thacher Road
Ojai, CA 93023
(805) 640-3210; Fax: (805) 640-9377
E-mail: admission@thacher.org
Web site: http://www.thacher.org

ORANGE

TIP Field Studies (Duke University Talent Identification Program)
June 15-August 6 (two-week programs)

See listing on page 182 for complete information.

SAN DIEGO

SeaWorld Adventure Camp
June-August (five-night sessions)

Ready for the ultimate summer camp? Spend five nights at SeaWorld San Diego and discover the many treasures of their 166-acre marine life adventure park. This overnight camp promises to be an experience like no other. It's fun to visit bottlenose dolphins, beluga whales, polar bears, penguins, and sharks, but at SeaWorld Adventure Camp, students will really get their feet wet and discover first-hand what it's really like to take care of SeaWorld's animals. The adventure doesn't end there, out-of-park excursions will immerse campers in San Diego's beautiful coastal landscapes and natural history. The thrills are non-stop in this animal experience of a lifetime. Students will stay in dormitories located at SeaWorld San Diego. Camp fees include transportation between SeaWorld San Diego and the San Diego Airport, lodging, meals, educational materials, supplies, and equipment.

Criteria: Registration.

Grade: 4-8.

Cost: Call for current costs.

Contact: Mike Dunn, Camp Manager
SeaWorld Adventure Camp
500 SeaWorld Drive
San Diego, CA 92109
(800) 380-3202; Fax: (619) 226-3634
Web site: http://www.seaworld.org

San Francisco

National Computer Camps
June-August

See listing on page 10 for complete information.

Santa Barbara

Summer Discovery Pre-College Enrichment Programs
June-August (three- to six-week programs)

See listing on page 12 for complete information.

Santa Cruz

Excel at UC Santa Cruz (Putney Student Travel)
June-August (Three-, four-, and seven-week programs)

See listing on page 9 for complete information.

Stanford

The Junior Statesmen Summer School (The Junior Statesmen Foundation)
June 29-July 24

Located on the Stanford University campus, The Junior Statesmen Summer School offers a rigorous academic challenge to outstanding high school students. The curriculum features seven college-level courses: AP American Government, AP Comparative Government, AP Economics, Constitutional Law, Political Communication, Public Speaking and the Law, and Speech Communication. These courses are enriched by a high-level speakers program and nightly sessions of a debate practicum, the Congressional Workshop. The collegiate academic environment stresses substantial reading, research, and writing. Students reside in Stanford University residence halls and use Stanford classrooms, libraries, and recreational facilities. Courses are taught by outstanding political scientists and top-ranked speech and debate instructors. Summer School students and faculty meet with guest speakers on campus for an in-depth exploration of politics and government in the nation's largest state. A cultural tip to San Francisco is also offered. Similar programs are conducted at Northwestern University, Georgetown University, Princeton University, and Yale University.

Criteria: Application; transcript; personal essay; recommendations.

Grade: Rising 10-12.

Cost:	$3,325 (includes room and board and all academic costs). Need- and merit-based scholarships are available.
Contact:	Admissions Director The Junior Statesmen Foundation 60 East Third Avenue, Suite 320 San Mateo, CA 94401-4032 (800) 334-5353, (650) 347-1600; Fax: (650) 347-7200 E-mail: jsa@jsa.org Web site: http://www.jsa.org

STANFORD

Summer College for High School Students (Stanford University)
June 21–August 17

World renowned for its excellence in teaching and research, Stanford University offers an eight-week program for students who are ready to explore the academic and personal challenges of a university environment. Participants select three to four undergraduate courses and earn Stanford University credit for completed work in the humanities, social sciences, natural sciences, and mathematics. Students live together in a dorm, and are supervised by an adult Program Director. A trained staff of Stanford undergraduates serves as Residence Counselors, providing support, guidance, and a first-hand perspective on life at Stanford University. Students also enjoy a full range of extracurricular and weekend activities, including intramural sports, house discussions with Stanford faculty and undergraduate admission officers, and visits to San Francisco, Yosemite, and Monterey. Local commuter students are also welcome.

Criteria:	Application (deadline: April 15); $25 application fee; transcript; personal essay; GPA; SAT; test scores; recommendations.
Grade:	Rising 12; entering college freshmen.
Cost:	$7,300 (residential); $2,300 (commuter); all costs are approximate. Limited need-based financial aid is available.
Contact:	Rafael Ulate, Director of Admission and Student Services Stanford Summer Session Building 590, 103 Stanford, CA 94305-3005 (650) 723-3109; Fax: (650) 725-6080 E-mail: summersession@stanford.edu Web site: http://summersession.stanford.edu

Stanford

Stanford Discovery Institutes (Stanford University)
June 1-August 17

The Stanford Summery Discovery Institutes offer students who have completed their sophomore year the opportunity to experience the excitement and challenge of being a student at Stanford University. Choosing one area from a variety of subjects (offerings in Summer 2001 included creative writing, environmental studies, philosophy, and theater), participants spend three intensive weeks delving deeply into that topic and studying closely with Stanford professors and visiting instructors who are experts in their fields. Students earn Stanford University credit for successfully completed coursework. Participants live together in a student residence under the supervision of an adult program director. Program staff members organize extracurricular activities which complement and reinforce the classroom instruction of each institute. Activities may include visits to San Francisco and Monterey; discussions with Stanford faculty; and public service projects.

Criteria: Application (deadline: April 15); $25 application fee; transcript; personal essay; test scores; GPA; PSAT; SAT; recommendations; sample of work (creative writing).

Grade: Rising 11-12.

Cost: $3,100-$4,800 (residential); $2,300-$4,000 (commuter); all costs are approximate. Limited need-based financial aid is available.

Contact: Rafael Ulate, Director of Admission and Student Services
Stanford Discovery Institutes
Building 590, Room 103
Stanford, CA 94305-3005
(650) 723-3109; Fax: (650) 725-6080
E-mail: summersession@stanford.edu
Web site: http://summerinstitutes.stanford.edu

SuperCamp® (Stanford University)
July-August

See listing on page 13 for complete information.

Valencia

InnerSpark (California State Summer School for the Arts)
July 12 - August 9

InnerSpark at the California State Summer School for the Arts is a rigorous pre-professional training program in the visual and performing arts, creative writing, animation, and film for talented artists of high school age. The month-long program is held at the California Institute of the Arts (CalArts) in Valencia. InnerSpark provides a supportive environment in which students hone acquired skills and explore new techniques and ideas for an intense and exciting learning experience. The school was created by the California Legislature and held its first session in 1987. Its purpose is to provide a training ground for future artists who wish to pursue careers in the arts and entertainment industries in California. California State Summer School for the Arts is a state agency funded through a unique public-private partnership.

Criteria: Application (and fee); recommendations; sample of work; gifted and talented; audition.

Grade: 9-12.

Cost: $1,590 (California residents); $3,885 (nonresidents). Financial aid is only available for California residents who are first-time participants.

Contact: Robert Jaffe, Director
InnerSpark
California State Summer School for the Arts
4825 J Street, Suite 120
Sacramento, CA 95819
(916) 227-9320; Fax: (916) 227-9455
E-mail: cynthia@csssa.org
Web site: http://www.csssa.org

COLORADO

STATE DIRECTOR

Leslie Chislett, Director of Gifted and Talented Program
Special Education Services Unit
Colorado Department of Education
201 East Colfax Avenue, Suite 300
Denver, CO 80203-1799
(303) 866-6652; Fax: (303) 866-6811
E-mail: chislett_l@cde.state.co.us

STATE ASSOCIATION

Colorado Association for the Gifted and Talented

Because all human beings have an inherent right to develop their full potential, the purpose of this organization is to foster an understanding of all gifted children and their exceptional needs and to advocate for appropriate education through partnerships with educators, parents, administrators, legislators, and the general public.

Jaquelin Medina, President
P.O. Box 473414
Aurora, CO 80047-3414
(303) 368-4401
E-mail: info@coloradogifted.org

REGIONAL TALENT SEARCH

Rocky Mountain Talent Search (University of Denver)
See listing on page 5 for complete information.

LOCATIONS THROUGHOUT COLORADO

Deer Hill Expeditions (Accredited by the Association for Experiential Education)
June 24-August 18 (three- to five-week programs)

Deer Hill has offered challenging wilderness expeditions, conservation service projects, and cross-cultural living and service in the canyons, rivers, and mountains of Colorado, Utah, Arizona, and New Mexico since 1984. Deer Hill's purpose is to enhance an individual's appreciation of the natural world, teach the skills of living in the wilderness with minimum impact, promote stewardship of the earth, and foster a tradition of service to our native lands and peoples. Deer Hill provides a challenging atmosphere in which people can grow as individuals and be integral members of a small group. Activities include whitewater rafting, whitewater canoeing, inflatable kayaking, canyoneering, mountaineering, rock climbing, leadership initiatives, cross-cultural living and service with Native Americans, and conservation projects with the U.S. Forest Service. Field staff average 25-30 years of age and have extensive experience leading young people in the backcountry. Deer Hill offers the opportunity to experience the natural beauty, human history, and diverse cultures of the American Southwest.

Criteria: Application (and fee); personal essays; teacher reference.

Grade: 7-12.

Cost: $3,300-$4,750.

Contact: Doug and Beverly Capelin, Directors
Deer Hill Expeditions
P.O. Box 180
Mancos, CO 81328
(800) 533-7221; Fax: (970) 533-7221
E-mail: info@deerhillexpeditions.com
Web site: http://www.deerhillexpeditions.com

COLORADO SPRINGS

SuperCamp® (Colorado College)
July-August

See listing on page 13 for complete information.

Fountain Valley School of Colorado
Academic Year

Fountain Valley School (FVS) of Colorado maintains a 70-year tradition of excellence, offering a comprehensive and challenging curriculum focused on academics, arts, and athletics. An accomplished and dedicated faculty, a rigorous academic program that includes AP and honors courses in every department, and the resources of a magnificent 1,100-acre Western campus offer unparalleled learning opportunities. Students develop leadership skills through a strong advising system and living in an environment distinguished by close peer and faculty relations. Fountain Valley enrolls 235 students from 15 states and 12 countries in grades 9-12. A $15 million residence hall master plan, campus-wide communication network, and a science building are among the new state-of-the-art facilities and resources added to the central campus, renowned for its setting and historical southwestern architecture. The broad range of extracurricular programs includes competitive athletics, outdoor education, horseback riding, and visual and performing arts. FVS graduates 100% of its seniors to selective four-year colleges and universities across the nation.

Criteria: Application (deadline: February 1); transcript; personal essay; recommendations; sample of work; test scores; SSAT; interview.

Grade: 9-12.

Cost: $27,350 (boarding); $15,550 (day). Need-based financial aid is available (Over $1 million is allocated to 34% of the student body annually).

Contact: Kilian J. Forgus, Director of Admission
Fountain Valley School of Colorado
6155 Fountain Valley School Road
Colorado Springs, CO 80911
(719) 390-7035; Fax: (719) 390-7762
E-mail: admis@fvs.edu
Web site: http://www.fvs.edu

COLORADO SPRINGS

Summer Seminar Program
(The Marie Walsh Sharpe Art Foundation)
June 8-21 (Session I); June 22-July 5 (Session II); July 6-19 (Session III)

The Marie Walsh Sharpe Art Foundation Summer Seminar Program is a scholarship program for artistically gifted high school juniors held on the campus of Colorado College. It is designed as an art institute offering an intensive visual-art studio program. Three two-week seminars are held each summer and allow each student to gain a stronger foundation of skills and understanding in the visual arts through experiencing college-level drawing and painting classes in a group setting. Artists-in-residence serve as the primary instructors. Students live in a dormitory, eat meals in the dining hall, and have access to all campus facilities. Sessions concerning careers in art, the development of a portfolio, and small group discussions with artists sharing their unique insights, technical expertise, and commitment to art, will be included. Students also enjoy a full schedule of evening activities. Trips are planned to draw and paint in the mountains and visit area museums.

Criteria: Personal essay; recommendations; slides of work.
Grade: Rising 12.

Cost: None. All expenses paid except for transportation.

Contact: Kim Taylor, Program Officer
The Marie Walsh Sharpe Art Foundation
830 N. Tejon, Suite 120
Colorado Springs, CO 80903
(719) 635-3220; Fax: (719) 635-3018

CORTEZ

Crow Canyon Archaeological Center
March-November (Non-dig programs, 1-5 days); May-September (Dig and non-dig programs, 5 days); June-August (Middle and high school programs for individual students)

Crow Canyon Archaeological Center in Cortez, Colorado, makes learning fun by incorporating diverse classroom subjects into an exciting, experiential format. In programs for school groups grades 4-12, students learn to look at science, social science, environmental studies, math, physics, and art in new ways through the discipline of archaeology. Students in grades 4-6 excavate in a simulated dig; 7th grade and older student groups may choose to dig alongside professional archaeologists in the field. Most programs include a full-day guided tour of Mesa Verde National Park. For individual students, Crow Canyon offers summer programs; a weeklong middle school archaeology program; a three-week high school field school offering intensive excavation experience; and a weeklong high school excavation program. Programs are held at Crow Canyon's scenic 110-acre campus, and include delicious meals and comfortable accommodations.

Criteria: Application; other criteria varies with program; may include personal essay and teacher recommendation.

Grade: 4-12 (school groups); 6-8 (middle school program); 9-12 (high school programs).

Cost: Varies with program. Limited financial aid is available.

Contact: School Programs Marketing Manager
Crow Canyon Archaeological Center
23390 Road 23
Cortez, CO 81321
(800) 422-8975, ext. 130; Fax: (970) 565-4859
E-mail: schoolprograms@crowcanyon.org
Web site: http://www.crowcanyon.org

ROCKY MOUNTAIN NATIONAL PARK

Wildlife Camp, Environmental Leadership Program, Environmental Backpacking, and Intern Instructor Programs (The Wilderness Education Institute)

Summer (seven- and fourteen-day sessions)

Wildlife Camp teaches campers (age 8-13) about natural systems and ecology, creates a community of campers and staff that values diversity and promotes intercultural learning, introduces campers to basic backpacking and rock climbing skills, and perpetuates the tradition of bluegrass music. **Leadership Training** gives teens (age 14-17) the opportunity to become environmental educators in the context of Wildlife Camp. **Environmental Backpacking** trips educate teens (age 13-17) about wildlife ecology, wilderness issues, backcountry skills, and environmental service on a multiple day backpacking trip in the National Park. Participants may also spend several days rock climbing, rafting, and exploring environmental careers. The **Intern Instructor** program hosts two individuals each summer (age 17-18) in a highly structured hands-on learning experience focused on exploring the career fields of outdoor and environmental education. The Institute operates a shuttle from Denver International Airport to base camp for all programs.

Criteria: Application.

Grade: 4-12; age 8-13 (Wildlife Camp); 14-17 (Leadership Training); 13-17 (Environmental Backpacking); 17-18 (Intern Instructor).

Cost: $690-$1,100. Financial aid is available.

Contact: Rob Alexander, Executive Director
Wildlife Camp, Environmental Leadership Program
2260 Baseline Rd. Suite #205
Boulder, CO 80302
(877) 628-9692
E-mail: information@weiprograms.org
Web site: http://www.weiprograms.org

The Road Less Traveled

Summer (one- to six-week sessions)

See listing on page 11 for complete information.

CONNECTICUT

STATE DIRECTOR

Dr. Jeanne Purcell, Consultant
Gifted and Talented Programs
Connecticut Department of Education
165 Capitol Avenue, Room 205
Hartford, CT 06106
(860) 713-6745; Fax: (860) 713-7018
E-mail: jeanne.purcell@po.state.ct.us

STATE ASSOCIATION

Connecticut Association for the Gifted

The mission of the Connecticut Association for the Gifted is to provide an organization for educators, psychologists, parents, policy makers, administrators, and others to learn about the unique educational and affective needs of gifted and talented children, and how to meet these needs effectively in our schools, families, and communities. It recognizes that gifted children come from all cultural and socioeconomic backgrounds and have diverse abilities and interests.

Sylvia Burke, President
155 Sycamore Drive
Torrington, CT 06790-4261
(203) 291-6586
E-mail: info@ctgifted.org

REGIONAL TALENT SEARCH

Center for Talented Youth (The Johns Hopkins Univerisity)
See listing on page 4 for complete information.

FAIRFIELD

National Computer Camps
June-August

See listing on page 10 for complete information.

FARMINGTON

Arts Alive! (Miss Porter's School)
June 29-July 26

As they explore a wide range of art forms, girls in grades seven through nine will strengthen their artistic and aesthetic talents in studio art, pottery, photography, jewelry making, dance, theatre, and writing. They will also enhance their overall academic skills, self-discipline, risk-taking skills, and self-confidence. Fun, friendship, and curiosity develop as girls explore the studio, performing, and literary arts through hands-on activities Classes are held in the recently renovated state-of-the-art computer labs; studio art, pottery, photography, and jewelry making studios; school theater; and dance studio. Related evening activities enhance Arts Alive! classes. A respected leader in girls' education since 1843, Miss Porter's School offers the demanding community that distinguish the finest boarding schools.

Criteria: Application ($30 application fee); transcript; personal essay; recommendations.

Grade: 7-9.

Cost: $3,500.

Contact: Wendy Allerton, Director of Summer Programs
Arts Alive!
Miss Porter's School
60 Main Street
Farmington, CT 06032
(860) 409-3692; Fax: (860) 409-3515
E-mail: summer_programs@missporters.org
Web site: mpsartsalive.org

FARMINGTON

MPS Summer Challenge (Miss Porter's School)
June 29-July 26

Girls in grades seven through nine can take the "MPS Summer Challenge." This academic program features challenging and fun science and math activities, athletics, field trips, and time to socialize. Girls come from around the United States and the world to participate in this unique program. Fun, friendship, curiosity, and confidence develop as girls explore the physical and mathematical worlds through hands-on education and problem solving activities. The program explores biology, chemistry, physics, and math through topics such as "Animal, Vegetable, or Mineral?" and "Where in the Solar System is...?" Classes are held in the fully networked Olin Arts & Sciences Center and take advantage of the school's extensive grounds, including the butterfly garden. A respected leader in girls' education since 1843, during the academic year Miss Porter's School offers the demanding curriculum, collaborative environment, and supportive community that distinguish the finest boarding schools (grades 9-12).

Criteria: Application (and $30 fee); recommendations; transcript; personal essay; female student.

Grade: 7-9.

Cost: $3,500. Limited need-based financial aid is available.

Contact: Wendy Allerton
Director, Summer Programs
Miss Porter's School
60 Main Street
Farmington, CT 06032
(860) 409-3692; Fax: (860) 409-3515
E-mail: Summer_Programs@missporters.org
Web site: http://www.summerchallenge.org

Kent

Kent School
Academic Year

Kent School, a coeducational, college preparatory, Episcopal Church school community, offers a demanding but supportive educational environment. The rural, 1,800-acre campus houses 500 boarding and 50 day students of all faiths from all over the United States and the world. Course placement is based on ability and background, not age or grade, thereby enabling progress to be as rapid as the individual's energy and talent will allow. Advanced Placement courses in all disciplines, including art and computer science, offer challenges to one-third of the student body. Independent study can be tailored to specially gifted students in approved areas not covered by the available curriculum. Particularly active and well-subscribed dramatic, vocal, and instrumental music programs, together with tremendously varied athletic options, ensure that the students' extracurricular lives are as rich and challenging as their curricular lives.

Criteria:	Application; transcript; personal essay; recommendations; test scores; SSAT (grades 9-10); PSAT or SAT (grades 11-12); interview.
Grade:	9-12, PG.
Cost:	$29,900 (boarding); $23,400 (day). Need-based financial aid is available ($3.5 million awarded annually).
Contact:	Marc L. Cloutier, Director of Admissions Kent School P.O. Box 2006 Kent, CT 06757 (800) 538-KENT, (860) 927-6111; Fax: (860) 927-6109 E-mail: admissions@kent-school.edu Web site: http://www.kent-school.edu

Middletown

Center for Creative Youth
(Capitol Region Education Council and Wesleyan University)
June 22-July 26

Located on the campus of Wesleyan University, the Center for Creative Youth (CCY) is a residential community of 200 artistically talented high school students. In the summer, the Center offers five weeks of advanced classes in creative writing, dance, instrumental and vocal music, technical theater, theater, musical theater, photography, filmmaking, and visual arts. This pre-college program provides a challenging learning opportunity for young artists from diverse backgrounds and cultures. Three elements of the program, which contribute to strong academic and personal growth, are: (1) association with talented and motivated peers, (2) recognition and evaluation of growth and skill development through intensive work with professional artists, and (3) accomplishment of an arts leadership project. This combination raises the awareness and aspiration levels of the program's students. Students study their desired art form with real artists and mentors who make their living from the arts. Interdisciplinary classes are also offered so students may engage in art forms beyond their major.

Criteria:	Application (and $20 fee); personal essay; recommendations; sample of work; nomination; interview; audition.
Grade:	Rising 10-12.
Cost:	$1,950 (tuition); $1,800 (room and board). Financial aid is available.
Contact:	Nancy Wolfe, Director Center for Creative Youth Capitol Region Education Council Wesleyan University 350 High Street Middletown, CT 06459 (860) 685-3307; Fax: (860) 685-3311 E-mail: ccy@wesleyan.edu Web site: http://www.crec.org/ccy

NEW HAVEN

Exploration Senior Program (Exploration Summer Programs)
June 29-August 9 (three-and six-week sessions)

Students come to Exploration Summer Programs from over 40 states and 40 countries to enjoy academic opportunities and extracurricular activities. Students entering tenth through twelfth grades attend our Senior Program on the campus of Yale University. Senior Program students live in the Old Campus, a beautifully landscaped quadrangle bordered by Gothic-style residences at the heart of the University. Exploration students have access to Yale's world-renowned academic facilities, museums, and libraries as well as its outstanding indoor and outdoor athletic and fitness facilities. The Senior Program offers high school students an exciting summer—the chance to experience innovative academic courses and mini-courses; meet other students from all over the world; engage in sports, activities, and discussions; get a taste of college life; and enjoy the cultural and recreational offerings of New York City and the Northeast.

Criteria:	Application; teacher report.
Grade:	Rising 10-12.
Cost:	$1,675 (one session, day); $3,395 (one session, residential). Limited financial aid is available.
Contact:	Becca Finer, Admissions Coordinator Exploration Summer Programs P.O. Box 368 470 Washington Street Norwood, MA 02062 (781) 762-7400; Fax: (781) 762-7425 Web site: http://www.explo.org

New Haven

The Junior Statesmen Summer School (The Junior Statesmen Foundation)
June 30-July 25

Located on the Yale University campus, The Junior Statesmen Summer School offers a rigorous academic challenge to outstanding high school students. The curriculum features four college-level courses: AP American Government, Constitutional Law, Public Speaking and the Law, and Speech Communication. These classes are enriched by a high-level speakers program in New York City and nightly sessions of a debate practicum, the Congressional Workshop. The collegiate academic environment stresses substantial reading, research, and writing. Students reside in a Yale University residence college and use Yale classrooms, libraries, and recreational facilities. Classes are taught by political scientists and top-ranked speech and debate instructors. Students meet with speakers for an in-depth look at politics, business, the media, and government in New York. Similar programs are conducted at Stanford University, Georgetown University, Northwestern University, and Princeton University.

Criteria:	Application; transcript; personal essay; recommendations.
Grade:	Rising 10-12.
Cost:	$3,325 (includes room and board and all academic costs). Need- and merit-based partial scholarships are available.
Contact:	Admissions Director The Junior Statesmen Foundation 60 East Third Avenue, Suite 320 San Mateo, CA 94401-4032 (800) 334-5353, (650) 347-1600; Fax: (650) 347-7200 E-mail: jsa@jsa.org Web site: http://www.jsa.org

New Milford

Buck's Rock Performing and Creative Arts Camp
June 25-August 16 (4-week sessions); June 25-August 16 (8-week session)

Since 1942, Buck's Rock Performing and Creative Arts Camp has offered teenagers (age 12-16) a wide range of activities in a freedom of choice, non-competitive teaching and learning environment. Creative arts include glassblowing, casting, lamp work, ceramics, woodworking, weaving, photography, video, computer, sculpture, fiber arts, publications and creative writing, radio broadcasting, etc. Performing arts include music, a digital recording studio, dance, theatre, clowning, and improvisation. In addition, there are opportunities to take part in sports, horseback riding, swimming, pioneering, fencing, martial arts, spelunking, animal and vegetable farming, and much more. At Buck's Rock, campers are given the freedom of choice to decide for themselves the activities in which they will become involved, and are allowed the time they need to pursue them. Campers work with qualified, professional artists and teachers who nurture and support their talents and skills as they perform and create in facilities that are equipped to professional standards.

Criteria:	Interview.

Grade: 6-12 (age 12-16).

Cost: $4,990 (4 weeks); $6,990 (8 weeks). Financial aid is available.

Contact: Mickey and Laura Morris
Buck's Rock Camp
59 Buck's Rock Road
New Milford, CT 06776
(860) 354-5030; Fax: (860) 354-1355
E-mail: bucksrock@bucksrockcamp.com
Web site: http://www.bucksrockcamp.com

New Milford

Canterbury School
Academic Year

Canterbury is a coeducational, boarding and day, college preparatory school guided by lay Roman Catholics since its founding in 1915. The campus is located in western Connecticut, 1 hour from Hartford, 1.5 hours from New York City, and 2.5 hours from Boston. Academic achievement at Canterbury is not limited to a traditional curriculum: there are 30 honors and Advanced Placement courses available. A 6:1 student-to-faculty ratio provides each student the opportunity to pursue learning outside a structured classroom. Independent study in a variety of academic and social areas is also available. Canterbury prides itself on creating a value-based community where every student experiences a broad and challenging program in a small school setting. The school's educational environment fosters academic rigor, athletic development, artistic enrichment, and spiritual growth. The hallmark of a Canterbury education is the School's willingness to accept students as they are, support them where necessary, stretch them where appropriate, and inspire them to become moral leaders in a secular world.

Criteria: Application (and fee); transcript; personal essay; recommendations; sample of work; test scores; GPA; SSAT; PSAT; SAT; interview.

Grade: 9-12, PG.

Cost: $30,500 (boarding); $21,500 (day). Need-based financial aid is available.

Contact: Keith R. Holton, Director of Admission
Canterbury School
New Milford, CT 06776
(860) 210-3832; Fax: (860) 350-1120
E-mail: admissions@cbury.org
Web site: http://www.cbury.org

Simsbury

Westminster School
Academic Year

Founded in 1888 by William Lee Cushing and inspired by the ancient Uppingham School in Rutland, England, Westminster School currently serves 365 boys and girls in a secondary school program (grades 9-12) and a small number of postgraduates. Day students constitute one-third of the student body. Just 20 minutes from downtown Hartford and 8 miles from Bradley International Airport, this 230-acre campus is an easy walk into Simsbury. Character, community, balance, and involvement comprise the core values. Opportunities for leadership exist alongside opportunities for a wide array of campus activities. Facilities for publications, art, music, drama, discussion clubs, chapel, and athletics are extensive. The close faculty/student relationships provide a haven for the gifted student who seeks to differentiate and go beyond what is covered in the classroom. T-1 lines and impressive, wireless technology network enhance students' capability to do research. Westminster offers an excellent college preparatory with 19 AP courses in all subject areas, enabling students to develop their optimal academic potential.

Criteria:	Application (deadline: January 25); $50 application fee ($100 for international applications); transcript; personal essay; recommendations; sample of work;, test scores; GPA; SSAT; interview.
Grade:	9-12, PG.
Cost:	$29,950 (boarding) $21,700 (day). Need-based financial aid is available (approximately $1.94 million).
Contact:	Jon C. Deveaux, Director of Admissions Westminster School 995 Hopmeadow Street Simsbury, CT 06070 (860) 408-3060; Fax: (860) 408-3042 E-mail: admit @westminster-school.org. Web site: http://www.westminster-school.org

Storrs

UConn Mentor Connection (University of Connecticut, Neag Center for Gifted Education and Talent Development)
July 7-25

UConn Mentor Connection is a three-week, residential, summer program for academically talented secondary students. The mission is to provide young people with opportunities to participate in creative projects and investigations directly with university mentors. High school juniors and seniors explore an area of interest through participation in real-world research and creative projects, and other works-in-progress. The goals of the program are to enable students to achieve to their highest potential, and to provide students with opportunities to interact with people from diverse backgrounds. If a student is eager to engage in exciting challenges, gain hands-on experience in an area of interest, experience college life, and meet new people who share common interests, he/she is a candidate for UConn Mentor Connection.

Criteria:	Application; transcript; GPA; personal essays; recommendations.
Grade:	Rising 11-12.
Cost:	$2,800.
Contact:	Heather L. Spottiswoode UConn Mentor Connection University of Connecticut 2131 Hillside Road, U-7 Storrs, CT 06269 (860) 486-0283; Fax:(860) 486-2900 E-mail: epsadm07@uconnvm.uconn.edu Web site: http://www.gifted.uconn.edu

WASHINGTON

The Gunnery
Academic Year

Founded in 1850, The Gunnery is a coeducational college preparatory boarding and day school dedicated to rigorous preparation for higher education. The school's name is derived from that of Frederick Gunn, its founder, whose mission was to establish a school that cultivated scholarship, personal integrity, social responsibility, and physical fitness—the four cornerstones on which he believed character is built. Today a student population of 270 is served in small classes, on the athletic fields, and in the dormitories by an exceptionally skilled, experienced, and committed faculty. Requirements include three years of language, mathematics, and laboratory science. Honors or Advanced Placement courses are offered in most disciplines in order to address the talents of gifted students. Superb facilities and a rich variety of extracurricular activities, including required athletics and fine and performing arts, are enjoyed by Gunnery students on a safe and scenic, 220-acre campus in the hills of western Connecticut.

Criteria:	Application (and fee); transcript (two years with current grades); writing sample; recommendations; SSAT, PSAT, or SAT; interview.
Grade:	9-12, PG.
Cost:	$30,100 (boarding); $21,800 (day). $1.6 million in financial aid is available, including merit scholarships for superior academic achievement.
Contact:	Thomas W. Adams, Director of Admissions The Gunnery 99 Green Hill Road Washington, CT 06793 (860) 868-7334; Fax: (860) 868-1614 E-mail: admissions@gunnery.org Web site: http://www.gunnery.org

WATERTOWN

The Taft School
Academic Year and Summer Session

The Taft School, a coeducational boarding and day school of 573 students, offers a diverse college-preparatory curriculum suited to the needs of the talented and gifted student. Taft offers admission only to those students who have demonstrated exceptional intellectual ability and have achieved considerable academic success. The inherent flexibility within the school's curriculum enables each student to progress at a speed commensurate with his or her abilities, and small classes (student-to-teacher ratio of 6:1) assure individual attention. Advanced Placement and Independent Study programs in every discipline enable advanced students to take on new challenges throughout their careers at Taft. In 2002, Taft students wrote 450 AP exams and earned an average of 4.2; approximately one-fifth of the seniors were recognized by the National Merit Scholarship Program. All Taft graduates go on to college. Recently Middlebury, Harvard, Williams, Georgetown, Yale, Trinity, Brown, Cornell, and Princeton have been the most popular choices. A summer session is also offered.

Criteria: Application (deadline: January 31); $35 application fee; transcript; personal essay; recommendations; test scores; PSAT; SSAT; SAT (grade 12 or PG candidates); interview.

Grade: 9-12, PG.

Cost: $29,100 (boarding); $21,000 (day). Need-based financial aid is available (34% of student body receives $3.8 million in aid).

Contact: Frederick H. Wandelt, III, Director of Admissions
The Taft School
110 Woodbury Road
Watertown, CT 06795
(860) 945-7777; Fax: (860) 945-7808
E-mail: admissions@taftschool.org
Web site: http://www.taftschool.org

Windsor

The Loomis Chaffee School
Academic Year

Located on a rural, three hundred-acre campus at the confluence of the Connecticut and Farmington Rivers, Loomis Chaffee is a coeducational boarding and day school enrolling 723 students (grades 9-12, and postgraduates). Students originate from 30 states and 15 foreign countries. The school features an extensive and rigorous curriculum of 179 courses, including Advanced Placement offerings in 14 subjects. The School Year Abroad Program offers opportunities to study in France, Spain, and Beijing. Additionally, German language students may study at a German boarding school the winter term of their senior year. The Loomis Chaffee campus includes a science center with ten fully equipped laboratories and a 58,000-volume library. A state-of-the-art visual art center includes studio facilities and classrooms. All dormitories are wired for full telecommunications capabilities including in-room telephones equipped with voice mail. Extracurricular activities include 30 interscholastic and intramural sports and extensive offerings in music, drama, art, and community service.

Criteria: Application (deadline: January 15); application fee; transcript; personal essay; recommendations; test scores; SSAT; interview; parent statement (optional).

Grade: 9-12, PG.

Cost: $29,200 (boarding); $21,900 (day). Financial aid is available.

Contact: Thomas Southworth, Director of Admissions
The Loomis Chaffee School
4 Batchelder Road
Windsor, CT 06095
(860) 687-6000; Fax: (860) 298-8756
E-mail: admissions@loomis.org
Web site: http://www.loomis.org

DELAWARE

State Director

Debora Hansen, Education Associate
Delaware Department of Public Instruction
P.O. Box 1402, Townsend Building
Dover, DE 19903
(302) 739-4885; Fax: (302) 739-3744
E-mail: dhansen@doe.k12.de.us

State Association

Delaware Talented and Gifted Association
Dr. Margaret Dee, Chair
P.O. Box 1402
Dover, DE 19903-1402
(302) 739-4885 x 3110
E-mail: mdee@state.de.us

Regional Talent Search

Center for Talented Youth (The Johns Hopkins University)
See listing on page 4 for complete information.

MIDDLETOWN

St. Andrew's School
Academic Year

St. Andrew's School offers gifted and energetic students the adventure, excitement, and challenge of a demanding curriculum, taught by a stimulating, creative, and supportive faculty. The location for Dead Poets Society, St. Andrew's is situated on 2,200 beautiful acres of fields, farms, forests, and tidal marshes, and is adjacent to a large pond used for environmental study, crew, and recreation. St. Andrew's enrolls 265 boys and girls, all of whom board, fostering a sense of belonging and a sense of community among the students. Small classes, a full range of AP courses (average score on national examinations is 4), along with extensive co-curricular programs in music, theater, visual arts, chapel, community service, student government, and 21 varsity athletic teams, provide tremendous opportunities for leadership, growth, discovery, and service. All students go on to college, with over 70% of the seniors enrolling at the most prestigious and competitive colleges.

Criteria:	Application (deadline: January 15); $35 application fee; transcript; math and English teacher recommendations; SSAT; interview.
Grade:	9-12 (boarding).
Cost:	$26,600 (2002-2003 costs). Need-based financial aid is available (approximately 45% of the students receive aid; $2.66 million awarded in 2002).
Contact:	Louisa H. Zendt, Director of Admission St. Andrew's School 350 Noxontown Road Middletown, DE 19709 (302) 378-9511; Fax: (302) 378-7120 E-mail: lzendt@standrews-de.org Web site: http://www.standrews-de.org

Newark

Summer College (University of Delaware)
June-July

Summer College is a five-week residential program for academically advanced, rising high school seniors. The program is designed to provide outstanding students the opportunity to experience the challenge of college-level studies and a social environment that allows them to deal with the freedom and responsibilities of college life. Students enroll in two freshman-level courses for which they may receive six or seven University of Delaware credits. The curriculum of 11 college courses includes Biology, Chemistry, English Literature, Western Civilization, Mass Communication and Culture, Philosophy in Film, World Religions, Critical Reading and Writing, Statistics, and General Psychology. These courses are open only to Summer College students, and class size is limited. Social, cultural, and recreational activities are planned for the students, including Saturday trips to nearby metropolitan areas and the Delaware seashore. Participants enjoy the challenge of academic study, develop a strong sense of community among themselves, and get a taste of college life, thereby easing the transition from high school.

Criteria:	Application; $30 application fee; transcript; personal essay; GPA; recommendations; PSAT or SAT.
Grade:	Rising 12.
Cost:	Approximately $1,595 (Delaware residents); $3,650 (nonresidents). Limited need- and merit-based financial aid is available.
Contact:	Elizabeth Reynolds, Coordinator Summer College/Honors Program University of Delaware 206 Elliott Hall Newark, DE 19716-1256 (302) 831-6560; Fax: (302) 831-4339 E-mail: summercollege@udel.edu Web site: http://www.udel.edu/summercollege

DISTRICT OF COLUMBIA

State Director

Mary Gill, Deputy Academic Officer-Elementary Programs
Office of Elementary and Secondary Programs
D.C. Public Schools
825 North Capitol Street Northeast, Rm 8084
Washington, DC 20002
(202) 442-5650
E-mail: mary.gill@k12.dc.us

Dr. Wilma Bonner, Deputy Academic Officer-Secondary Programs
Office of Elementary & Secondary Programs
D.C. Public Schools
825 North Capitol Street Northeast
Washington, DC 20002

Regional Talent Search

Center for Talented Youth (The Johns Hopkins University)
See listing on page 4 for complete information.

Congressional Student Leadership Conference
March-April (six-day programs); June-August (six- and ten-day programs)

See listing on page 8 for complete information.

The Junior Statesmen Summer School (The Junior Statesmen Foundation)
June 15-July 6 (Session 1); July 13-August 3 (Session 2)

Located on the Georgetown University campus, The Junior Statesmen Summer School offers a rigorous academic challenge to outstanding high school students. The curriculum includes four college-level courses (AP American Government, Constitutional Law, The Presidency, and U.S. Foreign Policy), a speakers program, and student debates on current issues. The collegiate environment stresses substantial reading, research, and writing. Students reside in a Georgetown University dormitory and use university classrooms, libraries, and recreational facilities. Nationally recognized political scientists teach the classes. Summer School students meet and question national leaders, including members of Congress, Presidential Cabinet members, Supreme Court justices, lobbyists, and journalists. Foreign Policy students meet with Pentagon and State Department officials and foreign ambassadors. Similar programs are conducted at Stanford University, Yale University, Northwestern University, and Princeton University.

Criteria: Application; transcript; personal essay; recommendations.

Grade: Rising 10-12.

Cost: $3,325 (includes room, most meals and all academic costs). Need- and merit-based scholarships are available.

Contact: Admissions Director
The Junior Statesmen Foundation
1140 Conneticut Avenue, NW, Suite 801
Washington, DC 20036
(800) 317-9338, (202) 296-7838; Fax: (202) 296-7839
E-mail: jsa@jsa.org
Web site: http://www.jsa.org

National Junior Leaders Conference (LeadAmerica Foundation)
June-August (six- and ten-day programs)

See listing on page 10 for complete information.

National Student Leadership Conference
Fall, Spring, and Summer

Since 1989, the National Student Leadership Conference (NSLC) has been preparing outstanding and motivated high school students from across the United States and over forty-five countries for leadership roles in high school, college, and beyond. Rather than lecturing students, professors use interactive teaching methods to immerse students in the learning process. Summer programs include: Business and Commerce; Congressional Process, Policy, and Politics; International Diplomacy; Law and Advocacy: "The Trial"; Advanced Law and Advocacy: "The Appeal"; and Medicine and Health Care. Mastering Leadership is available in the fall and spring. Curriculum is combined with leadership activities, field trips, and social activities to provide a complete experience for the students. Transferable college credit is available through American University for juniors and seniors. NSLC also offers summer programs for junior high students exploring leadership, justice, and democracy. For dates, locations, and to apply on-line, please visit the NSLC Web site.

Criteria: Application; teacher or counselor nominations; GPA.

Grade: 9-12.

Cost: $1,099-$1,799. Need-based scholarships are available.

Contact: Director of Admissions
National Student Leadership Conference
111 West Jackson Boulevard, Suite 700
Chicago, IL 60604
(800) 994-NSLC; (312) 322-9999; Fax: (312) 765-0081
E-mail: info@nslcleaders.org
Web site: http://www.nslcleaders.org

Summer Discovery Pre-College Enrichment Programs
June-August (three- to six-week programs)

See listing on page 12 for complete information.

FLORIDA

STATE DIRECTOR

Donnajo Smith, Program Specialist
Bureau of Instructional Support and Community Services
Florida Department of Education
614 Turlington Building
325 West Gaines Street
Tallahassee, FL 32399-0400
(850) 488-1106; Fax: (850) 922-7088
E-mail: donnajo.smith@fldoe.org

STATE ASSOCIATION

Florida Association for the Gifted

FLAG is a statewide organization whose mission is to inform, educate, and support schools and communities regarding quality policies and practices that prepare gifted and high ability learners for the challenges of the 21st century. FLAG Activities include sending a New Member Packet and publishing three newsletters per year, promoting the development of innovative programs at the school level, offering regional activities and events, hosting an Annual Conference with nationally recognized consultants and local practitioners sharing promising programs and practices, providing mini-grants for teachers and two annual competitive scholarships for gifted students.

Mary Ann Ratliff, President
P.O. Box 3408
Tampa, FL 33602
(813) 272-4460; Fax: (813) 272-4515
E-mail: maryann.ratliff@newideas.skhc.k12.fl.us

REGIONAL TALENT SEARCH

Duke University Talent Identification Program
See listing on page 2 for complete information.

LOCATIONS THROUGOUT FLORIDA

Governor's Summer Program for Gifted and High-Achieving Students
Summer

The purpose of the Governor's Summer Program is to provide an opportunity for outstanding gifted and high-achieving students to participate in and use the resources of the universities and colleges in the state of Florida. Institutions of higher education, public or private, submit proposals to provide day or residential summer programs for gifted and high-achieving students entering grades 8-12. Their aim is to provide learning experiences and instructional resources not available in the secondary education programs of participating students, and to utilize the academic strengths and unique instructional resources of the sponsoring institution. In the past, programs have focused on topics such as architecture, economic development, engineering, history, mathematics, science, public health, and theater. Information about programs selected for the Governor's Summer Program is sent to all Florida school districts to encourage the participation of outstanding secondary students from all the state's 67 school districts.

Criteria: Identification as gifted based on State Board of Education rules and other application criteria as specified by each program.

Grade: 8-12.

Cost: Variable costs with scholarships available.

Contact: Donnajo Smith
Program Development and Services
Florida Department of Education
325 W. Gaines Street, Suite 614
Tallahassee, FL 32399-0400
(850) 488-1106; Fax: (850) 922-7088
E-mail: donnajo.smith@fldoe.org
Web site: http://www.firn.edu

BIG PINE KEY

Seacamp (Seacamp Association Incorporated)
June 24-July 11; July 14-31; August 3-20

Seacamp's tropical location on the Big Pine Key offers teenagers an opportunity to explore the most exciting waters in the Lower Florida Keys. Students will move among coral reefs, sandy and grassy areas, mud flats, and natural tide pools, all of them rich in the sea plants and animals basic to the study of marine science. The marine science program is the heart of Seacamp and provides campers with a variety of coordinated activities under the guidance of academically trained marine science instructors. Seacamp offers several courses in SCUBA diving including basic and advanced certification. Seacamp also teaches the fun and skill of sailing and windsurfing. For enrichment, the program includes courses such as black and white photography, color photography, camp newspaper, and a variety of arts and crafts.

Criteria: Application; teacher report; recommendations.

Grade: Rising 7-12.

Cost: $2,550 (residential); $375 (SCUBA fees); $60 (transportation). Prices are for 2002 and subject to change.

Contact: Grace Upshaw, Director
Seacamp
1300 Big Pine Avenue
Big Pine Key, FL 33043
(305) 872-2331; Fax: (305) 872-2555
E-mail: info@seacamp.org
Web site: http://www.seacamp.org

Boca Raton

Saint Andrew's School
Academic Year

Saint Andrew's is a coeducational college-preparatory school serving day students in grades K-12 and boarding students in grades 9-12. Saint Andrew's mission is to develop intellectual curiosity and a desire for excellence while preparing students for advanced study in college and for responsible citizenship. In the Upper School, qualified students may select honors and Advanced Placement courses (22 are offered). Acceleration is also available. The Middle School program is designed to meet the needs of the gifted child. Traditional disciplines form the basic schedule and are supplemented by work in computers, the arts, Latin, and creative writing. The program encourages the intellectual growth of gifted children while allowing them to remain with age-mates for sports and social maturation.

Criteria: Application (and fee); transcript; recommendations; SSAT; personal essay; interview.

Grade: K-12 (day); 9-12 (boarding).

Cost: $11,300 (Lower School); $14,350 (Middle School); $15,650 (Upper School, day); $28,000 (boarding). Need-based financial aid is available.

Contact: Bradford L. Reed, Director of Admission
Saint Andrew's School
3900 Jog Road
Boca Raton, FL 33434
(561) 226-0214; Fax: (561) 487-4655
E-mail: admission@saintandrewsschool.net
Web site: http://www.saintandrewsschool.net

Coral Gables

Summer Scholar Program (University of Miami)
June 22-July 11

The University of Miami (UM) Summer Scholar Programs offer three-week intensive programs in six areas: broadcast journalism, endangered species, filmmaking, health and medicine, marine science, and sports management. Students experience college life at a major research university while taking a customized program of study that includes lectures, laboratories, and field trips. Summer Scholar courses are taught by outstanding University of Miami faculty for college credit. In addition to classes, students have the opportunity to visit local sites relevant to their field. Previous Summer Scholars visited local television studios, completed oceanic studies on the coral reefs of South Florida, produced their own short film, and participated in lab work.

Criteria: Application (and fee); transcript, personal essay; recommendations; GPA.

Grade: Rising 11-12.

Cost: $3,700. Financial aid is available (deadline: March 15, 2003).

Contact: Brian L. Blythe, Director of High School Programs
Summer Scholars Program
University of Miami
P.O. Box 248005
Coral Gables, FL 33124
(800) STUDY-UM; (305) 284-6107; Fax: (305) 284-2620
E-mail: ssp.cstudies@miami.edu
Web site: http://www.summerscholar.miami.edu

DAYTONA BEACH

Summer Aviation/Aerospace Programs (Embry-Riddle Aeronautical University)
June-August

Embry-Riddle offers summer programs focused on aviation and aerospace. **Sun Flight** (age 16-18) participants have three options: students stay for several weeks and learn to fly solo; stay eight weeks to earn a Private Pilot certificate and six college credits; or stay eight weeks to earn an instrument rating and four college credits. **Flight Exploration** (age 12-18) introduces students to flying and flight training. **Aerospace Summer Camp** (age 15-18) offers interactive classroom activities and tours to learn about developments in space technology including the history of space flight, space shuttle operations, teamwork in the aerospace industry, and interplanetary NASA programs while earning three college credits. **Careers in Aviation** (age 15-18) explores career opportunities in the fields of aviation and aerospace.

Criteria: Application (and deposit); letter of recommendation; essay; photo; GPA; a flight physical is required for all flight camps.

Grade: Age 12-18

Cost: $800-$7,500 (varies with program).

Contact: Director of the Summer Academy
Embry-Riddle Aeronautical University
600 S. Clyde Morris Boulevard
Daytona Beach, FL 32114
(800) 359-4550; Fax: (386) 226-7630
E-mail: summer@cts.db.erau.edu
Web site: http://www.erau.edu/summeracademy

Delray Beach

Unity School
Academic Year

Located on the shore of serene Lake Eden, Unity School is an independent, nonprofit, church-related school. It operates under the policies of Unity of Delray Beach Board of Directors, although no religious dogma is taught. The fundamental policies and philosophies of universal principles basic to Unity School include promoting the individual worth and dignity of each child. All aspects of the students' education are addressed: academic, physical, social, emotional, global awareness, and responsibility. Peace education and earthkeeping are also fundamental to Unity as the regional headquarters for Peaceful Schools International. Unity School was founded in 1964 by the congregation of Unity Church. Each classroom is enhanced with enrichment materials reflecting the latest advancements in technology and the educational techniques of a gifted curriculum. Median standardized test scores average an eight stanine score out of a possible nine. Enrichment programs include sports, Spanish, music (chorus, band, jazz band), multi-media production, art, lessons in living/leadership, computer, Web site design, theatre, and speech and debate.

Criteria: Application (and deposit); transcript; GPA; standardized test scores; recommendations; placement tests; interview.

Grade: PreK-8.

Cost: $5,550-$9,087.

Contact: Maria Barber, Headmistress
Unity School
101 N.W. 22nd Street
Delray Beach, FL 33444
(561) 276-4414; Fax: (561) 265-0990
E-mail: mbarber@unityschool.com
Web site: http://www.unityschool.com

Fort Lauderdale

University School (Nova Southeastern University)
Academic Year

University School is the only independent, college preparatory school in South Florida that is part of a major university, Nova Southeastern University. This unique affiliation provides students and faculty exceptional academic opportunities for study, research and teaching. University School's challenging academic programs are provided in a supportive environment enriched by exceptional performing arts, athletics, and service programs. The school is recognized as a Blue Ribbon School of Excellence by the U.S. Department of Education and is accredited by the Southern Association of Colleges and Schools, the Florida Council of Independent Schools, and the Association of Independent Schools of Florida. College and Advanced Placement courses are offered to qualified students, and 100% of each graduating class attend leading colleges and universities. University School is dedicated to providing students with a well-rounded academic program supported by character development, technological competence, extracurricular programs, community service, and the utilization of Nova Southeastern University's resources.

Criteria:	Application (and $100 fee); transcript; personal essay; recommendations; test scores; PSAT; entrance exam; interview.
Grade:	PreK-12.
Cost:	$8,420-$10,900. Limited financial aid is available.
Contact:	Kiki Kelrick, Director of Admissions University School of Nova Southeastern University 3301 College Avenue, Sonken Building Fort Lauderdale, FL 33314 (954) 262-4416; Fax: (954) 262-3535 E-mail: usadmin@nova.edu Web site: http://uschool.nova.edu

FORT MYERS

Canterbury School
Academic Year

Canterbury School is an independent, coeducational, college preparatory day school enrolling 660 students (grades preK-12). Located in southwest Florida, Canterbury offers a rigorous academic program preparing students to continue their education at select colleges and universities across the country. Last year's graduating class of 45 seniors received over $2 million in merit-based scholarships and averaged a score of 1240 on the SAT test. Outstanding opportunities also exist in athletics and the visual and performing arts. An exciting addition to the school's athletic facilities was made in August 1999 when a second gymnasium was opened. Canterbury School stresses the development of the whole individual through its integrated curriculum, including character education and a strong commitment to community service.

Criteria:	Application (and $75 fee); transcript; personal essay; teacher report; recommendations; test scores; GPA; SSAT; entrance exam; interview.
Grade:	PreK-12.
Cost:	$8,790-$12,490 (varies with grade level). Need-based financial aid is available ($800,000 awarded to 22% of students).
Contact:	R. Mason Goss, Director of Admission Canterbury School 8141 College Parkway Fort Myers, FL 33908 (239) 415-8945; Fax: (239) 481-8339 E-mail: mgoss@canterburyfortmyers.org Web site: http://www.canterburyfortmyers.org

Gainesville

Student Science Training Program—UF-SSTP (University of Florida)
June 16-August 2 (seven-week session)

The Center for Precollegiate Education and Training administers an intensive, seven-week residential, research participation program on the University of Florida campus. The University of Florida Student Science Training Program (UF-SSTP) features individually assigned laboratory work with research mentors in science, engineering, medicine, math and computers. Other components include research discussion groups, a science lecture series, ethics forums, communication workshops, conflict resolution training, a dual enrollment option, and various unique educational and recreational field trips.

Criteria: Application; transcript; personal essay; recommendations; PSAT, SAT or ACT.

Grade: Rising 11-12.

Cost: $2,600.

Contact: Dr. Mary Jo Koroly, Director
Center for Precollegiate Education and Training (CPET)
Box 112010
Room 334, Yun Hall
Gainesville, Fl. 32611-2010
(352) 392-2310
E-mail: sstp@cpet.ufl.edu
Web site: http://www.cpet.ufl.edu/sstp

Naples

Seacrest Country Day School
Academic Year

Seacrest was founded on the premise that each child has the potential for unlimited learning. Through Seacrest's program, students become aware that they can free themselves from self-imposed limitations and tap their own resources. Seacrest has been cited as providing a model for teaching into the next century. These accolades result from an educational system in which "learning to be everything you can be" in a rapidly changing world is a central theme. The faculty is carefully selected and represents the heart of the school. The copyrighted curriculum is strong yet flexible, and Seacrest's commitment to technology places it in the top five percent of schools for integrating technology into the curriculum. Strong parental involvement and community resources provide students with a broad spectrum of experiences. The success of Seacrest depends on its students' achieving an excellent academic foundation and responsible independence in the learning process. At Seacrest, creativity is nurtured and good humor nourished as students are readied for responsible adulthood.

Criteria: Application (and $75 fee); transcript; interview; recommendations; personal essay; test scores.

Grade: PreK-8.

Cost: $9,265-$10,255. Financial aid is available.

Contact:	Caroline H. Randall, Director of Admission
Seacrest Country Day School
7100 Davis Boulevard
Naples, FL 34104
(239) 793-1986; Fax: (239) 793-1460
E-mail: crandall@seacrest.org
Web site: http://www.seacrest.org

New Port Richey

Genesis Preparatory School
Academic Year

Genesis Preparatory School (GPS) is a coeducational college preparatory school that has served Florida's West Coast since 1993. A challenging and advanced curriculum is provided which allows each student to develop to his or her full potential. The school's technologically advanced laptop computer program enhances its rigorous curriculum. In addition to an emphasis in English, mathematics, sciences, and social studies, GPS provides a variety of experiences in art, music, and drama. Foreign language instruction and physical education round out the curriculum. Small class size and the wealth of talent and academic experience of the faculty enable students to receive individual attention as they progress academically, physically, and socially. All students are encouraged to participate in many extracurricular activities. GPS serves middle and upper school students (grades 6-12). The GPS student body consists of young men and women with a variety of talents and special interests. Consideration of applicants is given equally, regardless of race, gender, creed, or national or ethnic origin.

Criteria:	Application; transcript; test scores; recommendations; interview.
Grade:	6-12.
Cost:	$7,925 (Middle School); $8,175 (Upper School). Financial aid is available.
Contact:	Dr. Melissa Nurrenbrock, Head of School
Genesis Preparatory School
7710 Osteen Road
New Port Richey, FL 34653
(727) 846-8407; Fax: (727) 844-3601
Web site: http://genesisprep.com

Land O'Lakes

Academy at the Lakes
Academic Year and Summer

Academy at the Lakes is a coeducational day school enrolling students in PreK-12. The Academy was founded in 1992 and is accredited by the Florida Council of Independent Schools. The school's mission is to provide an outstanding educational experience to talented students in preparation for higher levels of educational challenge and attainment. The school experience offers 350 students opportunities in the fine arts, literature, community service, extended travel, capitalism, and a strong exposure to the Socratic virtues. In addition to its traditional, college preparatory curriculum, Academy at the Lakes offers ancillary programs and academic courses designed to enrich and broaden the individual learner. The summer camp offers youngsters (age 5-12) courses and experiences in the fine arts and athletics. Summer is a great time to explore the special interests and qualities of all students.

Criteria: Application ($50 application fee); transcript; personal essay; recommendations; sample of work; test scores; interview.

Grade: PreK-12.

Cost: $7,500-$12,000 (Financial aid is available).

Contact: Robert D. Sullivan, Admission Officer
Academy at the Lakes
2220 Collier Parkway
Land O'Lakes, FL 34639
(813) 948-6823; Fax: (813) 948-2943
E-mail: rdsullivan@academyatthelakes.org
Web site: http://www.academyatthelakes.org

Orlando

Lake Highland Preparatory School
Academic Year and Summer

Lake Highland Preparatory School (LHPS) is a coeducational, private day school located on a twenty-six acre campus in the heart of Orlando, Florida. Through its planned program of excellence, Lake Highland meets the academic needs of its students and promotes their spiritual, personal, and social development. The comprehensive, enriching education enables students to continue their academic studies successfully at the college level. A diversified curriculum, small class sizes, and personalized instruction by a staff of fully certified teachers are offered. The **LHPS Summer Spectacular** offers credit and non-credit classes for middle and high school students. Lower School students enjoy a wide range of enriching experiences. Summer classes include academics, creative writing, science topics, cultural awareness, arts, music, and crafts. All students have the opportunity to participate in athletic camps.

Criteria: Application (and fee); transcript; teacher recommendations; test scores (academic year); SSAT (grades 6-12).

Grade: PreK-12.

Cost:	$9,950 (academic year); summer cost varies according to program. Limited need-based financial aid is available for the academic year.
Contact:	Susan B. Clayton, Director of Admissions or Susan W. Keogh, Director of Summer Spectacular Lake Highland Preparatory School 901 North Highland Avenue Orlando, FL 32803 (407) 206-1900 Web site: http://www.lhps.org

ORLANDO

New School of Orlando
Academic Year

The New School of Orlando, now in its eighth year, is coeducational and non-denominational. The K through eighth grade program emphasizes an enriched/gifted program for all students. A rigorous academic curriculum is infused with the arts. All students are required to take literature-based language arts, science, social studies, math, and Spanish daily. Advanced algebra is taught to students who have completed basic math. Computer lab, art, dance, theatre-music, and physical education classes are an integral part of the curriculum. Chess is taught to students beginning in kindergarten through grade eight. Small class size allows teachers to individualize programming. Critical thinking and problem solving require students to diversify their thinking skills. Students are taught to become curious critical thinkers and constructively pro-active in their learning and social development.

Criteria:	Application (and fee); transcript; recommendations; sample of work; test scores; GPA; SAT; interview; audition; individual assessments.
Grade:	K-8.
Cost:	$7,000.
Contact:	Morris Sorin, Director New School of Orlando 130 East Marks Street Orlando, FL 32803 (407) 246-0556; Fax: (407) 246-0822 E-mail: director@newschoolorlando.org Web site: http://www.newschoolorlando.org

Orlando

SeaWorld/Busch Gardens Adventure Camps
(SeaWorld Orlando Adventure Park)
Year-round

SeaWorld Orlando's Adventure Camps offer real-world experiences with amazing animals for middle and high school students in the unique settings of SeaWorld Orlando and in field locations. Adventures include swimming with dolphins, rays, and tropical fish at Discovery Cove; snorkeling coral reefs in the Florida Keys; and discovering the rewards and challenges of working in a zoological park. Hands-on marine activities enable students to develop skills such as snorkeling, species identification, animal care, and teamwork. Camps focus on zoology, marine biology, and field biology—enabling students to explore a variety of careers. Group and individual program activities are designed to help fulfill National Education Standards. Summer camp internships are available to college students pursuing degrees in education, science, and recreation. Family and Teacher camps are also available.

Criteria:	Application; applicants should feel comfortable in a pool or deep water without assistance for programs that require swimming.
Grade:	6–12.
Cost:	$375–$1,875. Financial aid is not available.
Contact:	Education Reservations SeaWorld/Busch Gardens Adventure Camps 7007 SeaWorld Drive Orlando, FL 32821 (866) 4SW-CAMP; Fax: (407) 363-2399 Web site: http://www.seaworld.org

St. Petersburg

Admiral Farragut Academy
Academic Year

America's only Honors Naval Academy, Admiral Farragut Academy is a coeducational boarding school that offers PreK-12 students comprehensive leadership training. With 100% college acceptance, Farragut may nominate 17 cadets to service academies. Military practices and boarding begins in grade 6 and NJROTC is launched in grades 9-12. Located on Florida's Gulf Coast, cadets may take scuba, sailing, and flying. As a member of the Florida High School Activities Association, with 17 interscholastic sports, Farragut leads the state in sports excellence. Located on 55-acre waterfront property, the campus dorms house two to four students per room with private bathrooms and all facilities are air-conditioned. Teachers supervise the dorms and assist with mandatory evening study time. Out of 46 teachers, over 50% have advanced degrees. The Dual Enrollment Program provides over 70 college credits. Cadets average 1085 in SAT scores and exceed national averages on all other test scores. With 92% re-enrollment, cadets thrive in a positive environment.

Criteria:	Application (and fee); transcript; personal essay; recommendations; test scores; interview; tour.

Grade: PreK-12 (day); 6-12 (boarding).

Cost: $6,500-$7,000 (day, PreK-5); $9,800-$9,900 (day, 6-12); $21,000-$21,200 (boarding, 6-12). Prices are for tuition only and do not include books, uniforms, and other fees.

Contact: David Graham, Director of Admissions
501 Park Street North
St. Petersburg, FL 33710
(727) 384-5500; Fax: (727) 347-5160
E-mail: admissions@farragut.org
Web site: http://www.farragut.org

TALLAHASSEE

Maclay School
Academic Year and Summer

Maclay School is a coeducational, college preparatory private day school located on a one hundred-acre campus in Tallahassee. Maclay's philosophy is to provide its 1,050 students with an educational opportunity that enables each one to develop his/her inherent ability to the fullest—academically, emotionally, morally, and physically. An important part of the Maclay educational experience is the feeling of a close knit family, a school community involving parents, teachers, and students. The comprehensive, enriching educational experience enables students to continue their academic studies successfully at the college level. A diversified curriculum, small class size, and personalized instruction by certified teachers are offered. The **Maclay Summer Program** offers courses rich in academics, arts, and athletics. In addition to academic courses, the summer session offers a complete aquatics program, a fine arts program, and a complete sports program. Summer is a great time to explore the special qualities of all students.

Criteria: Application (and fee); transcript; recommendations; test scores; GPA.

Grade: PreK-12.

Cost: $4,150-$7,350. Limited need-based financial aid is available.

Contact: Michael Obrecht, Director of Admissions, or
Mark Gargiulo, Director of Summer Programs
Maclay School
3737 North Meridian Road
Tallahassee, FL 32312
(850) 893-2138; Fax: (850) 893-7434
Web site: http://www.maclay.org

Tampa

Berkeley Preparatory School
Academic Year and Summer

Berkeley Preparatory School is a coeducational day school enrolling students grades PreK-12. Berkeley was founded in 1960 and is accredited by the Florida Council of Independent Schools. The school's purpose is to enable its students to achieve academic excellence in preparation for higher education and to instill in them a strong sense of morality, ethics, and social responsibility. The school currently enrolls 1,175 students; 401 in the lower division, 294 in the middle division, and 480 in the upper division. In addition to its traditional, college preparatory curriculum, Berkeley offers summer programs for students at every grade level. Past course offerings have included: Kinderarts, Fine Arts, and an educational enrichment program in the lower school; academic courses including courses in history, government, economics, psychology, biology, physics, Spanish, French, Latin, etymology, geometry, precalculus, microcomputers, and architectural graphics design in the middle and upper school. Summer program offerings also include a graphing calculator workshop, sports camps, and several fine arts programs.

Criteria: Application (and fee); transcript; personal essay; recommendations; SSAT; interview; in-house testing.

Grade: PreK-12.

Cost: $10,210 (PreK-5); $12,020 (grades 6-8); $13,310 (grades 9-12); $695-$1,400 (summer programs). Financial aid and scholarships are available.

Contact: Mary Will Thomas, Director of Admissions
Berkeley Preparatory School
4811 Kelly Road
Tampa, FL 33615
(813) 885-1673; Fax: (813) 886-6933
E-mail: thomamar@berkeleyprep.org
Web site: http://www.berkeleyprep.org

SeaWorld/Busch Gardens Adventure Camps (Busch Gardens Tampa Bay)
Year-round

Busch Gardens Adventure Camps offer real-world experiences with amazing animals for middle and high school students in the unique settings of Busch Gardens Tampa Bay and in field locations. Students meet amazing animals with behind-the-scenes action, gain real-world experiences, and help care for endangered species. The camps focus on conservation, animal behavior, and biology—helping students explore a variety of careers. SeaWorld/Busch Gardens Adventure Camps are designed to help fulfill National Education Standards. Some schools and colleges provide course/school work credit for participation. Summer camp internships are available to college students pursuing degrees in education, science, and recreation. Family and Teacher camps are also available.

Criteria: Application; some camp sessions require personal essays, transcripts, and recommendations.

Grade: 4–12, PG.

Cost:	$295-$975. Financial aid is not available.
Contact:	Education Reservations SeaWorld/Busch Gardens Adventure Camps P.O. Box 9157 Tampa, FL 33674-9157 (800) 372-1797; Fax: (813) 987-5878 Web site: http://www.buschgardens.org

TAMPA

Tampa Preparatory School
Academic Year and Summer Program

Tampa Prep is an independent, coeducational day school for 600 students (grades 6-12). The school is housed in a new campus consisting of three buildings: an academic structure, a black box theater, and an athletic complex. Tampa Prep offers a college preparatory curriculum including 17 Advanced Placement courses. All graduates attend four-year colleges and universities. Tampa Prep exists to provide students with rigorous intellectual training and to instill values of fairness, decency, honor, diligence, and academic curiosity within an orderly and humane environment. Tampa Prep also offers a complete athletic program and a well-known program in the arts. Tampa Prep's summer programs include a summer school (grades 6-12) offering both credit and enrichment courses.

Criteria:	Application (and fee); transcript; personal essay; teacher recommendations; test scores (PSAT, SAT, ACT, ISEE, or SSAT); interview.
Grade:	6-12.
Cost:	$11,060 (grades 6-8); $11,690 (grades 9-12). Need-based financial aid is available.
Contact:	Andrew C. Hill, Director of Admissions and Financial Aid Tampa Preparatory School 727 West Cass Street Tampa, FL 33606 (813) 251-8481; Fax: (813) 254-2106 E-mail: admissions@tampaprep.org Web site: http://www.tampaprep.org

Tampa

Lee Academy for Gifted Education
Academic Year

Lee Academy provides gifted and talented students with the opportunity for academic acceleration in a non-institutional setting at its lakefront campus. Each student's curriculum and schedule is designed to meet his/her special needs, with emphasis given to self-expression and creative thought. A 10:1 student-to-teacher ratio ensures students individual attention and opportunity. In addition to its strong core curriculum, Lee Academy provides an extensive range of electives in fine arts, languages, computers, and advanced studies. Through its outstanding computer facilities, Lee Academy provides a significant resource base for class projects, experiments, and individual research. A diversified program of field trips allows the students to apply their learning to real world situations. For its upper level students, Lee Academy operates a dual enrollment program with the University of South Florida and conducts a foreign exchange program with various schools in Europe.

Criteria:	Application; transcript; personal essay; recommendations; sample of work; interview.
Grade:	PreK-12.
Cost:	$6,500-$7,500. Scholarships are available.
Contact:	Linda Lacey, Director Lee Academy for Gifted Education 8613 Twin Lakes Boulevard Tampa, FL 33614 (813) 931-3316; Fax: (813) 935-8612; E-mail: leeacademy@aol.com

West Palm Beach

Arthur I. Meyer Jewish Academy
Academic Year

Dedicated to providing the finest general education as well as an intensive Jewish education, the Arthur I. Meyer Jewish Academy empowers students to develop into strong, confident young adults. Students learn Hebrew in an immersion-type language program that begins in kindergarten. The Jewish Studies curriculum includes Bible studies, history, rituals, and values. Meyer Academy's accelerated math program allows students to complete honors programs in Algebra I, geometry, and Algebra II in middle school. Spanish is offered to elementary and middle school students. Chess, sign language, string and bass music programs are also available. Their facilities include state-of-the-art computer labs, science labs, a television production studio, and a media center. Meyer Academy's sports program utilizes the facilities of the adjacent JCC and teams participate in the Palm Beach County Private School League. The Arthur I. Meyer Jewish Academy is accredited by the Florida Council of Independent Schools and is a founding member of the Jewish community Day School Network.

Criteria:	Application; test scores; transcript; confidential evaluation (grades 1-8).
Grade:	K-8.
Cost:	$7.895. Need-based financial aid is available.

Contact:	Susan Lord, Director of Admissions
Arthur I. Meyer Jewish Academy
3261 North Military Trail
West Palm Beach, FL 33409
(561) 686-6520; Fax: (561) 686-8522
E-mail: susanlord@meyeracademy.com
Web site: http://meyeracacdemy.com

Winter Park

Trinity Preparatory School
Academic Year

Trinity Prep is an independent Episcopal, coeducational, day school with an enrollment of 805 students in grades 6-12. Its mission is to develop students who are able to excel in college and beyond, contribute to their communities, lead in a changing society, and grow spiritually. Trinity has never compromised its commitment to a rigorous curriculum, a highly qualified and caring faculty, a low student/teacher ratio, and exceptional college guidance program. The school is also known for its superior athletics and fine arts opportunities. The academic program offers 24 Advanced Placement courses, fields 47 teams in 12 sports (JH, JV, V), and includes many activities/clubs. Trinity students have taken responsibility for building their fourth Habitat for Humanity house this year. The average SAT score for the Class of 2002 was 1246. In the 103-member Class of 2003, 79% are taking at least one AP course; 44% are taking 3 or more. The class includes 8 National Merit Semi-finalists and 11 Commended Students.

Criteria:	Application (deadline: February 4); $50 application fee; transcript; personal essay; recommendations; test scores; ISEE; SSAT; PSAT; SAT; ACT; CTPIII; TOEFL (if English is second language); interview.
Grade:	6-12.
Cost:	$10,950 (and one-time enrollment fee). Need-based financial aid is available.
Contact:	Ethel S. Danhof, Director of Admission, Marketing, and Financial Aid
Trinity Preparatory School
5700 Trinity Prep Lane
Winter Park, FL 32792
(407) 671-4140; Fax: (407) 671-6935
E-mail: inquire@trinityprep.org
Web site: http://www.trinityprep.org

GEORGIA

State Director

Dr. Sally Krisel, Specialist
Gifted Education / Curriculum Services
Georgia Department of Education
1770 Twin Towers East
Atlanta, GA 30334-5040
(404) 657-0182; Fax: (404) 657-7096
E-mail: skrisel@doe.k12.ga.us

State Association

Georgia Association for Gifted Children

The Georgia Association of Gifted Children provides assistance to people throughout Georgia who seek to establish a support group for the gifted children in their community, maintains communication with regional and national gifted support organizations, publishes a quarterly newsletter, and sponsors an annual conference which offers a variety of informative and stimulating program sessions and an opportunity to meet other people who share like interests in gifted children. Distinguished service awards are presented at the annual conference including the Bynum Award, the Gifted Program Teacher of the Year, the Chapter of the Year, the Parent of the Year, a Leadership Award, and the Nicholas Green Award. In addition, Mini-Grants are awarded as funds are available. The GAGC also supports adequate training for gifted program teachers through contribution to the Margaret O. Bynum Scholarship Fund, encourages special recognition of Georgia's gifted youth, their parents, and educators through statewide observance of the annual Gifted Education Day in Georgia, supports the continuous efforts to have gifted education established as a certified teaching field in the State of Georgia, and offers fund-raising ideas and suggestions which can be implemented at the local level.

Kathy Kennedy, Executive Assistant
1579F Monroe Drive, #321
Atlanta, GA 30324
(404) 875-2284; Fax: (404) 875-2284
E-mail: bkas@attbi.com
Web site: http://www.gagc.org

Regional Talent Search

Duke University Talent Identification Program
See listing on page 2 for complete information.

ATLANTA

Academic Study Associates
June-August

See listing on page 7 for complete information.

Atlanta

Atlanta Workshop Players—"Destiny" Performing Arts Experience (Brenau University, and Oglethorpe University)
June 8-21 (one- and two-week residential sessions); July 7-11 (one-week day sessions)

"Destiny" Performing Arts Experience is the artistic adventure of a lifetime in residential and day programs. The intense, creative, learning environment is contagious fun! Students and Master teachers gather from all over the country to share a love of the arts. Their nationally-known instructors adore working with young people, and have successful careers in television, film, radio, dance, and on Broadway. The atmosphere is positive, supportive, and non-competitive. Students take classes in classical theatre, improv comedy, on-camera TV/film acting, commercial acting, videography, musical theatre, mime, juggling, audition techniques, diction, stage combat, choreography, acrobatics, jazz, tap, lyrical, swing, hip-hop, and African dance. They see and perform in shows nightly, have recreational activities, build self-esteem, increase communication skills, make life-long friends and have opportunities to audition for casting directors and talent agents. "Destiny" launches careers. A special two-week advanced production session is available for those who wish to step into the spotlight in a professionally produced show. Students may attend one, two, or all three weeks.

Criteria: Application; previous experience and resume required for the advanced production session.

Grade: 3-12.

Cost: $395 per week (commuter); $595 per week (residential); $1,190 (two-week advanced production session).

Contact: Lynn Stallings, Artistic Director
Atlanta Workshop Players
355 North Peak Dr.
Alpharetta, GA 30022
(770) 998-8111; Fax: (770) 993-6440
E-mail: awplayers@aol.com
Web site: http://www.awplayers.com

National Computer Camps
June-August

See listing on page 10 for complete information.

CARROLLTON

The Advanced Academy of Georgia (State University of West Georgia)
Academic Year and Summer

The Advanced Academy of Georgia, located on the campus of the State University of West Georgia, is a residential, early-entrance-to-college program for gifted and talented high school juniors and seniors. Academy students take university classes taught by university faculty for which they receive concurrent high school and university credit. Academy students reside in a residence hall on campus with their intellectual peers, young men in one wing and young women in the other. The residence hall director, who resides in the building, and a staff of well-trained resident assistants offer programs that encourage a healthy balance between academic pursuits and opportunities for leadership, recreation, and personal development. In addition, Academy scholars engage in a full range of campus activities including College Bowl competitions, original research, professional conferences, and contributing their talents to theatrical and musical events.

Criteria: Application (and fee); transcripts; recommendations; personal essay; GPA (minimum 3.5); SAT (minimum composite score: 1150; Verbal: 580, Math: 530) or ACT (minimum composite score: 25; English: 25, Math: 22); interview with parent(s) or guardian; high school approval form.

Grade: Rising 11-12.

Cost: $3,500 per semester (includes tuition and fees, room and board, and books). Out-of-state students add approximately $2,900 each semester. All costs are approximate and are quoted for 2002-2003 academic year. A limited number of out-of-state fee waivers and scholarships are available.

Contact: Susan Colgate, Director
The Advanced Academy of Georgia
Honors House
State University of West Georgia
Carrollton, GA 30118
(770) 836-4449; Fax: (770) 836-4666
E-mail: scolgate@westga.edu
Web site: http://www.westga.edu/~academy

LEARN to LIVE Together: Honors Leadership Academy for Young Women (LEARN to LIVE, Inc.)
July 6-11

LEARN to LIVE Together is a unique, residential program for young women (grades 7-12). Faculty lead structured sessions in science, technology, and the humanities. Session topics may include interpersonal skills, public speaking, debate, leadership styles, communication, conflict management, and diversity. The passion and commitment of the faculty to mentor young women and to share their life experiences with them make this program valuable and unique. Self-growth and initiative are encouraged through exploratory sessions. Early applicants receive discounted tuition rates and may influence the final selection of session topics. Utilizing the theme of **L**ove, **E**xplore, **A**chieve, **R**esearch, and **N**urture to **L**ove, **I**nitiate, **V**isualize, and **E**nergize, experiential activities provide the opportunity for each participant to refine her leadership potential in a supportive environment "**Together**." The program offers an opportunity for participants to become better prepared for higher education in an increasingly more diverse and complex world while living in a caring environment.

Criteria: Application; recommendations; personal essay.

Grade: 7-12.

Cost: $450 (if application is received by March 15); $550 (if application is received by May 15); $750 (if application is received by June 30). Prices include a $50 application fee.

Contact: Madhavi B. Sethna, Director
LEARN to LIVE Together: Honors Leadership Academy
LEARN to LIVE, Inc.
P.O. Box 876
Carrollton, GA 30112
(770) 214-0528
E-mail: L2L@charter.net
Web site: http://www.LEARN-to-LIVE.org

COCHRAN

GAMES—Georgia Academy of Mathematics, Engineering, and Science (Middle Georgia College)
Academic Year

The Georgia Academy of Mathematics, Engineering, and Science (GAMES) is a residential, joint-enrollment program for top-performing high school juniors and seniors. GAMES allows students who meet the strenuous admission requirements to obtain high school and college credit simultaneously while enrolled full-time in college courses. The program is designed for students who aspire to major in math, engineering, science, computers, or medicine; however, other majors are allowed. Students reside in a residence hall reserved for GAMES students. They take actual college courses accredited for transfer and benefit outside the classroom from the many enrichment activities designed by the academy personnel.

Criteria: Application (and fee); transcript; personal essay; recommendations; test scores; GPA (3.5 minimum); SAT (minimum total score: 1100; 560 Math, 530 Verbal); ACT (24 composite: 24 Math, 23 English); interview; high school disciplinary record.

Grade: 11-12.

Cost: $5,500 (Georgia residents); $9,000 (nonresidents). All costs are approximate.

Contact: Lisa Whitaker, Director of GAMES Admissions
GAMES
Middle Georgia College
1100 Second Street
Cochran, GA 31014
(478) 934-3471; Fax: (478) 934-3499
E-mail: games@warrior.mgc.peachnet.edu
Web site: http://www.mgc.peachnet.edu/

Gainesville

Firespark—School for Gifted Students in Fine Arts and Communications (Brenau University)
July 20-August 2

The Firespark program has combined creativity with outstanding technical and performance opportunities for the past twenty-five years. Students will receive 120 total hours of instruction during the two weeks in their choices of five subject areas. Firespark offers courses in: *Communications* (journalism, fiction writing, poetry, television production, introduction to radio, Web site design, advertising, and public relations); *Dance* (classical ballet, tap, modern, jazz, choreography, dance for stage and theater); *Drama* (acting, technical theater, lighting, makeup techniques, character improvisation, stage movement, scene study, musical theater); *Music* (theory, composition, electronic music and computer applications, audio recording, chorus, piano, organ, private voice lessons, experimental instrumental ensemble); and *Art and Design* (drawing, painting, ceramics, photography, sculpture, computer graphics, printmaking). Firespark employs practicing professionals as instructors in each area. The students are housed in on-campus dormitories with an adult supervisory staff, Firespark offers two weeks of intensive learning and creativity. Applications may be received by writing, calling, or visiting the Firespark Web site.

Criteria: Application (and $100 fee); personal essay; recommendations.

Grade: 7-12.

Cost: $998 (residential); $748 (commuter).

Contact: John D. Upchurch, D.M., Director
Firespark
Brenau University
One Centennial Circle
Gainesville, GA 30501
(770) 534-6741; Fax: (770) 534-6742
E-mail: jupchurch@lib.brenau.edu
Web site: http://www.firespark.org

Gainesville

Summer Opportunity and Academic Review Program (SOAR) and High Adventure Camp (Riverside Military Academy)
June 29-July 25 (SOAR); July 26-July 30 (High Adventure Camp)

The **Summer Opportunity and Academic Review Program** (SOAR) at Riverside Military Academy is a month-long residential session to help prepare students for the upcoming school year. A variety of courses are available in English, math, science, and languages. It is an excellent opportunity to improve study skills and strengthen educational backgrounds. A supervised evening study hall, with access to instructors, helps students maximize their potential. Believing there is a strong connection between physical and mental development, Riverside provides numerous recreational activities and field trips to keep learning fun and provide social experiences. Riverside's **High Adventure Camp** is designed to provide young men with the opportunity to experience outdoor high adventure activities in a safe, but challenging environment. Some of the experiences include hiking a portion of the Appalachian Trail, kayaking at the Olympic Rowing Venue on Lake Lanier, and canoeing on the Chattahoochee River.

Criteria: Application.

Grade: Rising 7-12.

Cost: $2,675 (SOAR); $725 (High Adventure Camp). A non-refundable deposit of $250 is required upon acceptance.

Contact: James Davis, Admissions Director
Riverside Military Academy
2001 Riverside Drive
Gainesville, GA 30501
(800) GO-CADET, (770) 532-6251; Fax: (678) 291-3364
E-mail: jdavis@cadet.com
Web site: http://www.cadet.com

MACON

MidSummer Macon Institute for the Arts (Wesleyan College)
June 14-28

MidSummer Macon Institute for the Arts is a two-week boarding program for students age 14-19. Students select their concentration of study from music, dance, theatre, creative writing, or visual arts. The two-week mini college curriculum includes a variety of evening performances by professionals in each art form.

Criteria: Application (deadline: May 16).

Grade: Rising 9-12.

Cost: $475-$775.

Contact: Jo Ann Green, Executive Director
MidSummer Macon
Wesleyan College
4760 Forsyth Road
Macon, GA 31210-4462
(478) 757-5174; Fax: (478) 757-3990;
E-mail: jogreen@wesleyancollege.edu
Web site: http://www.midsummermacon.com

Macon

SPECTACLES Math and Science Camps for Middle School Girls (Wesleyan College)
June 22-28 (Session 1); July 20-26 (Session 2)

Math and Science SPECTACLES, entering its 13th consecutive year, is a one-week residential math and science camp for middle school girls sponsored by Wesleyan College in Macon, Georgia. The camp offers one week of exciting activities that will change the way middle school girls see their world. Field trips and a career planning workshop, which allows conversation with women who have pursued math and science-related fields, will open students' eyes to their place in the world of math and science. Students work in the college's science labs, electronic classrooms, in the arboretum and wildlife sanctuary, and study with math and science faculty. A wide range of extracurricular activities is provided. Students live in one of the college's air-conditioned residence halls.

Criteria:	Application; educators' recommendations; personal essay; female student.
Grade:	Rising 6-7 (Session 1); rising 8-9 (Session 2).
Cost:	$625.
Contact:	Rejeana Cassady, Coordinator SPECTACLES Wesleyan College Academic Affairs Office 4760 Forsyth Road Macon, GA 31210-4462 (478) 757-5228; Fax: (478) 757-2430 E-mail: rcassady@wesleyancollege.edu Web site: www.wesleyancollege.edu/community/spectacles

Rabun Gap

Rabun Gap-Nacoochee School
Academic Year

Rabun Gap-Nacoochee School offers challenging college preparation for day and boarding students in grades 6-12. The 1,300-acre campus is two hours from Atlanta in the beautiful mountains of northeast Georgia. The curriculum ensures development of strong writing and math skills and includes AP and honors courses, ESL, environmental studies, and fine arts. All students participate in an after-school program, which combines campus work assignments, community service, and extracurricular activities, including interscholastic sports, outdoor and equestrian programs. All students have supervised Internet access and personal e-mail. A separate residence hall faculty provides 24-hour supervision for boarding students. Worship, an important aspect of the school's Presbyterian heritage, has been part of community life since its founding in 1903. All students attend weekly chapel services.

Criteria:	Application (deadline: July 15); $50 application fee; transcript; recommendations; PSAT; SAT; ACT; SSAT; interview; ISEE.

Grade:	6 (day); 7-12 (boarding).
Cost:	$20,500 (boarding); $8,500 (day). Additional fees for books and uniforms. Merit scholarships and need-based grants are available.
Contact:	J. Timothy Martin, Director of Admission Rabun Gap-Nacoochee School 339 Nacoochee Drive Rabun Gap, GA 30568 (800) 543-7467, (706) 746-7467; Fax: (706) 746-2594 E-mail: admission@rabungap.org Web site: http://www.rabungap.org

ROME

Darlington School
Academic Year and Summer (June 1-August 1)

Founded in 1905, Darlington School, coeducational and college-preparatory, serves boarders (9-PG) and day students (PreK-12) with challenging academics, leadership, service, arts, athletics, a family-like atmosphere, excursions, trips, and travel. Located in Rome, Georgia, near Atlanta and Chattanooga, the school covers 500 acres. New facilities include a softball field and athletic center with swimming, indoor track, aerobics, weight room, wrestling, basketball, and volleyball courts, and a field house. Nearly half of the 400 upper school students live in six houses with 80 instructors providing supervision and academic support. Families serve as "Rome Parents" for boarders. Parents and students follow academic progress through confidential student pages on the Internet. **Darlington Summer Camps** give middle schoolers an opportunity outside the ordinary. Choices include outdoor adventures, caving, horseback riding, steel band, musical theatre, football, golf, tennis, rockets, robotics, fast-pitch softball, volleyball, soccer, basketball, and environmental science.

Criteria:	Application; application fee ($50: boarding, $40: day, $75: international); transcript; personal essay; student questionnaire; recommendations; SSAT; interview.
Grade:	9-12 (boarding); PreK-12 (day).
Cost:	$26,100 (boarding); $10,500 (day); $10,000 (6-8); $8,500 (K-5). Call for Darlington Summer Camps fees. Up to eight partial or full merit scholarships are available.
Contact:	Director of Admission Darlington School 1014 Cave Spring Road Rome, GA 30161 (800) 368-4437; (706) 235-6051; Fax: (706) 232-3600 E-mail: admission@darlingtonschool.org Web site: http://www.darlingtonschool.org

Valdosta

Governor's Honors Program
June-August

The Georgia Governor's Honors Program centers on intensive study in one of sixteen academic, technology/career education, agriculture education, or fine arts areas. Students choose an additional minor area. The 675 participants in this residential program are chosen from 2,400 nominees from public and private schools in Georgia. Students attend the program on the campus of Valdosta State University in Valdosta.

Criteria: Application; recommendations; interview or audition.

Grade: Rising 11-12.

Cost: No charge to participants. The program is funded by the state of Georgia.

Contact: Dr. Joe Searle, Director
Governor's Honors Program
1770 Twin Towers East
Atlanta, GA 30334-5040
(404) 657-0183; Fax: (404) 657-7096
E-mail: jsearle@doe.k12.ga.us

HAWAII

STATE DIRECTOR

Betsy Moneymaker, Gifted Education Specialist
Instructional Services Branch
Hawaii Department of Education
475 22nd Avenue Room 119
Honolulu, HI 96816
(808) 733-4780x320; Fax: (808) 735-8228
E-mail: betsy_moneymaker@notes.k12.hi.us

STATE ASSOCIATION

Hawaii Gifted Association
Lynell Soares, President
P.O. Box 22878
Honolulu, HI 96823-2878
(808) 732-1138

REGIONAL TALENT SEARCH

Center for Talented Youth (The Johns Hopkins University)
See listing on page 4 for complete information.

IDAHO

STATE DIRECTOR

Gary Marx, Gifted and Talented Specialist
Special Education Services
Idaho Department of Education
P.O. Box 83720

ILLINOIS

STATE DIRECTOR

Carol McCue, Principal Consultant
Gifted & Talented Education
Illinois Board of Education
100 North First Street
Springfield, IL 62777
(217) 782-3810; Fax: (217) 782-7171
E-mail: vmccue@isbe.net

STATE ASSOCIATION

Illinois Association for Gifted Children

The Illinois Association for Gifted Children is an organization of parents, educators, and other committed to the education and development of children with diverse gifts and talents. We educate, support, and influence those who touch the lives of children and focus our energies to meet the needs of children with gifts and talents in Illinois. Our committees consist of Professional Development, Standards, Advocacy, Communications, Convention, Recognition, Finance, Membership, Parent Affiliate, and Affective. We provide professional development opportunities throughout the year as well as hosting a convention in February at the Downtown Marriot in Chicago. Our communication consists of a newsletter, The Courier, published 2-3 times per year plus a Journal that addresses an area of interest in depth. The journal is published once a year. Our recognition committee recognizes and honors the Nicholas Green Scholar for Illinois, as well as offering two scholarships to IAGC events.

Dr. Sally Walker, Executive Director
800 East Northwest Highway, Suite 610
Palatine, IL 60074
(847) 963-1892; Fax: (847) 963-1893
E-mail: sywalker@earthlink.net
Web site: http://iagcgifted.org

REGIONAL TALENT SEARCH

Center for Talent Development (Northwestern University)
See listing on page 3 for complete information.

Aurora

Illinois Mathematics and Science Academy
Academic Year

Decidedly different. That is how to describe IMSA's residential educational program. Students are able to conduct high level research with scientists and scholars, and learn from the world's "masters." Students also have unlimited opportunities to "give back" to the community. These one-of-a-kind learning opportunities, coupled with a first-class curriculum in mathematics, science, the humanities, English, arts, and music, make IMSA truly unique. Students also enjoy 18 interscholastic sports, co-curricular activities, and numerous student-run clubs and organizations. IMSA faculty and staff include Presidential Award winners, distinguished authors, and fellowship winners. A physicist, who won the Nobel Prize, serves as resident scholar. The entire faculty holds advanced degrees with 39% holding a Ph. D. IMSA has a strong history of preparing students for success. *Worth* magazine recently listed IMSA as one of the top 50 public high schools in the nation for having a successful record placing their graduates within Harvard, Yale, and Princeton.

Criteria: Application (and fee); transcript; personal essay; recommendations; SAT; gifted and talented; Illinois resident.

Grade: 10-12.

Cost: No cost for tuition or room and board; some activity fees are assessed. Need-based financial aid is available.

Contact: Amy Conyers, Coordinator of Admission
Illinois Mathematics and Science Academy
1500 West Sullivan Road
Aurora, IL 60506-1000
(630) 907-5028; Fax: (630) 907-5887
E-mail: aconyers@imsa.edu
Web site: http://www.imsa.edu

Chicago

Congressional Student Leadership Conference
March-April (six-day programs); June-August (six- and ten-day programs)

See listing on page 8 for complete information.

Chicago

Discovery Approach to Science EnHancement—DASH
(Illinois Institute of Technology)
July 1-August 2

The Illinois Institute of Technology (IIT) offers a five-week, nonresidential science exploration program for students who have completed the ninth or tenth grade and have received a 'B' or better in their math and science courses. The Discovery Approach to Science EnHancement (DASH) is offered on the IIT main campus. Participants spend three weeks exploring the physical concepts regarding the relationship between acceleration, velocity, and distance and the physiological factors of space travel. During the final two weeks, students are introduced to the world of engineering and manufacturing through the designing, building, and launching of model rockets. Classroom sessions are complemented by hands-on experiments, computer assignments, Internet exploration, Web page development, and field trips, including a "Physics Day" at Great America Theme Park. IIT faculty, assisted by top IIT students who serve as project leaders and mentors, guide participants through an exciting and innovative approach to science and engineering topics.

Criteria:	Application (and fee).
Grade:	9-10.
Cost:	None.
Contact:	Dr. Peter Johnson, BCPS Department DASH Illinois Institute of Technology 3105 South Dearborn Chicago, IL 60616 (312) 567-3440; Fax: (312) 567-3210 E-mail: peter.johnson@iit.edu Web site: http://www.iit.edu/~iitnsf/dash.html

Summer Programs for High School Students (University of Chicago)
June 21-August 30

The University of Chicago Summer Session offers talented students opportunities for intellectual adventures in the city of Chicago and around the world. Five programs are offered: **Research in the Biological Sciences** trains students in a broad range of techniques used in cutting edge molecular and cellular biological research laboratories; **Stones and Bones** students join renowned paleontologist Paul Sereno on a Wyoming expedition in search of dinosaur and other fossils; **Insight** courses provide intensive hands-on exploration of a particular field such as animal behavior, child development or Egyptology; **ChicaGO! The Traveling Academy** takes students on an in-depth tour of the language(s), culture, and history of an intriguing locale (Greece is scheduled for Summer 2003); **Summer College** gives participants a taste of college life at a competitive institution, as they take classes with University of Chicago undergraduates.

Criteria:	Application (deadline: May 15); $50 application fee; transcript; personal essay; recommendations.
Grade:	Rising 10-12.

Cost: $1,875-$6,000 (tuition); $1,200-$2,400 (board). Financial aid is available for tuition cost.

Contact: Valerie Huston, Secretary
Summer Session
University of Chicago
1427 E. 60th Street
Chicago, IL 60637
(773) 702-6033; Fax: (773) 702-6814
E-mail: uc-summer@uchicago.edu
Web site: http://www.grahamschool.uchicago.edu/summer

CHICAGO

The Junior Statesmen Summer School (The Junior Statesmen Foundation)
June 30-July 25

Located on the campus of Northwestern University, The Junior Statesmen Summer School offers a rigorous, academic challenge to outstanding high school students. The curriculum includes four college-level courses: AP American Government, Political Philosophy, Political Communication, and Speech Communication. These classes are enriched by a high-level speakers program and nightly sessions of a debate practicum, the Congressional Workshop. The collegiate, academic environment stresses substantial reading, research, and writing. Students reside in a Northwestern University dormitory and use university classrooms, libraries, and recreational facilities. Classes are taught by outstanding political scientists and top-ranked speech and debate instructors. For two days, Summer School students and faculty meet with guest speakers in Chicago for an in-depth, behind-the-scene exploration of politics and government. Similar programs are conducted at Stanford, Yale, Princeton, and Georgetown Universities.

Criteria: Application; transcript; personal essay; recommendations.

Grade: Rising 10-12.

Cost: $3,325 (includes room and board and all academic costs). Need- and merit-based scholarships are available.

Contact: Admissions Director
The Junior Statesmen Foundation
60 East Third Avenue, Suite 320
San Mateo, CA 94401-4032
(800) 334-5353, (650) 347-1600; Fax: (650) 347-7200
E-mail: jsa@jsa.org
Web site: http://www.jsa.org

National Junior Leaders Conference (LeadAmerica Foundation)
June-August (six- and ten-day programs)

See listing on page 10 for complete information.

PALATINE

Quest Academy
Academic Year

Quest Academy is an independent day school for the academically gifted and talented that enrolls 320 students (grades PreK-8). Based on a traditional liberal arts education with equal emphasis on the sciences, the humanities, and the arts, the curriculum includes language arts, social studies, science, mathematics, computers, art, music, drama, physical education, and French. Class work revolves around hands-on, interdisciplinary projects that allow students to delve into subjects in depth. Character development as well as critical thinking and reasoning abilities are taught and applied across content areas. An atmosphere dedicated to excellence and joy in learning fosters self-discipline, confidence, initiative, responsibility, leadership, and self-worth. Field trips, utilizing resources offered by Chicago and its environs, enhance classroom study in academics and the arts.

Criteria: Application; transcript; recommendations; test scores; interview; IQ testing; student visit.

Grade: PreK-8.

Cost: $6,500-$11,080. Need-based financial aid is available.

Contact: Judy Jankowski, Director of Admission
Quest Academy
500 N. Benton
Palatine, IL 60067
(847) 202-8035; Fax: (847) 202-8085
Web site: http://www.questacademy.org

PEORIA

World of Wonder (Bradley University Institute for Gifted and Talented Youth)
June 2-27

Bradley University offers the best in high-interest instruction. Classes meet for two hours Monday through Friday. Over 90 courses offer challenging instruction in small classes. Class selections may include: mini-medical school, mini-veterinary school, news journalism, movie production, scuba, rocketry, Math Masters, photography, mini-law school, biology, planetarium visits, literature, interviews of sport celebrities, space missions, world studies, and the visual and performing arts.

Criteria: Application (deadline: May 1); most recent report card; home scholars must submit an essay.

Grade: 1-8.

Cost: $85.00 per ten-hour class. Financial aid is available.

Contact: Cathy Sherlock or Dr. Mary Ann Manos
College of Education and Health Sciences
206 Westlake Hall
Bradley University
Peoria, IL 61625
(309) 677-3181, (309) 677-2614; Fax: (309) 677-2952
E-mail: mmanos@bradley.edu
Web site: http://www.bradley.edu

URBANA

Exploring Your Options (University of Illinois College of Engineering)
June 15-August 2 (one-week sessions)

Exploring Your Options (EYO) is a week-long residential program that introduces high school freshmen, sophomores, and juniors to the field of engineering. EYO is held at the University of Illinois at Urbana-Champaign. Participants interact with engineering students and faculty members, plan and build a project, and engage in hands-on activities prepared by departments within the College of Engineering. Two sessions (June 15-21 and July 27-August 2) are open to rising sophomores and juniors; a third session (July 6-12) is open to rising freshmen.

Criteria:	Application (deadline: May 9); $50 application fee; personal essay; recommendations; ACT.
Grade:	Rising 9-11.
Cost:	$550.
Contact:	Toni Pitts, Interim Director of Worldwide Youth in Science and Engineering 400 Engineering Hall 1308 W. Green Street Urbana, IL 61801 (800) 843-5410, (217) 333-2860; Fax: (217) 244-2488 E-mail: wyse@uunc.edu Web site: http://www.engr.uiuc.edu/wyse/

INDIANA

STATE DIRECTOR

Cheryl Boyer-Schrock, Program Consultant
Gifted and Talented Unit
Indiana Department of Education
State House, Room 229
Indianapolis, IN 46204-2798
(317) 232-9107; Fax: (317) 232-9121
E-mail: cschrock@doe.state.in.us

STATE ASSOCIATION

Indiana Association for the Gifted

IAG is a united body of parents, educators, and concerned citizens, committed to the advocacy and advancement of educational practices and resources which will meet the unique learning needs of gifted/talented students. IAG hosts an annual state professional conference, a free-fare resource show, and regional parent presentations. IAG publishes a quarterly journal, a 179 page resource guide, and a guide to summer programs. IAG gives awards to outstanding educators, supporters, and students and awards scholarships. IAG advances legislation and state education policies that improve educational opportunities for high ability Indiana students.

Dr. Tracy Cross, President
P.O. Box 641
Carmel, IN 46082
(317) 705-1660; Fax: (317) 705-1660
E-mail: iagdirect@iquest.net
Web site:http://www.iag-online.org

REGIONAL TALENT SEARCH

Center for Talent Development (Northwestern University)
See listing on page 3 for complete information.

BLOOMINGTON

High School Journalism Institute (Indiana University)
July 7-11; July 13-17; July 19-23

The Indiana University High School Journalism Institute (HSJI) is an intensive five-day workshop designed for students who have accepted a position in high school media or for those interested in learning about journalism. It is also a great way to explore Indiana University as a possible college choice. Participants will examine the role of the media, analyze their own and other student publications and electronic media, and develop the skills needed to produce quality publications and broadcast productions. Excellent faculty members from Indiana and around the country will guide the participants' study during the 57th consecutive journalism workshop program.

Criteria: Returned registration form with full payment (deadline: June 6).

Grade: 9-12.

Cost: $295.

Contact: Jack Dvorak, Director
High School Journalism Institute
Indiana University
940 E. 7th Street
Bloomington, IN 47405-7108
(812) 855-0895; Fax: (812) 855-0901
E-mail: dvorakj@indiana.edu
Web site: http://www.journalism.indiana.edu/workshops/hsji

CULVER

The Batten Scholars Program (The Culver Academies)
Academic Year

The Batten Scholars Program offers incoming ninth- and tenth-graders who demonstrate academic, citizenship, and character excellence, the opportunity to obtain a four-year, full-tuition scholarship to The Culver Academies. The scholarship, which also provides for two fully funded educational enrichment opportunities, is renewable annually based on evaluation by a faculty/staff committee. Six Batten Scholarships are to be awarded for the 2003-2004 school year. The Batten Scholars Program is an opportunity for competent, qualified students to benefit from The Culver Academies' nine-month, college preparatory environment. Academics, citizenship, and character excellence have long been mainstays of the programs at The Culver Academies for students in grades nine through twelve. Culver offers Advanced Placement and accelerated courses, plus classes such as aviation and horsemanship in addition to a wealth of athletic and extracurricular experiences.

Criteria: Application (deadline: February 1); $30 application fee; transcript; personal essay; recommendations; test scores; SSAT; interview.

Grade: 9-10.

Cost: $25,400 (plus books and uniforms; 2002-2003 costs). Financial aid is available.

Contact: Mike Turnbull, Director of Admissions
The Culver Academies
1300 Academy Road #157
Culver, IN 46511
(800) 528-5837; Fax: (574) 842-8066
E-mail: admissions@culver.org
Web site: http://www.culver.org

Notre Dame

Paula Program for Young Female Scholars
July 6-12 and July 13-19

The Saint Mary's College Paula Program is designed for young women entering grades 8-11 with a thirst for knowledge. The program offers two distinct weeks centered around a specific content area. July 6-12: visual and performing arts and July 13-19: math and science explorations. Each week of this residential enrichment program offers a range of courses and activities to enhance critical thinking skills, problem solving techniques, and creativity.

Criteria:	Application (deadline: May 31); $100 application fee; transcript; personal essay; recommendations.
Grades:	Rising 8-11.
Cost:	$475 (before April 30); $525 (after April 30). Costs are for one week.
Contact:	Andrea Dunn, Director Paula Program for Young Female Scholars St. Mary's College Notre Dame, IN 46556 (574) 284-4778; Fax: (574) 284-4784 E-mail: camps@saintmarys.edu Web site: http://www.saintmarys.edu

Richmond

Explore-A-College
June 22-July 5

Now entering its 22nd year, Explore-A-College is a two-week residential program designed for college-bound high school students who will be entering the 10th, 11th, or 12th grade in the fall of 2003. It is an opportunity for them to get a taste of college before making their final college choice. While the academic benefits are obvious to students, they also learn many other things while they are on campus: how to manage their time better, how to be independent, and how to meet peers and make friendships with students from all over the United States and abroad. In addition, students receive two semester hours of college credit upon successful completion of the course of their choice.

Criteria:	Application (and fee); transcript; recommendations; test scores, GPA (if available); SAT (approximately 530 V/480 M).
Grade:	Rising 10-12.
Cost:	$1,150 (tuition, room and board). Limited, need-based financial aid is available.
Contact:	Dee Ball Johnson, Director of Summer Studies Explore-A-College Earlham College Drawer 188 Richmond, IN 47374 (800) EARLHAM; Fax: (765) 983-1560 E-mail: ballde@earlham.edu Web site: http://www.earlham.edu/~eac

IOWA

State Director

Rosanne Malek, Coordinator
Gifted and Talented Education
Iowa Department of Education
Grimes State Office Building
400 East 14th Street
Des Moines, IA 50319-0146
(515) 281-3199; Fax: (515) 242-6025
E-mail: rosanne.malek@ed.state.ia.us

State Association

Iowa Talented and Gifted Association

ITAG, an affiliate of the National Association for Gifted Children, is a tax exempt, 501(c)3, organization which was organized more than 25 years ago with a vision that gifted/talented children in the state of Iowa should receive an education commensurate with their abilities and needs. ITAG promotes advocacy at the state and local levels; pre- and in-service training in gifted education; parent, guardian, and community awareness, education, and involvement. ITAG is parents, guardians, educators, other professionals, and community leaders who share an interest in the growth and development of gifted and talented individuals in Iowa.

Bobbi Chester, President
8345 University Boulevard, Suite F-1
Des Moines, IA 50325
(515) 225-2323; Fax: (515) 225-6363
E-mail: iowatag@aol.com

Regional Talent Search

Duke University Talent Identification Program
See listing on page 2 for complete information.

AMES

Challenges for Youth-Talented and Gifted—CY-TAG (Iowa State University)
June 15-July 5 (Session 1); July 6-26 (Session 2)

Iowa State University (ISU), in conjunction with the Office of Precollegiate Programs for Talented and Gifted (OPPTAG), is proud to offer individualized, intensive, and accelerated studies for academically talented students. The goal of the CY-TAG program is to provide an in-depth and challenging learning experience for gifted students in an atmosphere of warmth, excitement, and fun. Students enroll in one three-week class taught by ISU instructors totaling over 100 hours of instructional time. Teaching assistants are utilized to maintain low student-to-faculty ratios and to individualize learning experiences. Courses offered include Psychology, Precalculus Mathematics, Computer Programming, Introductory and Advanced Genetics, Engineering, Physics, Chemistry, Forensic Science, Literature and Composition, and mentorship opportunities. Students live under supervision in an air-conditioned dormitory located on campus. Stimulating academics are complemented by a wide variety of exciting social, recreational, and cultural activities.

Criteria: Application (and fee); ACT; SAT.

Grade: 7-11.

Cost: $1,400 (approximate cost). Financial aid is available.

Contact: Zachary H. Osborn, Administrator of Programs
CY-TAG
Iowa State University
310 Pearson Hall
Ames, IA 50011-2200
(515) 294-1772; Fax: (515) 294-3505
E-mail: opptag@iastate.edu
Web site: http://www.opptag.iastate.edu

EXPLORATIONS! (Iowa State University)
June 15-July 26 (one-week sessions)

EXPLORATIONS!, a one-week alternative to the CY-TAG program, is an exciting and challenging enrichment opportunity offered by Iowa State University (ISU) in conjunction with the Office of Precollegiate Programs for Talented and Gifted (OPPTAG). EXPLORATIONS! is a program designed to introduce students to cutting edge concepts within topic areas not traditionally taught in their local schools. Students are immersed in stimulating activities and laboratories for this exciting summer residential program. Enthusiastic instructors explore a variety of interesting topics such as ancient Egyptians, astronomy, computer programming, digital photography, modern mythology (*Harry Potter, Star Wars, Lord of the Rings*), physics, robotics, art and design, architecture, and Medieval history. Students live in a supervised, air-conditioned dormitory located on the ISU campus and participate in a variety of well-structured recreational, social, and cultural activities.

Criteria: Application (and fee); recommendations; test scores; ACT; SAT.

Grade: 6-10.

Cost: $500 (approximately). Financial aid is available for those who participate in at least three of the six EXPLORATIONS! sessions.

Contact: Zachary H. Osborn, Administrator of Programs
EXPLORATIONS!
Iowa State University
310 Pearson Hall
Ames, IA 50011-2200
(515) 294-1772; Fax: (515) 294-3505
E-mail: opptag@iastate.edu
Web site: http://www.public.iastate.edu/`opptag_info

Iowa City

National Scholars Academy (The Belin-Blank International Center for Gifted Education and Talented Development)
June 15-20 (Session 1); June 22-27 (Session 2)

The National Scholars Academy (NSA) is a one-week, residential program that offers students (rising grades 10-12) an opportunity to engage in college-level course work. NSA will be offered in two sessions; students may attend one or both sessions. Possible course offerings include Trial Style and Litigation, Mathematical Problem Solving, Modern Approaches to Biomedical Research, and Narrative Nonfiction Writing. Students must be members of the National Recognition Program for High School Scholars (NRPHSS), members of the Belin-Blank Exceptional Student Talent Search (BESTS), or be a past scholarship winner to attend NSA.

Criteria: Application; test scores; membership in NRPHSS or BESTS; or former Blank Scholars, Governor's Scholars, Environmental Health Sciences Scholars, or Wallace Scholars.

Grade: Rising 10-12.

Cost: $600 (per session). Financial aid is available.

Contact: Jan Warren, Program Administrator
National Scholars Academy
University of Iowa
210 Lindquist Center
Iowa City, IA 52242
(800) 336-6463; Fax: (319) 335-5151
Web site: http://www.uiowa.edu/~belinctr

Iowa City

Academy for Creative Engineering (ACE) and Academy for Legal Thought and Action (ALTA) (The Belin-Blank International Center for Gifted Education and Talented Development)
June 15-27

The Academy for Creative Engineering (ACE) and the Academy for Legal Thought and Action (ALTA) are programs designed to provide students in grades 9-11 an opportunity to learn about the professional fields of engineering and law. Students will research engineering problems or legal cases and will present their findings. ACE is done in collaboration with The University of Iowa's College of Engineering and ALTA in collaboration with The University of Iowa's College of Law.

Criteria:	Application; test scores; NRPHSS, BESTS, or past Belin-Blank scholarship participant.
Grade:	9-11.
Cost:	$1,300 (room, board, activities, materials, and instruction). Financial aid is available.
Contact:	Jan Warren, Program Administrator ACE/ALTA The University of Iowa 210 Lindquist Center Iowa City, IA 52242 (800) 336-6463; Fax: (319) 335-5151 Web site: http://www.uiowa.edu/~belinctr

KANSAS

STATE DIRECTOR

Zo Ann Torrey, State Director
Special Education Services
Kansas Department of Education
120 Southeast 10th Street
Topeka, KS 66612-1182
(785) 291-3097; Fax: (785) 296-1413
E-mail: ztorrey@ksde.org

STATE ASSOCIATION

Kansas Association for Gifted, Talented, and Creative
The purpose of the organization shall be to provide services and support for gifted students; and to provide professional development, research information, networking, support, and encouragement to educators and parents of gifted and talented students in Kansas.

Pam Fellingham, President
P.O. Box 8078
Shawnee Mission, KS 66208-0078
E-mail: fellinghamp@aol.com

Kansas Parent Information Network
Donna House, Chair
426 Olivette
McPherson, KS 67460
(316) 241-5654

REGIONAL TALENT SEARCH

Duke University Talent Identification Program
See listing on page 2 for complete information.

HUTCHINSON

Future Astronaut Training Program (Kansas Cosmosphere and Space Center)
May-August (weeklong sessions)

Entering its 19th year, the Cosmosphere's Future Astronaut Training Program is one of the nation's premier space training programs. Designed by the Cosmosphere's own space science educators, the program simulates astronaut training through teamwork, problem solving, and training in state-of-the-art simulators. Sessions are limited to 40 students, which allows everyone to participate in everything. The main simulators include the full motion-based space shuttle, centrifuge, mission control, three axis trainer, 1/6 gravity trainer, manned maneuvering unit, advanced flight simulator, lunar rover, robotics challenge, and stress simulator. Students attend briefings on spaceflight, astronaut requirements, the International Space Station, all aspects of the shuttle and NASA's unmanned probes. The students build and launch rockets; study astronomy using telescopes and the Cosmosphere's Planetarium; attend IMAX® films; and take advantage of the Hall of Space Museum, housing one of the most comprehensive collections of American and Russian space artifacts in the world, including the actual Apollo 13 command module *Odyssey*.

Criteria: Application (and fee); good physical health.

Grade: Rising 7-10.

Cost: $585.

Contact: Jody Gilley, Registrar
Future Astronaut Training Program
Kansas Cosmosphere and Space Center
1100 North Plum
Hutchinson, KS 67501-1449
(800) 397-0330; (620) 662-2305, ext. 304; Fax: (620) 662-3693
E-mail: jodyg@cosmo.org
Web site: http://www.cosmo.org

KENTUCKY

STATE DIRECTOR

Carla Garr, Consultant for Gifted and Talented Education
Kentucky Department of Education
Division of Professional Development
500 Mero Street, 18th Floor
Frankfort, KY 40601
(502) 564-2106, extension 4725; Fax: (502) 564-9848
E-mail: cgarr@kde.state.ky.us

STATE ASSOCIATION

Kentucky Association for Gifted Education

The Kentucky Association for Gifted Education (KAGE), officially organized in 1979, is a non-profit volunteer group of parents, teachers, administrators, other educators, and all citizens interested in being advocates for appropriate educational opportunities for gifted and talented youth in Kentucky.

Lynette Baldwin, Executive Director
P.O. Box 9610
Bowling Green, KY 42102-9610
(271) 745-4301; Fax: (270) 745-6279
E-mail: kage@wku.edu

REGIONAL TALENT SEARCH

Duke University Talent Identification Program
See listing on page 2 for complete information.

Cooperative Program

VAMPY/Summer Program for Verbally and Mathematically Precocious Youth
June 29-July 19

For the twentieth summer, Western Kentucky University offers a three-week residential program of academic, cultural, and recreational experiences which are appropriate for very bright students who have completed the seventh through tenth grades during the current academic year. Students enroll in one fast-paced, challenging course which meets six hours each weekday. Classes of 14-16 students are taught by outstanding teachers, each aided by a teaching assistant. The residential experience is an integral part of VAMPY. Students live in an air-conditioned dormitory, and residential counselors provide supervision when students are not in class. Activities include theater outings, guest speakers, films, sports, and other recreational activities. Students have access to the university library and recreational facilities. Courses include Ancient Civilizations; Chemistry; Computer Programming (C++); Expository Writing; Field Ecology; Genetics; Humanities; Mathematics; Medieval Literature; Movies and American Culture; Nazi Germany and the Holocaust; and Physics. **This program is offered through cooperative efforts with the Duke University Talent Identification Program.**

Criteria: Application; test scores (minimum scores: SAT: Math 500, Verbal 500; ACT: Math 18, English 21, for grade 7). Score criteria may vary depending on course, age, and grade level.

Grade: Rising 8-11.

Cost: $1,550 (tuition, books, room, board, and recreational activities). Need-based financial aid is available.

Contact: Dr. Julia Roberts, Director
The Center for Gifted Studies
Western Kentucky University
1 Big Red Way
Bowling Green, KY 42101-3576
(270) 745-6323; Fax: (270) 745-6279
E-mail: gifted @wku.edu
Web site: http://www.wku.edu/gifted/

Bowling Green

SCATS—Summer Camp for Academically Talented Middle School Students
(Western Kentucky University, The Center for Gifted Studies)
June 15-27

For the twenty-first summer, Western Kentucky University offers a two-week summer camp for academically talented students entering grades 7-9. Most participants reside on campus, where they participate in a variety of educational, cultural, and recreational activities. Students enroll in four classes from approximately thirty choices that include art, computer science, foreign language, literature, writing, mathematics, music, science, and social studies. Classes of 14-16 students meet for one hour and a half each weekday. Teachers are Western Kentucky University professors and other experienced educators who are interested in teaching academically talented young people. Students have opportunities to develop skills, expand interests, and make friends with young people who share similar interests. The residential experience is an integral part of SCATS. Students live in an air-conditioned dormitory, and residential counselors provide supervision when students are not in class. Activities may include a theater outing, guest speakers, cookouts, sports, and other recreations.

Criteria:	Eligibility for gifted services.
Grade:	Rising 7-9.
Cost:	$950 (residential); $350 (nonresidential). Need-based financial aid is available.
Contact:	Dr. Julia Roberts, Director The Center for Gifted Studies Western Kentucky University 1 Big Red Way Bowling Green, KY 42101-3576 (270) 745-6323; Fax: (270) 745-6279 E-mail: gifted@wku.edu Web site: http://www.wku.edu/gifted/

Danville

Governor's Scholars Program (Also in Highland Heights and Richmond)
June-July

Designed to motivate and empower Kentucky's brightest young people to become contributing citizens, the Governor's Scholars Program seeks to broaden the horizons of its 1,000 participants. Through nontraditional courses and independent learning, students are encouraged to develop their conceptual and critical thinking skills. The curriculum features an in-depth experience in a focus area, chosen from courses that cover biological issues; modes of mathematical thinking; and social, political, and economic theory. Each student also participates in a service learning project that takes real world ideas considered in class and "tests" them in the community. The Governor's Scholars Seminars focus on personal growth and explore such topics as interpersonal communications, college choices, civic responsibility, and relationships. Planned evening and weekend activities along with visits from noted scientists, writers, and community leaders complete this stimulating summer experience.

Criteria:	Application (deadline: Jan 31); transcript; personal essay; recommendations; test scores; GPA; PSAT, SAT, or ACT; student profile of activities, honors, and personal interests; Kentucky resident.
Grade:	Rising 12.
Cost:	None.
Contact:	Sherleen Sisney, Executive Director Governor's Scholars Program 1024 Capital Center Drive, Suite 210 Frankfort, KY 40601 (502) 573-1555; Fax: (502) 573-1641 E-mail: jerritinsley@mail.state.ky.us Web site: http://www.kygsp.org

Georgetown

Pre-College Academic Experience in Mathematics and Science (Georgetown College)
June 15-27

The Georgetown College Pre-College Academic Experience in Mathematics and Science (PAEMS) is designed for rising high school sophomores, juniors, and seniors who have an exceptional interest in math, science, and/or computer science. The two-week residential program will integrate classroom and hands-on learning opportunities in biology, chemistry, computer science, mathematics, and environmental science. Full-time Georgetown College professors teach all classes. The program seeks to challenge students academically, stimulate their interest in science and math, expand their perspectives of global issues, foster creativity, and promote a team concept to problem solving. Classes and activities on campus will be combined with field trips to nationally known research and industrial facilities, as well as natural areas.

Criteria: Transcript; recommendations; GPA; PSAT.

Grade: Rising 10-12.

Cost: $700. Need-based financial aid is available.

Contact: Dr. William R. Harris, Program Coordinator
Pre-College Academic Experience in Math and Science
Georgetown College
400 East College Street, Box 234
Georgetown, KY 40324
(502) 863-7921; Fax: (502) 863-7744
E-mail: paems@georgetowncollege.edu
Web site: http://www.georgetowncollege.edu/departments/paems

Murray

Summer Challenge Camps (Center for Gifted Studies at Murray State University)
June 23-27; June 20-July 4; July 6-18 (Summer Challenge in Spain)

The Summer Challenge Camps offered by the Center for Gifted Studies are designed to enrich the gifted student through a variety of options. Beginning with Summer 2003, the Center offers an exchange program to Spain, where students (rising 9-11) can study at a Center for Gifted Studies in Spain, thereby increasing their language proficiency while they pursue enrichment activities. The setting for the on-campus camps is Murray State University, located in the beautiful lake region of Western Kentucky. Examples of on-campus offerings are Advanced Robotics, Chess, and Photography. In both settings, students have challenging experiences at a reasonable cost with a highly qualified faculty. Kentucky residents may be eligible for financial assistance through the KAGE Foundation.

Criteria: Application; recommendations; test scores; basic language proficiency for program in Spain.

Grade: Rising 5-11; rising 9-11 (Summer Challenge in Spain).

Cost: $225 (commuter); $325 (residential); $750 (Summer Challenge in Spain: includes tuition, room, and board). Financial aid is available for Kentucky residents.

Contact: Dr. Joy L. Navan, Director
Center for Gifted Studies
Murray State University
P.O. Box 9
Murray, KY 42071
(270) 762-2539; Fax: (270) 762-3799
E-mail: joy.navan@coe.murraystate.edu
Web site: http://www.murraystate.edu/coe/centers/gifted/default.htm

LOUISIANA

STATE DIRECTOR

Eileen Kendrick, Coordinator of Gifted and Talented Programs
Louisiana Department of Education
1453 Patrick Drive
Baton Rouge, LA 70810
(225) 342-5295; Fax: (225) 342-5880
E-mail: ekendrick@mail.doe.state.la.us

STATE ASSOCIATION

Association for Gifted and Talented Students
Gay Arnold, President
3301 Old Spanish Trail
Westlake, LA 70669
(337) 882-0234, extension 249
E-mail: garnold@hal.calc.k12.la.us

REGIONAL TALENT SEARCH

Duke University Talent Identification Program
See listing on page 2 for complete information.

COOPERATIVE PROGRAM

The ADVANCE Program for Young Scholars (Northwestern State University)
June 8-28

The ADVANCE Program for Young Scholars is a summer residential program for talented youth that offers intensive, fast-paced courses in the humanities, mathematics, natural science, and computer science. Students selected to participate in ADVANCE enroll in one course during the three-week term and complete the equivalent of one year of high school, or one semester of college-level study. By working with carefully selected instructors and teaching assistants, each student is given the opportunity to attain maximum academic growth. Residential life is an equally important aspect; balanced leisure and cultural activities complement the intensive academic program. The residential staff organizes a wide array of extracurricular activities for each evening to encourage relaxation and socialization. Classes are generally limited to 15 students and are structured to allow students to progress at their own pace. Although courses are not offered for high school credit, many students test out of courses via state approved final examinations given during the program or through their home schools. Courses include Algebra I, Algebra II, Biology, Chemistry, Computer Science (C++), Creative Writing, Film Studies, Forensic Science, Geometry, Physics, Precalculus, Psychology, Shakespeare and Performance, Spanish, and Web Design. **This program is offered through cooperative efforts with the Duke University Talent Identification Program.**

Criteria: Application (and $100 deposit); SAT or ACT. Call for information regarding their alternate admission policy.

Grade: Rising 8-12.

Cost: $1,550. Limited need-based financial aid is available.

Contact: ADVANCE Program for Young Scholars
Northwestern State University
P.O. Box 5671
Natchitoches, LA 71497
(800) 259-4438 (LA only), (318) 357-4500; Fax: (318) 357-4547
E-mail: palmerh@nsula.edu

BATON ROUGE

LSU Youth Programs (Louisiana State University)
June 9-27 (non-credit); June 9-July 18 (credit)

Under the umbrella of LSU Youth Programs are several program options. Secondary students may enroll in a variety of non-credit, three-week long mini-courses on numerous topics ranging from art and ethics to math and science. High school students wishing to complete one unit of honors high school credit can enroll in math, science, humanities, or computer classes. Special one-week, non-credit camps focusing on different topics are also available each year. Topics in the past have included cartooning, oceanography, space, genetic engineering, forensic science, and video production. All program options emphasize small classes and hands-on involvement.

Criteria: Application; transcript; GPA.

Grade: 7-12.

Cost: Non-credit: $100 (per course) or $995 (residential). Credit: $395 (per course) or $1,695 (residential). Limited need-based financial aid is available.

Contact: Janet Sheldon, Manager, LSU Youth Programs
Louisiana State University
177 Pleasant Hall
Baton Rouge, LA 70803
(800) 388-3883, (225) 578-3144; Fax: (225) 578-7503
Web site: http://www.youth.lsu.edu

LAFAYETTE

**Summer Scholars Residential Program
(University of Louisiana at Lafayette)**
June 8-13

The Summer Scholars Program offers a one-week residential experience for academically talented students completing grades 7-8. Each student selects three academic and/or arts classes and schedules a fourth class designed to develop interpersonal communication and leadership skills.

Criteria:	Documentation of high potential in academics, arts, or leadership.
Grade:	Rising 8-9.
Cost:	$375 (Louisiana residents); $500 (nonresidents). Need-based financial aid is available (priority is given to Louisiana residents).
Contact:	Marlene Beard, Director of Summer Enrichment Programs Center for Gifted Education University of Louisiana at Lafayette P.O. Box 43251 Lafayette, LA 70504-3251 (337) 482-6701; Fax: (337) 482-5842

LAKE CHARLES

Governor's Program for Gifted Children (McNeese State University)
June 8-July 26

Established in 1959, the Governor's Program for Gifted Children provides an opportunity for educational enrichment to intellectually gifted middle (grades 6-8) and high school (grades 9-10) students. The program integrates the fundamentals of subject material, research, and lab work with active participation in the arts and sciences. The "Grand Finale" includes performance opportunities in chorus, orchestra, drama, stage tech, debate, art, and a full-scale musical production. In each discipline, students are encouraged to think and act independently. Without neglecting the physical and aesthetic needs of the child, the program attempts to embody Shakespeare's statement: "It is the mind that makes the body rich."

Criteria:	Application (and fee); transcript; personal essay; recommendations; sample of work; test scores; GPA; ACT (grades 9-10 only); interview (when feasible); audition (musically gifted only).
Grade:	Rising 6-10.
Cost:	$1,995 (includes tuition, room and board, damage deposit, student allowance, and fees). Scholarship information available upon request.
Contact:	Dr. George Middleton, Director Governor's Program for Gifted Children McNeese State University Box 91490 Lake Charles, LA 70609 (337) 475-5446; Fax: (337) 475-5447 E-mail: office@gpgc.org Web site: http://www.gpgc.org

Natchitoches

Louisiana School for Math, Science, and the Arts
Academic Year

The Louisiana School for Math, Science, and the Arts (LSMSA) was recently selected as one of the 25 best secondary schools in the nation. LSMSA is one of only a few public residential high schools for academically talented students in the United States and the only one that stresses both academics and the arts. The outstanding faculty, of which approximately sixty percent hold doctorates, allows the Louisiana School the opportunity to offer an extensive curriculum in mathematics, sciences, humanities, computer science, and the creative and performing arts. This curriculum, along with the residential life activities, helps in the development of a community of scholars. The comprehensive residential life program includes intramurals, student government, clubs, student publications, and some athletics. The living/learning environment provides opportunities for field trips, tutorials, guest speakers, and attendance at a variety of cultural events.

Criteria: Application; transcript; personal essay; parent statement; recommendations; test scores; GPA; SAT; ACT; interview; audition; Louisiana resident.

Grade: 11-12.

Cost: $750 (room and board); $130 (student activity fee). Fee reductions and exemptions are available.

Contact: Dr. Richard Loftin, Director of External Affairs
Louisiana School for Math, Science, and the Arts
715 College Avenue
Natchitoches, LA 71457
(800) 259-3173 (LA only), (318) 357-3173; Fax: (318) 357-3189
Web site: http://www.lsmsa.edu

MAINE

STATE DIRECTOR

Wanda Monthey, Gifted and Talented Director
Maine Department of Education
23 State House Station
Augusta, ME 04333
(207) 624-6831; Fax: (207) 624-6821
E-mail: wanda.monthey@state.me.us

STATE ASSOCIATION

Maine Educators of the Gifted and Talented

Maine Educators of the Gifted and Talented (MEGAT) has been organized in order to further the common good of gifted child education in the State of Maine. The association publishes newsletters, including scholarly articles addressing current issues and practices related to gifted child education both in Maine and nationally, for members. MEGAT also holds regular regional meetings to provide mutual support and the exchange of information relative to gifted child education in the region. To foster the professional growth of educators, the association sponsors conferences and workshops annually to provide exposure to the ideas and professional contributions of national leaders in gifted child education. MEGAT also works cooperatively and collaboratively with the State Department, university system and other appropriate organizations in providing training statewide on issues relating to gifted education.

Nancy Patterson, President
20 Forrest Avenue
Ellsworth, ME 04605
(207) 667-6494
E-mail: npatterson@mail.hctc.k12.ne.us

REGIONAL TALENT SEARCH

Center for Talented Youth (The Johns Hopkins University)
See listing on page 4 for complete information.

BETHEL

Young Scholars Program (Gould Academy Summer School)
June 29-July 26

Young Scholars is a residential program designed specifically for high-aptitude, motivated students. The program combines intensive, accelerated, total-immersion instruction in one area of study with a uniquely powerful social and community living experience. The academic program is built around teachers who are successful, inspirational scholars and is complemented by small classes of 6-10 motivated, able students. All courses are full-credit equivalent and make use of Gould Academy's advanced computer system with full Internet access. Offerings include high school level writing, math (pre-algebra through precalculus), biology, earth science, foreign language, and art. Ideally located for outdoor pursuits, activities include mountain hiking, swimming, and canoeing; sports such as soccer and basketball; studio arts; trips to the ocean; overnight camping; Boston museums; and local festivals. Student-organized games, dances, performances, newspaper, and literary magazine are encouraged and supported. A talented and supportive residential staff provides close supervision. The overall staff-to-student ratio is 1:4.

Criteria: Application (deadline: June 1); $25 application fee; transcript; personal essay; test scores.

Grade: Rising 7-9.

Cost: $2,800 (boarding); $1,900 (day). Financial aid is available.

Contact: Tami Johnson, Director
Gould Academy Summer School
P.O. Box 860
Bethel, ME 04217
(207) 824-7777; Fax: (207) 824-2926
E-mail: johnsont@gouldacademy.org
Web site: http://www.gouldacademy.org

SEAL HARBOR

Acadia Institute of Oceanography
June 22-July 5, July 20-August 2 (Basic sessions); July 6-19, August 3-16 (Advanced sessions)

Located on Mt. Desert Island, Maine, the Acadia Institute of Oceanography (AIO) is a one-of-a-kind educational experience for students age 12-18. Since 1975, AIO has introduced young people to the world of marine science through a unique curriculum that combines the basic elements of biological, physical, and chemical oceanography with field, classroom, offshore, and laboratory work. The edge of the sea is AIO's classroom and its academic activities follow the tides. AIO seeks highly motivated students for participation in the program. The program offers two basic sessions (age 12-15) and two advanced sessions in which completion of a high school biology or chemistry course is required. All participants are expected to arrive with a curious mind and a commitment to learn. Graduates of advanced sessions are eligible to apply for the tropical marine biology program held at the Hofstra University Marine Lab in Jamaica and the Bermuda Biological Station for Research. A one-week career seminar for students interested in marine biology will be offered in 2003.

Criteria: Application (and $200 deposit); recommendations (one from science teacher).

Grade: Rising 5-12 (age 12-18).

Cost: $1,750. A limited number of scholarships are available; requires 2 recommendations and a personal essay.

Contact: Sheryl Gilmore, Executive Director
Acadia Institute of Oceanography
P.O. Box 2220
Saint Augustine, FL 32085
(904) 829-1112; Fax: (904) 829-1112
E-mail: aio@aug.com
Web site: http://www.acadiainstitute.com

Wiscasset

The Maine Coast Semester (The Chewonki Foundation, Inc.)
August 28-December 17 (Fall); January 29-May 31 (Spring)

The Maine Coast Semester offers a small number of 11th grade students the chance to live and work on a 400-acre saltwater peninsula to explore the interrelationship between people and the environment through courses in natural science, environmental issues, art, history, literature, and writing. The academic program is designed to support and enrich the junior year curriculum. The buildings are rustic, the atmosphere is informal, and the community is small-only 36 students and 13 faculty members. Students and faculty jointly share responsibility for all aspects of the program. In addition to their studies, students work to maintain the facilities and a working farm and woodlot. The students who attend the Maine Coast Semester are highly motivated and very academically capable.

Criteria: Application; transcript; personal essay; recommendations; sample of work.

Grade: 11.

Cost: $14,600. Financial aid is available.

Contact: Paul Arthur, Admissions Director
or Scott Andrews, Director
The Maine Coast Semester
485 Chewonki Neck Road
Wiscasset, ME 04578
(207) 882-7323; Fax: (207) 882-4074
E-mail: parthur@chewonki.org; sandrews@chewonki.org
Web site: http://www.chewonki.org

MARYLAND

STATE DIRECTOR

Dr. Carolyn R. Cooper, Specialist of Gifted and Talented Education
Maryland Department of Education
200 West Baltimore Street
Baltimore, MD 21201-2595
(410) 767-0363; Fax: (410) 333-2050
E-mail: ccooper@msde.state.md.us

STATE ASSOCIATION

Maryland Coalition for Gifted and Talented Education
Joan Roache, President
6401 Old Chapel Terrace
Bowie, MD 20720
(301) 262-9551
E-mail: jroache@ids2.idsonline.com

REGIONAL TALENT SEARCH

Center for Talented Youth (The Johns Hopkins University)
See listing on page 4 for complete information.

BALTIMORE

Johns Hopkins Summer Pre-college Program (Johns Hopkins University)
June 30-August 1

Johns Hopkins Summer Pre-college Program attracts academically talented students who want to stretch their minds and earn college credit. Students complete two Hopkins undergraduate courses in one of seven areas of concentration: American government/pre-law, college preview, computer applications/business, earth and space science/engineering, humanities, international relations, and medical science. Applicants may also select the English as a Second Language program or take courses on-line. Small classes and the internationally-known Hopkins faculty provide an atmosphere of excellence. Participants tour the well-known Hopkins research and medical facilities and enjoy day trips to Washington, D.C., a college fair, talent show, community service projects, dances, sports, music, and other activities. Residential students live in dormitories under the supervision of residential advisors. The Hopkins summer catalog and Web site list courses and application forms.

Criteria:	Application (deadline: April 25); $40 application fee; transcript; personal essay; recommendations; test scores; GPA, ACT, SSAT, PSAT, or SAT.
Grade:	Rising 11-12, PG (minimum age is 16).
Cost:	$5,200 (residential: includes room, board, tuition, and activities); $495 (commuters: per credit). Limited financial aid is available.
Contact:	Summer Programs, Krieger School of Arts and Sciences The Johns Hopkins University Suite G1/Wyman Park Building, 3400 N. Charles St. Baltimore, MD 21218 (410) 516-4548; Fax: (410) 516-5585 E-mail: summer@jhu.edu; Web site: http://www.jhu.edu/summer

GLENCOE

Oldfields School
Academic Year

Founded in 1867, Oldfields continues to provide young women with the opportunity to make the most of their academic and personal potential. Oldfields is nationally known for its individualized college-preparatory curriculum, which includes AP courses and a flexible dual-track system for girls in grades 8-12. Eighty percent of the 185 girls are boarding students representing 9 countries and 27 states. Oldfields is the only all-girls, private, pilot school taking part in the Microsoft/Toshiba Laptop Program, which has resulted in 100% of the faculty and 100% of the students using personal laptop computers on a fully networked campus. Oldfields offers overseas and off-campus programs as part of a two-week May program. Fine and performing arts, athletics, horseback riding, dance, and other extracurricular activities are offered and encouraged. Extensive extracurricular programs offered on weekends are enhanced by the school's proximity to Baltimore, Washington, D.C., and Philadelphia.

Criteria:	Application (and fee); transcript; personal essay; recommendations; test scores; WISC; ISEE; PSAT; SSAT; interview; female student.
Grade:	8-12.
Cost:	$29,500 (boarding); $18,600 (day). Financial aid is available. Application deadline for financial aid is February 15.
Contact:	Kimberly C. Loughlin, Director of Admission and Financial Aid Oldfields School 1500 Glencoe Road Glencoe, MD 21152 (410) 472-4800; Fax: (410) 472-6839 E-mail: admissions@oldfields.pvt.k12.md.us Web site: http://www.oldfieldsschool.org

ST. JAMES

Saint James School
Academic Year

A coeducational boarding and day school of 220 students established in 1842, Saint James maintains high scholastic standards, excellence in athletics, and the development of students of sound character. A nurturing environment supports a challenging and traditional curriculum, which is successful in providing students with a depth of knowledge that serves as a foundation for academic achievement at the collegiate level. Recent graduates have matriculated at schools such as Amherst, Bryn Mawr, Bucknell, Davidson, Furman, Wake Forest, Georgetown, Vanderbilt, Johns Hopkins, Rice, University of Virginia, and the University of North Carolina at Chapel Hill. The historic campus is located on 700 acres of land just south of Hagerstown, Maryland. The proximity to cultural opportunities in the Baltimore-Washington region enhances weekend activities.

Criteria:	Application (deadline: January 31); $40 application fee; transcript; math, English, and guidance counselor recommendations; test scores (PSAT, SAT, or SSAT); interview.
Grade:	8-12.

Cost: $23,000 (boarding); $15,400 (day). Financial aid is available.

Contact: William W. Ellis, Jr., Director of Admissions and Financial Aid
Saint James School
College Road
St. James, MD 21781
(301) 733-9330; Fax: (301) 739-1310
E-mail: admissions@stjames.edu
Web site: http://www.stjames.edu

STEVENSON

St. Timothy's School
Academic Year

St. Timothy's School is a girls boarding and day school for grades 9-12 and postgraduate. The campus is in a rural setting, only 15 minutes from downtown Baltimore and one hour from Washington, D.C. The students receive individualized instruction from a highly qualified and dedicated faculty in classes averaging between 8 to 10 girls. The school offers a rigorous college-preparatory program with Advanced Placement classes in ten subject areas, as well as additional honors courses. One hundred percent of St. Timothy's girls enter college, with many accepted by highly selective college and universities in the United States and abroad. The school's facilities include a new state-of-the-art athletic complex, eight tennis courts, equestrian center with indoor and outdoor arena, 350-seat theater, two dormitories, art barn, 20,000 volume library, hardwired classrooms, and three computer labs with a 2:1 computer to student ratio.

Criteria: Application (deadline: February 10); $40 application fee; transcript; personal essay; recommendations; SSAT or ISSE; interview.

Grade: 9-12, PG.

Cost: $29,400 (boarding); $17,750 (day). All costs are for 2002-2003 year. Financial aid is available.

Contact: Patrick Finn, Director of Admissions
St. Timothy's School
8400 Greenspring Avenue
Stevenson, MD 21153
(410) 486-7400; Fax: (410) 486-1167
E-mail: admis@sttimothysschool.com
Web site: http://www.sttimothysschool.com

MASSACHUSETTS

STATE DIRECTOR

Linda DeLorenzo, Content Specialist
Gifted Education
Massachusetts Department of Education
350 Main Street
Malden, MA 02148
(781) 388-3389; Fax: (781) 388-3396

Susan Wheltle, Temporary Contact
Office of Special Services
Massachusetts Department of Education
350 Main Street
Malden, MA 02148
(781) 338-6239

STATE ASSOCIATION

Massachusettes Association for Advancement of Individual Potential
Mark Anderson, President
P.O. Box 1265
Barnstable, MA 02630-2265
(781) 394-5526
E-mail: president@massgifted.org

REGIONAL TALENT SEARCH

Center for Talent Development (The Johns Hopkins University)
See listing on page 4 for complete information.

AMHERST

Academic Study Associates
June-August

See listing on page 7 for complete information.

Excel at Amherst College (Putney Student Travel)
June-August (Three-, four-, and seven-week programs)

See listing on page 9 for complete information.

SuperCamp® (Hampshire College)
July-August

See listing on page 13 for complete information.

ANDOVER

Phillips Academy Summer Session (Phillips Academy)
July 1-August 6

The nation's oldest boarding school, situated 25 miles north of Boston, offers a five-week summer program to students from all over the world. This pre-college experience includes demanding classes, invigorating afternoon activities, and welcoming dormitories that prepare students for collegiate residential life. For five weeks, in a multicultural setting, students with impressive goals prepare for the rigors of the best colleges and for the rigors of thriving and surviving in this complex world. There are over sixty course offerings in the arts, literature and writing, mathematics, music, computer science, natural sciences, philosophy, social sciences, languages, English as a Second Language, and SAT preparation. The average class size is 14.

Criteria:	Application; $45 application fee ($80 for international students); transcript; personal essay; recommendations; corrected English essay.
Grade:	9-12.
Cost:	$4,800 (boarding); $3,400 (day). Financial aid is available.
Contact:	Maxine Grogan, Dean of Admissions Phillips Academy Summer Session 180 Main Street Andover, MA 01810 (978) 749-4400; Fax: (978) 749-4414 E-mail: summersession@andover.edu Web site: http://www.andover.edu/summersession

Ashburnham

Cushing Academy
Academic Year

Founded in 1865, Cushing Academy is an independent, college-preparatory boarding school for girls and boys in grades 9 through 12 and postgraduate. In the New England tradition of educational excellence, Cushing students come from across the country and around the world to pursue a challenging academic curriculum, engage in competitive athletics, and forge creative pathways in the visual and performing arts. The Academy offers more than 18 Advanced Placement and honors classes, 46 varsity and junior varsity teams, and arts offerings that include silversmithing and stained glass. Such variety coupled with small classes, a talented and dedicated faculty, a strong support network, and state-of-the-art facilities provide Cushing students with the tools needed to achieve excellence at the secondary school level.

Criteria:	Application (and fee); transcript; personal essay; recommendations; test scores; PSAT, SAT, or SSAT; interview.
Grade:	9-12, PG.
Cost:	$31,500 (boarding); $21,890 (day). Need-based financial aid is available ($1.6 million).
Contact:	T. Mark Aimone, Director of Admission Cushing Academy 39 School Street Ashburnham, MA 01430 (978) 827-7300; Fax: (978) 827-6253 E-mail: admission@cushing.org Web site: http://www.cushing.org

Boston

Congressional Student Leadership Conference
March-April (six-day programs); June-August (six- and ten-day programs)

See listing on page 8 for complete information.

National Junior Leaders Conference (LeadAmerica Foundation)
June-August (six- and ten-day programs)

See listing on page 10 for complete information.

BOSTON

Program in Mathematics for Young Scientists—PROMYS
(Boston University)
July 6–August 16

PROMYS offers a lively mathematical environment in which ambitious high school students explore the creative world of mathematics. Through their intensive efforts to solve a large assortment of unusually challenging problems in number theory, the participants practice the art of mathematical discovery: numerical exploration, formulation and critique of conjectures, and techniques of proof and generalization. More experienced participants may also study algorithms, modular forms, and combinatorics. Problem sets are accompanied by daily lectures given by research mathematicians. Labs and problem-solving seminars meet in the afternoons. In addition, 15 highly competent, college-age counselors live in the dormitories and are always available to discuss mathematics with students. Each participant belongs to a problem solving group that meets with a professional mathematician three times per week. Special lectures by outside speakers offer a broad view of mathematics and its role in the sciences.

Criteria:	Application; transcript; teacher reports; personal essay; applicant's solutions to a set of challenging problems included with the application packet.
Grade:	Rising 10-12.
Cost:	$1,600 (approximate cost for room and board). Need-based financial aid is available; PROMYS is dedicated to the principle that no student will be unable to attend because of financial need.
Contact:	PROMYS Boston University Department of Mathematics 111 Cummington Street Boston, MA 02215 (617) 353-2563; Fax: (617) 353-8100 E-mail: promys@bu.edu Web site: http://www.promys.org

Cambridge

Minority Introduction to Engineering, Entrepreneurship and Science—MITE²S Program (Massachusetts Institute of Technology)
June 18-August 2

MITE²S is a rigorous six-week summer program designed to introduce underrepresented minority high school students to careers in engineering, entrepreneurship, and science. Participants are selected from a nationwide pool of applicants: juniors in high school who are Native American, African American, or Hispanic American. The students selected for the program spend six weeks at MIT totally immersed in campus life. Classroom work centers on math, physics, biochemistry/chemistry, engineering design, writing, and hi-tech entrepreneurship, with daily assignments and periodic exams, all designed to help students develop scientific and engineering skills in a university environment. Also scheduled are presentations by MIT engineering and science faculty, by practicing engineers, scientists, and graduate students, and by college admissions, financial aid, and career counselors. Trips to industrial and laboratory sites and to the lighter and more cultural side of local life are scheduled.

Criteria: Application (postmark deadline: February 7); transcript; recommendations; personal essays; GPA; PSAT; SAT; underrepresented minority student; proof of U.S. citizenship or copy of green card.

Grade: Rising 12.

Cost: No cost except transportation to and from MIT.

Contact: Karl W. Reid, Director, MITE²S Program
Massachusetts Institute of Technology
Room 1-211, 77 Massachusetts Avenue
Cambridge, MA 02139
(617) 253-3298; Fax: (617) 253-8549
E-mail: mites@mit.edu
Web site: http://web.mit.edu/mites/www

Research Science Institute (Center For Excellence in Education and Massachusetts Institute of Technology)
June 22-August 2

Sponsored by the Center for Excellence in Education in collaboration with Massachusetts Institute of Technology, the twentieth annual Research Science Institute provides students with an intense one-on-one research experience with mentor scientists from MIT, Harvard, and surrounding private research institutions. Classes in scientific communication, computer use, research methods, as well as a series of "professional lectures" in biology, chemistry, physics, and mathematics prepare students for research. A guest lecture series runs throughout the program and features nationally recognized figures in science and the humanities. Field trips to cultural and scientific sites occur on weekends. Throughout the program a residential staff of counselors and teachers supports student research. Students, counselors, and teachers come from all states and are joined by international students for the six-week program. In prior years, professors from MIT, Harvard University, University of Washington, Yale University, and Columbia University have led the professorial staff.

Criteria: Application (deadline: February 1); transcript; recommendations; PSAT (minimum score approximately 140); personal essay.

Grade: Rising 12, PG (or student who has completed the equivalent of three years of high school).

Cost: No cost except transportation to and from the Institute.

Contact: Maite P.Ballestero, Director of Administration
Center for Excellence in Education
140 Park Street, SE, 2nd Floor
Vienna, VA 22180-4627
(703) 938-9062; Fax: (703) 938-9121
E-mail: maite@cee.org
Web site: http://www.cee.org/rsi

Cambridge

Harvard Secondary School Program (Harvard University)
June 22-August 15

Harvard Summer School's Secondary School Program offers intensive eight-week college-credit courses for students who have finished their junior or senior year. Courses include: anthropology, astronomy, biology, chemistry, classics, computer science, drama (acting and directing), economics, English, expository and creative writing (including writing humor, fiction, poetry, scriptwriting, journalism), languages, government, mathematics, philosophy, physics, psychology (including Law and Psychology, and Crime and Justice), visual and environmental studies, and women's studies. Students live in dormitories with other secondary school students. (Those about to enter college live with other such students.) Students "shop" during the first week to choose two four-unit courses. Activities include dances, a talent show, a trivia bowl, intramural sports, a tennis tournament, a swim meet, trips to other colleges (last year to Brown, Yale, Dartmouth, and Bates), a college fair, day trips to Tanglewood, Newport, and Provincetown, and social events within dormitories.

Criteria: Application (and fee); transcript; teacher reports; recommendations; test scores (if available).

Grade: Rising 12 and entering college freshmen.

Cost: $6,900 (room, board, and tuition: 2002 rates). Limited financial aid is available.

Contact: Harvard Secondary School Program
Harvard Summer School
51 Brattle Street
Cambridge, MA 02138-3722
(617) 495-3192; Fax: (617) 495-9176
E-mail: hewitt@hudce.harvard.edu
Web site: http://www.ssp.harvard.edu

Concord

Concord Academy
Academic Year

The individuality, diversity, and quality of Concord Academy's faculty and student body distinguish it from other highly competitive academic boarding and day schools. Life at Concord Academy is creative and inquisitive, the people are impassioned and involved, and the school is academically demanding. Students study intensely and participate actively in a broad range of artistic, athletic, and extracurricular activities. Though rigorous, the school is also nurturing. Large enough to offer 349 students a comprehensive academic and extracurricular program, it is small enough to provide an intimate, caring, boarding community. Set in a small, historic town near Cambridge and Boston, Concord Academy is a close and vibrant community enhanced by its culturally rich environment.

Criteria:	Application; $45 application fee ($100 for international applications); transcript; personal essay; recommendations; test scores; SSAT, PSAT, SAT, ISEE (or equivalent); interview.
Grade:	9-12.
Cost:	$30,460 (boarding); $24,280 (day). Need-based financial aid is available (1.5 million).
Contact:	Pamela J. Safford, Associate Head for Enrollment and Planning Concord Academy 166 Main Street Concord, MA 01742 (978) 402-2250; Fax: (978) 287-4302 E-mail: admissions@concordacademy.org Web site: http://www.concordacademy.org

Middlesex School
Academic Year

Middlesex School preserves an intellectual tradition marked by small, highly interactive classrooms in which students learn to express themselves articulately and solve problems creatively. Over a century old, the magnificent 350-acre campus is located in Concord, Massachusetts, just 20 miles west of Boston. A remarkably diverse, close-knit community, the school enrolls 333 students from 26 states and 11 countries. New courses in science writing and the scientific media, bio-ethics, and Mandarin Chinese enhance the challenging curriculum that also includes 24 Advanced Placement courses. The experienced, dedicated faculty prepares Middlesex students for study at the most selective colleges and universities in the country. From the intellectually rigorous academic program to the rich and varied arts program to strong, competitive athletics complemented by a wide range of extracurricular opportunities, the sense of common purpose which binds the Middlesex community is the pursuit of excellence in all areas of school life.

Criteria:	Application (deadline: January 31); $50 application fee; transcript; personal essay; recommendations; sample of work; test scores; SSAT.
Grade:	9-12.

Cost:	$31,250 (boarding); $25,000 (day). Financial aid is available ($2 million).
Contact:	Sibyl F. Cohane, Director of Admissions Middlesex School 1400 Lowell Road Concord, MA 01742 (978) 369-2550; Fax: (978) 371-6939 E-mail: admission@middlesex.edu Web site: http://www.middlesex.edu

DEERFIELD

Deerfield Academy
Academic Year

Deerfield Academy, a coeducational, college-preparatory boarding school founded in 1797, is known for its high academic standards and cohesive school spirit. Deerfield nurtures its 598 students' intellectual curiosity with a rigorous curriculum, as well as encourages responsible citizenship. The outstanding faculty prepares students for competitive universities, challenging students in an academic program that includes Advanced Placement in 19 subject areas, two math courses beyond BC Calculus, an extensive spring term elective program, and domestic and foreign off-campus study. In addition to taking honors and AP classes, students with a deep interest and gift in a field—be it mathematics, the visual or performing arts, science, writing or the humanities—may enroll in advanced tutorials or independent study. Deerfield's 280-acre campus includes the Boyden Library, housing over 72,000 items and over 400 periodicals in five languages; an Arts Center; a Science Center housing New England's second largest planetarium; a 12,000 square-foot open laboratory; and a new Computer Technology Center.

Criteria:	Application; transcript; personal essay; teacher recommendations; sample of work; test scores; SSAT; interview.
Grade:	9-12, PG.
Cost:	$28,000 (boarding); $21,500 (day). Financial aid is available (over $4.2 million in financial aid awarded to 37% of students in 2002).
Contact:	Patricia L. Gimbel Dean of Admission and Financial Aid Deerfield Academy Main Street Deerfield, MA 01342 (413) 774-1400; Fax: (413) 772-1100 E-mail: admission@deerfield.edu Web site: http://www.deerfield.edu

Easthampton

The Williston Northampton School
Academic Year

For over 150 years, The Williston Northampton School has offered a carefully designed and challenging program to its students. In 1991, the school was named an Exemplary Secondary School by the U.S. Department of Education. The rigorous, college preparatory curriculum is enriched by the culturally diverse and stimulating environment near Amherst, Smith, Mt. Holyoke, and Hampshire Colleges, and the University of Massachusetts. Special programs include English-Speaking Union, School Year Abroad, directed studies, intensive English and history electives, a strong fine and performing arts department, a comprehensive athletic program, and many opportunities for student leadership. 550 students from around the United States and the world enjoy state-of-the-art facilities including the Technology Center, Science Tech Lab, Williston Theatre, Athletic Center, and Reed Campus Center. Williston educates for maturity, growth, independence, and responsibility. The school's faculty and staff respect personal style, ideology, and diverse talents and provide an environment conducive to the realization of each individual's potential.

Criteria: Application (and fee); transcript; personal essay; recommendations; test scores; PSAT, SAT, ACT, or SSAT; interview.

Grade: 7-12, PG (day only); 9-12, PG (boarding and day).

Cost: $29,500 (boarding); $20,500 (day). Over $3 million in need-based financial aid is available.

Contact: Allison Marsland, Associate Director of Admission
The Williston Northampton School
19 Payson Avenue
Easthampton, MA 01027
(413) 529-3282; Fax: (413) 527-9494
E-mail: admission@williston.com
Web site: http://www.williston.com

Great Barrington

Simon's Rock College of Bard
Academic Year

Serious students in tenth and eleventh grades often crave the academic challenge and social responsibility of college. College-style summer enrichment programs tend to enhance this craving. Simon's Rock College is designed to give these academically able students the opportunity to begin college study. Of the several fine "early entrance" programs in the United States, Simon's Rock is the oldest, largest, and the only one exclusively devoted to younger scholars. With an enrollment of 390 students, Simon's Rock offers individually tailored programs of study. The college awards both B.A. and A.A. undergraduate degrees in the liberal arts and sciences. The admissions staff looks for students who show evidence of a lively intellect, sustained achievement, and scholarly potential. Through its Acceleration to Excellence Program, accomplished high school sophomores compete for scholarships ranging from $5,000 to full tuition and fees.

Criteria:	Application (and fee); transcript; GPA; two personal essays; recommendations; sample of work; test scores; PSAT, SAT or ACT; interview.
Grade:	10-11.
Cost:	$34,860 (tuition and fees). Need- and merit-based financial aid is available.
Contact:	Mary King Austin, Dean of Admission Simon's Rock College of Bard 84 Alford Road Great Barrington, MA 01230-9702 (800) 235-7186; Fax: (413) 528-7334 E-mail: admit@simons-rock.edu Web site: http://www.simons-rock.edu

Great Barrington

Young Writer's Workshop (Simon's Rock College of Bard)
June 29-July 19

The Young Writer's Workshop began at Simon's Rock in 1983 and has served as a model for summer workshops at other colleges around the country. Each year 70-80 talented students are selected to participate. Unlike conventional workshops in creative or expository writing, the focus is on using informal, playful, expressive writing as a way to strengthen skills of language and thinking. The subjects range from stories and poems the group has read to personal experience, natural phenomena, and works of art. Out of this informal writing, using techniques of peer response, students develop more polished pieces from poems and stories to reflective essays. Classes are small and emphasize an atmosphere of trust and collaboration. During the three weeks students have the opportunity to attend plays, concerts, and other cultural activities that are part of summer life in the Berkshires. Former participants have gone on to enroll in such colleges as Amherst, Bard, Harvard, Haverford, Princeton, Simon's Rock, Smith, Williams, and Yale.

Criteria:	Application; personal essay; recommendations.
Grade:	Rising 10-12.
Cost:	$1,775 (tuition, room, board, and fees). Need-based financial aid is available.
Contact:	Dr. Jamie Hutchinson, Director Summer Young Writer's Workshop Simon's Rock College of Bard 84 Alford Road Great Barrington, MA 01230 (413) 528-7231; Fax: (413) 528-7365 E-mail: jamieh@simons-rock.edu Web site: http://www.simons-rock.edu

Groton

Groton School Scholars Program
Academic Year

Groton School, a coeducational boarding school of 360 students, offers a special program for gifted and talented students who enter in the eighth, ninth, or tenth grade. This program requires study of both a classical and a modern language in addition to an accelerated liberal arts curriculum. In the last five years, Groton students have taken 2,254 Advanced Placement exams in 23 different subject areas, scoring 3, 4, or 5 on 2,032 exams. Groton is a well-endowed school with diverse students who create a special sense of community. The school combines an inspiring faculty with talented students from 32 states and 16 foreign countries. Groton's students are from a wide spectrum of academic, economic, religious, and ethnic backgrounds; they share with the faculty a commitment to intellectual growth, academic excellence, spiritual development, and service to others.

Criteria: Application (and fee); transcript; personal essay; teacher recommendations; SSAT; interview.

Grade: 8-12.

Cost: $32,160 (residential); $24,115 (day). Financial aid is available ($2.3 million dollars in financial aid was awarded last year to 94 students).

Contact: John M. Niles, Director of Admission
Groton School
P.O. Box 991
Groton, MA 01450
(978) 448-7510; Fax: (978) 448-9623
E-mail: admission_office@groton.org
Web site: http://www.groton.org

Lawrence Academy
Academic Year

An academically demanding curriculum combines traditional teaching with student centered learning through seminars, projects, and independent study opportunities. Signature programs, which encourage hands on learning, include the Ninth Grade Program, Combined Studies Course, Winterim, and Lawrence II. Extensive arts offerings in dance, drama, music, and visual arts, as well as a competitive sports program, a warm community environment, international diversity, daily advisor meetings, e-mail and Internet, radio station, and recording studio enhance the program.

Criteria: Application (deadline: February 1); $50 application fee; transcript; personal essay; recommendations; test scores; PSAT; SAT; SSAT; interview.

Grade: 9-12.

Cost: $31,200 (boarding); $23,400 (day). Need-based financial aid is available.

Contact: Barbara M. Krein, Director of Admissions
Lawrence Academy
P.O. Box 992
Groton, MA 01450
(978) 448-6535; Fax: (978) 448-9208
E-mail: admiss@lacademy.edu
Web site: http://www.lacademy.edu

Medford

Tufts Summer Study
Summer

Tufts Summer Study is a coeducational day program for rising juniors and seniors. Students can choose from one or two summer programs. **The Health Science Program** introduces students to the world of health care, combining classroom experience with visits to a local medical facility. **The Writing Program** focuses on expository writing, helping students develop a writing style that appeals, convinces, educates, and entertains. **The Computer Science Explorations Program** is for students with no prior programming experience, who wants to know more about computers and computer science. In the **College for Juniors Program**, seniors can take up two college classes. College credit is available for those who qualify.

Criteria:	Application; $25 application fee; transcript; personal essay; recommendations; test scores; GPA; PSAT; SAT.
Grade:	Rising 11-12.
Cost:	$1,275. Financial aid is available.
Contact:	Steve McDonough Tufts Summer Study Tufts University 108 Packard Avenue Medford, MA 02155 (617) 627-3454; Fax: (617) 627-3295 E-mail: highschool@tufts.edu Web site: http://ase.tufts.edu/summer

North Andover

Brooks School
Academic Year

Brooks' diverse student body of 350 students includes 17% American students of color, 12% international students, and 46% girls. Two thirds of the faculty live on the 251-acre campus that strives to challenge and support students in both their academic and personal development. The school has recently added the Henry Luce III Library, the Lehman Art Center, the Kingsbury Computer Center and the F. Fessenden Wilder Dining Hall and Student Center, and plans are underway to add a new athletic facility in the next two years. The computer center includes more than 50 computers with Internet and e-mail access and a brand new language lab used extensively by the modern language classes. All students have their own e-mail account, and each dormitory room is wired for Internet, telephone, and other modern media advances. There are 17 Advanced Placement courses offered as well as overseas exchange opportunities in Scotland, Hungary, Kenya, and South Africa.

Criteria: Application (and fee); transcript; personal essay; teacher report; recommendations; test scores; GPA; PSAT; SAT; SSAT; interview.

Grade: 9-12.

Cost: $29,325 (boarding); $21,135 (day). $1.6 million in financial aid is available.

Contact: Casey Bobo
Brooks School
1160 Great Pond Road
North Andover, MA 01845
(978) 686-6272, (978) 686-6271; Fax: (978) 725-6298
E-mail: admission@brooksschool.org
Web site: http://www.brooksschool.org

Northampton

Smith College Summer Science and Engineering Program
June 29-July 26

Girls with dreams of careers in science, engineering, and medicine should make the Smith College Summer Science and Engineering Program (SSEP) part of their plan. Participants report that SSEP prepares them to tackle tough science courses and to know what to expect in college. Smith College is one of the top-rated colleges in America. SSEP participants are taught by Smith science and engineering faculty, live in a college house alongside Smith undergraduate interns, and have access to all campus facilities. SSEP courses emphasize asking questions and learning by doing. Participants learn how scientists formulate questions, work on sophisticated scientific instruments, and develop critical thinking skills. Research courses for 2003 include investigations such as Your Genes, Your Chromosomes: A Laboratory of Human Genetics and Designing Intelligent Robots. During free time participants choose from organized sports, recreational and cultural activities, weekend field trips to local arts festivals, museums, and theatrical performances.

Criteria: Application (deadline: May 1); $50 application fee (refundable); transcript; personal essay; recommendations.

Grade:	9-12.
Cost:	$3,750. Need-based financial aid is available.
Contact:	Gail Scordilis, Director of Educational Outreach Smith College Clark Hall Northampton, MA 01063 (413) 585-3060; Fax: (413) 585-3068 E-mail: gscordil@smith.edu Web site: http://www.smith.edu/summerprograms/ssep

PITTSFIELD

Miss Hall's School
Academic Year

Founded in 1898, Miss Hall's School was one of the first girls' boarding schools established in New England. Today the school is a nationally recognized, independent secondary school offering a rigorous and innovative college-preparatory program for 140 boarding and day students from twenty states and eleven countries. The student-to-teacher ratio is 5:1, and the average class size is nine. The academic program offers a varied curriculum, an honors tier, a wide range of Advanced Placement courses, and an Academic Skills Center for one-on-one skills development. There is a three-level English as a Second Language program for international students. The Expressive Arts Program includes music, studio arts, theatre, photography, choreography, and modern dance. Girls participate in ten team sports, in addition to wilderness, alpine skiing, riding, and Tae Kwon Do. Through the weekly Horizons program, students explore community service, career development internships, and the cultural riches of the Berkshires.

Criteria:	Application (deadline: February 15); $40 application fee; transcript; personal essay; recommendations; test scores; SSAT; interview; female student.
Grade:	9-12.
Cost:	$29,925 (boarding); $17,535 (day). Financial aid is available.
Contact:	Kimberly Boland, Acting Director of Admission Miss Hall's School 492 Holmes Road Pittsfield, MA 01201 (413) 443-6401; Fax: (413) 448-2994 E-mail: info@misshalls.org Web site: http://www.misshalls.org

SOUTHBOROUGH

Exploration Junior Program (Exploration Summer Programs)
June 29-August 9 (three-and six-week sessions)

The Exploration Junior Program at St. Mark's School was founded to provide an opportunity for young people to explore academic, artistic, and athletic interests in a relaxed and creative environment that encourages a lifelong love of learning. Students entering grades four through seven come to Exploration Junior Program from over 35 states and more than a dozen countries to take part in residential and day programs. St. Marks School is one of the country's oldest and most prominent coeducational, college preparatory schools. Students at Exploration have the opportunity to choose from a wide variety of academic courses including Archeology, Journalism, Ceramics, and Chemistry. The campus offers 250 acres of fields, woodlands, and ponds. In addition to the superb classroom facilities, there are art studios, a theater, and an award-winning science center. The campus houses a multi-million dollar sports complex, which includes eight playing fields, eight tennis courts, and a pool.

Criteria: Teacher recommendation.

Grade: Rising 4-7.

Cost: $1,575 (day); $3,195 (residential). Limited financial aid is available.

Contact: Becca Finer, Admissions Coordinator
Exploration Summer Programs
P.O. Box 368
470 Washington Street
Norwood, MA 02062
(781) 762-7400; Fax: (781) 762-7425
Web site: http://www.explo.org

SOUTH HADLEY

SummerMath (Mount Holyoke College)
June 29-July 26

SummerMath is designed to engage young women in the process of learning and creating mathematics. During the four weeks of SummerMath, students take a mathematics class, a computer class, and two 2-week workshops that are drawn from topics such as chemistry, astronomy, architecture, robotics, anatomy, brain-imaging, confidence-building, and statistics. In all classes, students take charge of their own education by actively exploring new ideas and learning to take a creative approach to problems. SummerMath students develop powerful problem-solving strategies and increased understanding and confidence. Other activities include sports, arts and crafts, speakers, discussions, theater, a Boston museum trip, movies, and dances. Students come to SummerMath from all over the United States as well as from countries around the world. Together, these participants create a college-like experience on a campus located in a region rich in natural and cultural resources.

Criteria: Application (deadline: May 1); $25 application fee; personal essay; female student.

Grade: Rising 9-12.

Cost: $3,900 (boarding); $3,100 (day). Need-based financial aid is available.

Contact: Charlene and James Morrow, Directors
SummerMath
Mount Holyoke College
50 College Street
South Hadley, MA 01075-1441
(413) 538-2608; Fax: (413) 538-2002
E-mail: summermath@mtholyoke.edu
Web site: http://www.mtholyoke.edu/proj/summermath

WELLESLEY

Dana Hall School
Academic Year

Dana Hall, located 12 miles west of Boston in Wellesley, Massachusetts, is a college preparatory school for girls in grades 6-12. Boarding is offered for grades 9-12. Originally founded in 1881 as a preparatory school for students entering Wellesley College, Dana Hall has maintained a tradition of excellence and academic rigor through the decades. Dana Hall students represent a diversity of talents and interests, and students come from 18 states and 14 countries to pursue their education before entering college. Graduates attend outstanding colleges and universities across the country where they study disciplines with confidence and experience. Each year, the Congdon Prize Scholarship is awarded to two entering sophomore boarding students from outside New England who demonstrate exceptional academic and personal promise, a potential for leadership, and a responsibility to the community-at-large. The scholarship provides a $2,500 prize and includes an additional award based on financial need.

Criteria: Application (and fee); transcript; personal essay; recommendations; test scores; SSAT; interview (recommended); female student.

Grade: 6-12.

Cost: $30,210 (boarding); $22,675 (day). $2,500 merit scholarship and need-based financial aid are also available.

Contact: Olive B. Long, Director of Admission and Financial Aid
Dana Hall School
45 Dana Road
Wellesley, MA 02482
(781) 235-3010; Fax: (781) 235-0577
E-mail: admission@danahall.org
Web site: http://www.danahall.org

WELLESLEY

Exploration Intermediate Program (Exploration Summer Programs)
June 29-August 9 (three-and six-week sessions)

The Exploration Intermediate Program at Wellesley College was founded to provide an opportunity for young people to explore academic, artistic, and athletic interests in a relaxed and creative environment that encourages a lifelong love of learning. Students come to Exploration from over 40 states and 40 countries to take part in day and residential programs. Students entering grades eight and nine have attended the Intermediate Program for the past 17 years. The Intermediate Program offers trips to a variety of cultural, recreational, and educational attractions throughout the Northeast. Exploration offers a unique environment for students to pursue a range of interests from Law and Ethics to Sculpture and Architecture. The Intermediate Program provides excellent preparation for a student's high school years. A multi-million dollar sports center, beautiful dormitories, historic classroom buildings, tennis courts, playing fields, and a lake on campus make Wellesley an ideal place to spend the summer.

Criteria:	Teacher report.
Grade:	Rising 8-9.
Cost:	$1,625 (day); $3,295 (residential). Limited financial aid is available.
Contact:	Becca Finer, Admissions Coordinator Exploration Summer Programs P.O. Box 368 470 Washington Street Norwood, MA 02062 (781) 762-7400; Fax: (781) 762-7425 Web site: http://www.explo.org

WILLIAMSTOWN

Excel at Williams College (Putney Student Travel)
June-August (Three-, four-, and seven-week programs)

See listing on page 9 for complete information.

WILBRAHAM

Wilbraham and Monson Academy
Academic Year

Wilbraham & Monson Academy is an independent, coeducational, college preparatory school enrolling students in grade six through a postgraduate year. Strongly committed to the educational values inherent in a residential community, the Academy has designed its program to be a total experience, which addresses every aspect of an individual's growth. Beyond providing preparation for the challenge of higher education, the Academy ensures that its students possess the knowledge, critical thinking skills, and moral framework needed to lead constructive and fulfilling adult lives. The primary goals of the Academy are to promote broad intellectual development, good physical health, personal accountability, mutual respect, and commitment to service. Each student is encouraged to meet the highest standards of intellectual and personal responsibility in preparation for the challenges of higher education and for success as a contributing participant in an interdependent world. Visit their Web site for additional information.

Criteria: Application (deadline February 1); $50 application fee; transcript; personal essay; interview; recommendations; sample of work; test scores; SSAT.

Grade: 6-12, PG.

Cost: $29,200 (boarding); $18,500 (day).

Contact: Christopher Moore, Director of Admissions
Wilbraham and Monson Academy
423 Main Street
Wilbraham, MA 01095
(413) 596-6811; Fax: (413) 599-1749
E-mail: cmoore@WMAnet.org
Web site: http://www.wmacademy.org

Woods Hole

Science at Sea (Sea Education Association)
August 4-23

Science at Sea is an interdisciplinary academic program for secondary school students interested in the ocean environment. The program combines rigorous scientific research with the opportunity to develop skills in leadership, teamwork, communication, and critical thinking. Students spend ten days at the SEA campus in the world-renowned oceanographic center of Woods Hole preparing to embark on a ten-day voyage at sea aboard a 130-foot brigantine.

Criteria: Application ($10 application fee); transcript; personal essay; recommendations; test scores.

Grade: 10-12.

Cost: $3,500.

Contact: Brian R. Hopewell, Dean of Enrollment
Science at Sea
Sea Education Association
Box 6, 171 Woods Hole Road
Woods Hole, MA 02543
(800) 552-3633; Fax: (508) 540-0558
E-mail: admission@sea.edu
Web site: http://www.sea.edu

MICHIGAN

STATE DIRECTOR

David Mills, Consultant, Talent Development
Office of Education Options
Michigan Department of Education
608 West Allegan
Lansing, MI 48909
(517) 373-4213
E-mail: millsd@michigan.gov

STATE ASSOCIATION

Michigan Alliance for Gifted Education

The Michigan Alliance for Gifted Education is a state wide organization of parents, educators, and others interested in appropriate educational opportunities for gifted students, support for parents, and professional development. The Alliance provides leadership and advocacy to seek differentiated education and services for the diverse needs of over 50,000 gifted, talented, and creative students in Michigan.

3300 Washtenaw Avenue, Suite 220
Ann Arbor, MI 48104
(734) 677-4404; Fax: (734) 677-2407
E-mail: rtavares@ucia2.com
Web site: http://www.migiftedchild.org

REGIONAL TALENT SEARCH

Center for Talent Development (Northwestern University)
See listing on page 3 for complete information.

ANN ARBOR

Camp CAEN (University of Michigan College of Engineering)
June 15-August 15 (two-week sessions)

Camp CAEN is a world-class computer and technology camp offered by the Computer Aided Engineering Network (CAEN) at the University of Michigan College of Engineering. Knowledgeable staff, that include enthusiastic engineering student mentors, teach beginning and advanced classes ranging from Java programming and Web site development to virtual reality. From digital video production to an immersive virtual reality CAVE, high-tech is at Camp CAEN. The coed program also includes a new all-girls "Discover Yourself through Technology" class. Camp CAEN offers an opportunity for students to broaden their horizons beyond the typical high school and enables them to become acquainted with the UM College of Engineering.

Criteria: Personal essay; teacher recommendation.

Grade: 7-12.

Cost: $875 (commuter); $1,595 (residential). Limited financial aid is available.

Contact: James Todd, Camp Coordinator
Camp CAEN
University of Michigan
2318 Media Union, 2281 Bonisteel Boulevard
Ann Arbor, MI 48109-2094
(734) 647-6812; Fax: (734) 936-2486
E-mail: campcaen@engin.umich.edu
Web site: http://campcaen.engin.umich.edu

Ann Arbor

Summer Discovery Pre-College Enrichment Programs
June-August (three- to six-week programs)

See listing on page 12 for complete information.

Bloomfield Hills/Birmingham

The Roeper School
Academic Year and Summer

The structure of the curriculum at The Roeper School emphasizes conceptual learning and gifted education and provides specific goals for individuals in accordance with their characteristics, needs, and interests. In the **Lower School**, homerooms serve as centers for language arts activities, social studies, and mathematics. Additional classes in music, art, science, French, drama, dance, physical education, library, and computer skills are part of the daily curriculum. The **Middle School** curriculum includes English literature, composition, social studies, French, Spanish, mathematics, computer study, science, studio and performing arts, and physical education/intramural sports. Courses in the **Upper School** include English core courses and electives in many areas; and Advanced Placement courses in English, physics, biology, chemistry, foreign languages, and social studies. The fine arts program provides many opportunities for performance and participation at all levels. Roeper is a coeducational day school. A summer camp is also offered.

Criteria: Application (and fee); transcript; personal essay; recommendations; test scores.

Grade: PreK-12.

Cost: $11,300-$15,400. Over $1 million is available in scholarships and financial aid.

Contact: Lori Zinser, Director of Admissions
The Roeper School
41190 Woodward Avenue
Bloomfield Hills, MI 48304
(248) 203-7316; Fax: (248) 203-7310
E-mail: zinserl@roeper.org
Web site: http://www.roeper.org

East Lansing

The Mathematics-Science-Technology Program (Michigan State University)
July 27-August 9 (two-week sessions)

The Mathematics-Science-Technology (MST) Program is a two-week, summer residential program for academically talented students who are currently in grades seven and eight. The program is conducted on the East Lansing campus of Michigan State University and is designed to serve 110 students identified as academically talented. Qualifying students of all races and religious backgrounds are encouraged to apply. The program has been designed to stimulate students to learn about new developments in career fields of mathematics, science, and technology. The goal of the program is to match intellectual abilities of talented adolescents with rigorous and challenging course work that provides enrichment but does not duplicate or accelerate work that is part of regular school curriculum. Classes offered are mathematics, genetics, astronomy, physics, robotics, and mechanical engineering. Special clinics in creative writing, tae kwan do, musical theater, visual arts, basketball, and magic are also offered.

Criteria: Application (deadline: April 30); $100 application fee; transcript; personal essay; recommendations; GPA; ACT; SAT.

Grade: 7-8.

Cost: $1,125.

Contact: Jenny McCampbell
Michigan State University
188 Bessey Hall
East Lansing, MI 48824-1033
(517) 432-2129
E-mail: mccampbe@msu.edu
Web site: http://www.msu.edu/user/gifted

Houghton

Explorations in Engineering (Michigan Technological University)
July 13-19

The Explorations in Engineering Workshop (EIE) provides young minority and/or economically disadvantaged men and women who are academically talented in mathematics or science the opportunity to investigate careers in engineering and science. Through an intensive one-week residential workshop, the participants explore several areas of engineering and science. Sessions are led by minority engineers, role models and speakers from industry, and university faculty. Each session includes a hands-on laboratory experience that demonstrates the information each engineering and science area uses. Recreational and evening activities include a career roundtable, variety show, career planning, beach outings, movies, team building, and more.

Criteria: Application; transcript; GPA; personal essay; recommendations; minority, academically, or educationally disadvantaged student.

Grade: 9-11.

Cost: $50 registration fee (payable upon acceptance). All accepted students receive a scholarship; the program is supported entirely by Michigan Technological University and corporations.

Contact: John Lehman, Coordinator for MTU Youth Programs
Michigan Technological University
1400 Townsend Drive
Houghton, MI 49931
(906) 487-2219; Fax: (906) 487-3101
E-mail: yp@mtu.edu
Web site: http://www.youthprograms.mtu.edu

HOUGHTON

Honors Orchestra Program (Michigan Technological University)
Late June-early July

The Honors Orchestra Program is for talented high school musicians who are serious about playing their instruments. The students will have the opportunity to perform alongside professional musicians and to accompany a major operatic production with the Pine Mountain Music Festival. The Festival attracts world famous singers and musicians to the scenic Upper Peninsula of Michigan. Intensive daily rehearsals and master classes introduce students to the rewarding world of the professional musician.

Criteria: Recommendations; sample of work (tape).

Grade: 9-12 (age 15-18).

Cost: No cost except for $100 registration fee (transportation is not included).

Contact: John Lehman, Coordinator for MTU Youth Programs
Michigan Technological University
1400 Townsend Drive
Houghton, MI 49931
(906) 487-2219; Fax: (906) 487-3101
E-mail: yp@mtu.edu
Web site: http://www.youthprograms.mtu.edu

Houghton

Women in Engineering (Michigan Technological University)
July 6-12

The Women in Engineering Workshop (WIE) provides young women who are academically talented in mathematics and/or science the opportunity to investigate careers in engineering and science. WIE is open to all young women, but economically and educationally disadvantaged students are the main focus. Through an intensive one-week residential workshop, participants explore several areas of engineering and science. Educators, university faculty, and practicing minority engineers from industry and the government lead informative sessions and discussions. Each session includes a hands-on laboratory that demonstrates the information and equipment each engineering and science area uses. Recreational and evening activities include a career roundtable, a variety show, career planning, beach outings, movies, team building, and more.

Criteria: Application; transcript; GPA; personal essay; recommendations; female student.

Grade: Rising 10-12.

Cost: $50 registration fee (payable upon acceptance). All accepted women receive a scholarship; the program is supported by Michigan Technological University and corporations.

Contact: John Lehman, Coordinator for MTU Youth Programs
Michigan Technological University
1400 Townsend Drive
Houghton, MI 49931
(906) 487-2219; Fax: (906) 487-3101
E-mail: yp@mtu.edu
Web site: http://www.youthprograms.mtu.edu

INTERLOCHEN

Interlochen Center for the Arts
Academic Year and Summer

In 1928, Joseph E. Maddy's dream of a permanent training ground for young artists was realized in the formation of the National High School Orchestra Camp at Interlochen. Today, Interlochen Center for the Arts is well established as one of America's true cultural treasures, continuing as the country's premier site for young musicians, dancers, actors, visual artists and writers to explore and develop their talents. Named one of the top 10 nonprofits in the country by Independent Sector, Washington, D.C., Interlochen Center for the Arts is home to the Interlochen Arts Camp, which provides intensive training each summer to talented youngsters from around the world, and Interlochen Arts Academy, which has produced more Presidential Scholars in the Arts than any other high school in the United States. The Center has grown to include Interlochen Public Radio, a national leader in listener support, and the Interlochen Arts Festival, which presents more than 750 concerts and exhibits annually by students, faculty, and the nation's preeminent artists. In June 2000, Interlochen merged with The Pathfinder School, an independent school serving pre-kindergarten through eighth-grade students of the Grand Traverse region.

Criteria: Application (and fee); personal essay; recommendation letters; sample of work; audition.

Grade: 3-12 (Camp); 9-12 (Academy).

Cost: Varies. Contact their admissions office for a complete list of tuition rates and available financial assistance.

Contact: Tom Bewley, Director of Admissions
Interlochen Center for the Arts
P.O. Box 199
Interlochen, MI 49643-0199
(231) 276-7472; Fax: (231) 276-7464
E-mail: admissions@interlochen.org
Web site: http://www.interlochen.org

MINNESOTA

State Director

Mary S. Pfeifer
Minnesota Department of Children, Families, and Learning
Children, Families, and Learning Department
1500 Highway 36 West
Roseville, MN 55113-4266
(651) 297-7204
E-mail: mary.pfeifer@state.mn.us

State Association

Minnesota Council for the Gifted and Talented

Minnesota Council for the Gifted and Talented (MCGT) is a state-wide, not-for-profit organization. Its members are mainly parents, educators, and other professionals. MCGT provides information, literature and referral services, publishes a bi-monthly newsletter, conducts occasional topical seminars, sponsors an annual state conference with special children's programs, promotes advocacy at all levels for gifted and talented children, is active in legislative efforts on behalf of kids in collaboration with the Minnesota Educators of the Gifted and Talented, and participates in a national network through its affiliation with the National Association for Gifted Children and other organizations.

Deb Corhouse, President
5701 Normandale Road
Edina, MN 55424
(952) 848-4906
E-mail: info@mcgt.net
Web site: www.mcgt.net

Regional Talent Search

Center for Talent Development (Northwestern University)
See listing on page 2 for complete information.

Locations Throughout Minnesota

Concordia Language Villages
June 9-August 23

Concordia Language Villages is an internationally recognized world language and culture education program specializing in thirteen world languages: Chinese, Danish, English, French, Finnish, German, Italian, Japanese, Korean, Norwegian, Russian, Spanish, and Swedish. Concordia Language Villages is a program of Concordia College in Moorhead, Minnesota, and draws nearly 9,500 participants from across the United States and many other countries. The mission of the program is to prepare young people for responsible citizenship in the global community. Concordia Language Villages stresses immersion in language and culture because it promotes learning that cannot be duplicated in any classroom setting. Young people learn to communicate with confidence and cultural sensitivity in another language. The program simulates any trip abroad.

Participants enjoy cuisine, architecture, and other aspects authentic to the target culture. Villagers staying at Concordia Language Villages have an unparalleled opportunity to explore another country without ever leaving the north woods of Minnesota.

Criteria:	Application (and fee).
Grade:	Age 7-18.
Cost:	$545 (one week); $1,100 (two weeks); $2,455 (four weeks). Scholarships and need-based financial aid are available.
Contact:	Public Relations Director Concordia Language Villages 901 8th Street South Moorhead, MN 56562 (800) 222-4750, (218) 299-4544; Fax: (218) 299-3807 E-mail: clv@cord.edu Web site: http://www.ConcordiaLanguageVillages.org

FARIBAULT

Shattuck-St. Mary's School
Academic Year and Summer

Founded in 1858, Shattuck-St. Mary's is one of the oldest midwestern boarding schools, with a strong emphasis on college preparation. The 300 students enjoy an average class size of 12. All teachers and students are provided a Gateway 450X notebook computer; every classroom and dormroom is connected to the Internet. Gifted students may enroll in a variety of honors, accelerated, Advanced Placement, and independent study courses. Because of their coursework at Shattuck-St. Mary's, graduates have enrolled with advanced standing at Georgetown, Kenyon, Macalester, Mount Holyoke, Princeton, and Vassar. Extensive extracurricular and athletic programs, including a nationally ranked ice hockey program, provide cultural and competitive opportunities for all students. The award-winning choir and orchestra are complemented by a full range of drama and dance courses. The school's athletic facilities include an eighteen-hole golf course and an indoor hockey arena. A month-long summer program, with courses in English and mathematics, is also offered.

Criteria:	Application (and fee); transcript; personal essay; recommendations; test scores; GPA; SSAT; gifted and talented; interview.
Grade:	6-12, PG.
Cost:	$25,600 (boarding); $17,500 (day). Financial aid and academic scholarships are available.
Contact:	Phillip R. Trout, Director of Admissions Shattuck-St. Mary's School 1000 Shumway Avenue, P.O. Box 218 Faribault, MN 55021 (800) 421-2724; Fax: (507) 333-1661 E-mail: admissions@s-sm.org Web site: http://www.s-sm.org

Morris

Summer Scholars (University of Minnesota)
July 13-25

The Summer Scholars Program is designed to give academically gifted high school juniors an opportunity to do college-level work and experience college life. The program emphasizes skills necessary for success in college—writing, critical thinking, using the library, discussion, interdisciplinary perspectives, and campus life. Students choose one of the following courses, each carrying two college credits. *Human Reproduction and Biotechnology* examines the biological sciences of the new techniques used to tinker with human reproduction and the social implications of using biotechnology to affect human reproduction. *Writing Workshop: Growing Up American*, develops skills of written expression through examination of the topic of 'growing up in America' as reflected in literature, history, and film. Both courses are taught by award-winning professors. Student assistants provide academic guidance and live with Scholars in the residence hall. Applicants should be in the top 20 percent of their class and recommended by a teacher or administrator.

Criteria: Application (deadline: April 20); personal essay; recommendations; GPA.

Grade: 11.

Cost: $700.

Contact: Karen Ellis, Program Director
Summer Scholars
University of Minnesota, Morris
600 East Fourth
Morris, MN 56267
(800) 842-0030; Fax: (320) 589-1661
E-mail: elliskj@mrs.umn.edu
Web site: http://www.mrs.umn.edu/cerp/youth/summerscholars

Northfield

Summer Writing Program (Carleton College)
July 6-25

Every summer more than 80 high school juniors gather on the campus of Carleton College for three weeks of intensive writing instruction, fun, and friendship. Emphasizing a writing process approach, the program helps students learn to compose academic papers that are similar to those they will write in college. Classes are small and intimate, designed to encourage all students to become active participants in the learning process. Students will read both contemporary and traditional literature which will then become the focus of their essays. Students will be given written evaluations of their three main papers. Academic credit (six Carleton credit hours) will be awarded to those participants who successfully complete the program.

Criteria: Application; transcript; expository writing sample.

Grade: Rising 12.

Cost: $1,950. A limited number of scholarships are available.

Contact: Becky Fineran-Gardner, Program Coordinator
Summer Academic Programs
Carleton College
One North College Street
Northfield, MN 55057
(507) 646-4038; Fax: (507) 646-4540
E-mail: summer@carleton.edu
Web site: http://www.carleton.edu/campus/sap

Saint Cloud

Advanced Program in Technology and Science (St. Cloud State University)
July 27-August 15

The Advanced Program in Technology and Science is a residential program for high ability, high potential students who have completed grades 11 and 12 and who are seriously interested in a future in technology and science. Students of color and females are encouraged to apply. The goals of the program are to focus on scientific research; to expose students to career options in technology and science; to provide role models in these fields; and to encourage mentor/mentee relationships.

Criteria: Application (deadline: May 9); $10 non-refundable application fee; personal essay; GPA; parent statement; proof of income.

Grade: Rising 12 and rising college freshman.

Cost: Tuition, academic fees, room and board, and books are provided.

Contact: Dr. Robert C. Johnson, Director
Ethnic Studies Program, CH 214
St. Cloud State University
720 4th Avenue South
St. Cloud, MN 56301
(320) 255-4928; Fax: (320) 229-5660
E-mail: ethstudies@stcloudstate.edu
Web site: http://pipeline.stcloudstate.edu/applications.html

St. Cloud

Scientific Discovery Program (St. Cloud State University)
July 13-August 15

The Scientific Discovery Program is a residential program for students who have completed grades 9-10, are of high ability and potential, and who demonstrate a strong interest in science and/or mathematics. Participants experience biological, chemical, computer, mathematical, social, and statistical sciences through laboratories, special demonstrations, presentations, field trips, and lectures related to water quality and solid waste management. Students of color and females are encouraged to apply.

Criteria:	Application (deadline: May 2); $10 application fee (non-refundable); transcript; personal essay; recommendations; test scores; parent statement; proof of income.
Grade:	Rising 10-11.
Cost:	Tuition, academic fees, room and board, and books are provided.
Contact:	Dr. Robert C. Johnson, Director Ethnic Studies Program, CH 214 St. Cloud State University 720 4th Avenue South St. Cloud, MN 56301 (320) 255-4928; Fax: (320) 229-5660 E-mail: ethstudies@stcloudstate.edu Web site: http://pipeline.stcloudstate.edu/applications.html

Math-Science-Computer Camps (St. Cloud State University)
June 8-July 10 (five-day sessions)

The Math-Science-Computer Camps are intensive, five-day, residential programs featuring mathematics, science, and computers. Students are exposed to science and math in fun and innovative ways. While specially designed to interest students of color and females in rising grades 4-9, the programs are open to all. The camp experience includes field trips, recreation, and outdoor activities.

Criteria:	Application (deadline: April 11) $10 registration fee (non-refundable); teacher recommendations; parent statement; proof of income.
Grade:	Rising 4-9.
Cost:	$650. Fees are determined by family income (Because most students are subsidized by the program sponsors, the cost for most families is between $0 and $150). Financial assistance is available.
Contact:	Dr. Robert C. Johnson, Director Ethnic Studies Program, CH 214 St. Cloud State University 720 4th Avenue South St. Cloud, MN 56301 (320) 255-4928; Fax: (320) 229-5660 E-mail: ethstudies@stcloudstate.edu Web site: http://pipeline.stcloudstate.edu/applications.html

MISSISSIPPI

State Director

Dr. Conrad S. Castle, Coordinator of Gifted Programs
Mississippi Department of Education, Rm. 372
Office of Deputy Superintendent
P.O. Box 771
Jackson, MS 39205-0771
(601) 359-2586; Fax: (601) 359-2040
E-mail: ccastle@mde.k12.ms.us

State Association

Mississippi Association for Gifted Children
Jane Everly, President
630 South State Street
Jackson, MS 39201
(601) 960-8344; Fax: (601) 973-8682
E-mail: jeverly@jackson.k12.ms.us
Web site: http://www.magc.org

Regional Talent Search

Duke University Talent Identification Program
See listing on page 2 for complete information.

Cooperative Program

Summer Program for Academically Talented Youth
(The Frances A. Karnes Center For Gifted Studies, The University of Southern Mississippi)
July 6-25

The Frances A. Karnes Center for Gifted Studies at The University of Southern Mississippi will offer its annual three-week summer residential program for academically talented youth. Students who qualify based on SAT or ACT results will enroll in one intensive, fast-paced course. Classes meet six hours per day, Monday through Friday, and three hours on Saturday. Regular attendance at the evening study hall is required. The program is designed to develop the potential of the students to the fullest. Instructors include university faculty, outstanding teachers from secondary school, and advanced graduate students experienced in teaching academically talented students. This three-week program is designed to include appropriate academic, cultural, and recreational experiences. The University of Southern Mississippi is located approximately 100 miles from Jackson, Mississippi; New Orleans, Louisiana; and Mobile, Alabama. Courses include Precalculus Mathematics, (Algebra I and II, Geometry, Trigonometry, and Modern Analysis), Human Anatomy and Physiology, Art Appreciation, Southern Writers and Literature, Creative Writing, Physics, Marine Biology, Psychology, World History, Technical Writing, Forensic Science, Polymer Science, Geology, Personal Finance, and Legal Systems in Business. **This program is offered through cooperative efforts with the Duke University Talent Identification Program.**

Criteria: Test scores.

Grade: 7-10.

Cost: $1,150. Need-based financial aid is available.

Contact: Frances A. Karnes, Director
The Frances A. Karnes Center for Gifted Studies
The University of Southern Mississippi
Box 8027
Hattiesburg, MS 39406-8207
(601) 266-5236; (601) 266-5246; Fax: (601) 266-4978
E-mail: gifted.studies@usm.edu
Web site: http://www-dept.usm.edu/~gifted

Columbus

The Mississippi School for Mathematics and Science
(Mississippi State Department of Education)
Academic Year

The Mississippi School for Mathematics and Science (MSMS), the nation's fourth state-supported residential high school for academically able students, is located in Columbus, Mississippi. Housed on the campus of the Mississippi University for Women, it offers a "campus within a campus" setting. Room and board are provided at no cost to the students. The curriculum emphasizes mathematics and science while providing strong programs in English, social science, foreign language, computer science, art, and music. Research, writing, and computer usage are emphasized across the curriculum. Students graduate with over 24 course units and will be prepared for a rigorous college or university program. The academic day, held Monday-Friday from 8:00 a.m. to 4:30 p.m., mimics a college schedule. After-school activities include varsity, intramural, physical education activities, club and organization meetings, and time in the residence halls to visit and relax.

Criteria:	Application; transcript; teacher, counselor, and principal recommendations; writing samples; test scores (PLAN, ACT); GPA; interview; Mississippi resident.
Grade:	11-12. Applications are accepted during sophomore year.
Cost:	None. MSMS is a state-supported public school.
Contact:	Farrah Robinson, Assistant for School Advancement The Mississippi School for Mathematics and Science P.O. Box W-1627 Columbus, MS 39701 (800) 553-6459 (MS only); (662) 329-7687; Fax: (662) 329-8570 E-mail: frobinson@msms.k12.ms.us Web site: http://www.msms.k12.ms.us

HATTIESBURG

Summer Gifted Studies Program
(The Frances A. Karnes Center for Gifted Studies, The University of Southern Mississippi)
June 22-27

The Summer Gifted Studies Program is designed to enhance the abilities of gifted students through enrichment/acceleration activities. This one-week residential program is a combination of intellectual and recreational activities. *Business Leaders–Today and Tomorrow:* Students learn about planning and starting a business, public relations, and budgeting. *Inventions:* Students create inventions to address current world problems and explore methods of marketing their inventions. *Money, Money, Money:* Students learn about the fundamentals and history of money, including the stock market and principles of economics and finance. *Mind Power:* Students explore the relationship between the brain and mind. *Design Studio:* Students develop an awareness of the various principles relating to design. *Write On!:* Students discuss and practice the process of writing from brainstorming and topic information to organization, analysis, and revision of works produced. *World Cultures:* Students will be involved in a systematic investigation of historical and contemporary issues of selected world culture.

Criteria:	Application; test scores; students may qualify with one of the following: IQ test (120 on WISC-R, WISC-III, or Stanford-Binet); group achievement test scores at the 90th percentile or above on Total Reading, Total Math, Total Language, or Total Battery.
Grade:	4-8.
Cost:	$395. Need-based financial aid is available.
Contact:	Frances A. Karnes, Director The Frances A. Karnes Center for Gifted Studies The University of Southern Mississippi Box 8207 Hattiesburg, MS 39406-8207 (601) 266-5236; Fax: (601) 266-4978 E-mail: gifted.studies@usm.edu Web site: http://www-dept.usm.edu/~gifted

Hattiesburg

Leadership Studies Program (The Frances A. Karnes Center for Gifted Studies, The University of Southern Mississippi)
June 15-20

The Leadership Studies Program has served young leaders from many states. The one-week residential *Leadership I* session is a systematic, comprehensive approach for training students with leadership potential. It includes training in areas necessary to leadership development: written and oral communication, group dynamics, problem solving, planning, personal skills, and decision making. Each student develops a "Plan for Leadership" to be implemented in his/her school, community, or religious affiliation. Guest speakers, films, and simulations are used to supplement the training. *Leadership II* is an extension of the first program (prerequisite: Leadership I). This course focuses on situational leadership, assertiveness training, and psychology of leadership to further develop leadership potential. *Leadership III* is an extension of the second program (prerequisite: Leadership II). Training will focus on the legal aspects of leadership, responsibilities of various positions of leadership, developing personal power, and leadership for the future.

Criteria: Application; school official's signature.

Grade: 6-11.

Cost: $395. Need-based financial aid is available.

Contact: Frances A. Karnes, Director
The Frances A. Karnes Center for Gifted Studies
The University of Southern Mississippi
Box 8207
Hattiesburg, MS 39406-8207
(601) 266-5236; Fax: (601) 266-4978
E-mail: gifted.studies@usm.edu
Web site: http://www-dept.usm.edu/~gifted

MISSOURI

STATE DIRECTOR

David Welch, Director of Gifted Education Programs
Missouri Department of Elementary and Secondary Educucation
P.O. Box 480
Jefferson City, MO 65102
(573) 751-2453; Fax: (573) 751-9434; E-mail: dwelch@mail.dese.state.mo.us

STATE ASSOCIATION

Gifted Association of Missouri
Susan Berti, President
P.O. Box 1495
Jefferson City, MO 65102
(573) 769-2803; Web site: http://www.mogam.org

REGIONAL TALENT SEARCH

Duke University Talent Identification Program
See listing on page 2 for complete information.

COLUMBIA

Missouri Scholars Academy (Missouri Department of Elementary and Secondary Education, University of Missouri-Columbia)
June

The Missouri Scholars Academy is designed to give gifted students from the state of Missouri an opportunity to pursue studies differing from traditional programs. Guest lecturers, forums, films, and other events in the academy enhance and extend the curriculum. The curriculum is organized into four areas of study. *Area I-Academics (Major)*: Each student selects one course of study from the four major academic offerings-mathematics, science, social studies, and humanities. *Area II-Academics (Minor)*: Students will study a second academic field of their choice for one hour each afternoon. *Area III-Personal and Social Dynamics*: All students attend an Area III class each afternoon. The curriculum in this area relates to the unique personal and social problems faced by gifted students. *Area IV-The Co-curricular and Recreational Program*: The Missouri Scholars Academy provides participants a diverse range of afternoon, evening, and weekend opportunities.

Criteria:	Application; personal essay; GPA; IQ and achievement test scores; school nomination; Missouri resident.
Grade:	Rising 11.
Cost:	None. Funded by the state of Missouri.
Contact:	David Welch, Director, Gifted Education Missouri Scholars Academy Missouri Department of Education P.O. Box 480 Jefferson City, MO 65102 (573) 751-2453; Fax: (573) 751-9434 E-mail: dwelch@mail.dese.state.mo.us Web site: http://www.moscholars.org

Kirksville

The Joseph Baldwin Academy for Eminent Young Scholars (Truman State University)
June 7-28 (Session 1); July 5-26 (Session 2)

The Joseph Baldwin Academy offers students (rising 8-10) the opportunity to engage in an intensive, three-week residential program with an academically challenging curriculum. The program also provides rich learning experiences and the opportunity for talented students across the nation to interact and encourage each other's development all within the university environment. Students enroll in one concentrated college course, which meets six hours each weekday and three hours on Saturdays. Classes are taught by university faculty. The curriculum includes the following courses: Arthur, King of Britain; Biology; Latin; Chemistry; The Historian as Detective; Psychology; Science of Secrecy; Shakespeare; Studio Art; Acting; Computer Programming; Creative Writing; Criminal Justice; Italian; Physics; and World Mythology.

Criteria: Application; (deadline: December 2); nomination; test scores; PSAT; SAT; ACT.

Grade: Rising 8-10.

Cost: $995 (some classes have additional fees for special field trips). A limited number of partial scholarships are available.

Contact: Jana Morton, Assistant to the Dean
Truman State University
100 E. Normal, 203 McClain Hall
Kirksville, MO 63501
(660) 785-5406; Fax: (660) 785-7460
E-mail: jmorton@truman.edu
Web site: http://jba.truman.edu

St. Louis

College Horizons (Whitman College and Washington University)
June 14-18 (Session 1); June 28-July 2 (Session 2)

See listing on page 265 for complete information.

High School Summer Scholars Program (Washington University)
June 8-July 12 (Session 1); July 13-August 15 (Session 2)

Washington University's High School Summer Scholars Program provides academically-talented rising seniors with a rare and special experience—five weeks of serious fun, rewarding academic challenge, and the excitement of living and bonding with fellow students from around the country and the world. Participants get a head start on college courses (and learn the study skills required to be successful), garner helpful hints on admissions and financial aid, and experience the independence of college life. In this small, selective program, participants can earn up to seven units of college credit, choosing from stimulating introductory college courses ranging from the arts and humanities to science and social science. Scholars live in a residence hall on campus, enjoy a variety of social and cultural opportunities, and make lasting friendships.

Criteria:	Application (deadline: May 2 for Session 1; June 6 for Session 2); $35 application fee ($70 for international applications); transcript; personal essay; test scores; GPA; recommendations.
Grade:	Rising 12.
Cost:	$4,400. Financial aid is available.
Contact:	Marsha Hussung, Director High School Summer Scholars Program Washington University Box 1145, 1 Brookings Drive St. Louis, MO 63130 (866) 209-0691 (toll-free); (314) 935-6834; Fax: (314) 935-4847 E-mail: mhussung@artsci.wustl.edu Web site: http://ucollege.wustl.edu/hssp

St. Louis

Thomas Jefferson School
Academic Year

A coeducational boarding and day school for grades 7-12, Thomas Jefferson School offers one of the most rigorous academic programs in the country, an outstanding college-placement record, a lively and diverse peer group, and a friendly, comfortable environment. Short, focused classes give students freedom to plan much of their own time for study. Students have ready access to teachers (the student/teacher ratio is 6:1). Moreover, pleasant dorms (all with access to telephone, e-mail, and the Internet), good food, and vacations averaging four weeks provide an enjoyable lifestyle for students who take their education seriously. Students with high aptitude can accelerate in some areas, including mathematics and foreign languages. In English, students meet a curriculum that requires unusual care and depth, and discover that there are no easy answers in literature. Sports, fine arts, and extracurricular activities round out an exceptional academic program.

Criteria:	Application (deadline: February 15); transcript; recommendations; SSAT; ISEE (or in-house entrance exam); interview.
Grade:	7-12.
Cost:	$25,200 (full-time boarding); $23,900 (five-day boarding); $15,600 (day). Need-based financial aid is available.
Contact:	Marie De Jesus, Director of Admissions Thomas Jefferson School 4100 South Lindbergh Boulevard St. Louis, MO 63127 (314) 843-4151; Fax: (314) 843-3527 E-mail: admissions@tjs.org Web site: http://www.tjs.org

Springfield

Precollege Summer Academy (Southwest Missouri State University)
June 9-August 1

The Precollege Summer Academy allows rising seniors to enroll in university classes. While such enrollment is permitted any time during the senior year, this special program is offered during the summer between the junior and senior year. Students may choose a residential or commuter program. All students take a non-credit university orientation course and choose a specially designed, interdisciplinary, two-semester-hour course. They also take additional course work from regular summer offerings. Students who choose to live on campus are housed in the same residence hall, and all participants have full use of university recreational facilities. Co-curricular activities are planned to provide educational enrichment as well as recreational opportunities. All academic fees are covered by admission to the program.

Criteria:	Application (deadline: April 28); transcript; recommendations; GPA; test scores (PSAT, SAT, ACT, or PLAN).
Grade:	Rising 12.
Cost:	$175 (program fee); $860 (room and board).
Contact:	Dr. Curtis P. Lawrence, Dean of University College Precollege Summer Academy Southwest Missouri State University 901 South National Avenue Springfield, MO 65804 (417) 836-6370; Fax: (417) 836-6372 E-mail: cpl142f@ smsu.edu Web site: http://www.smsu.edu/ucollege/precollege/precollege.html

SUMMERSCAPE (Drury University)
June 15-26; July 6-17

SUMMERSCAPE is designed for students who have completed grades 6-9. Courses are selected and planned to provide an academic challenge and creative experiences. Classes are limited to 16 students. Thirty-eight courses could be offered in the areas of archaeology, music, debate, theater, computer science, journalism, video production, high-tech concepts, foreign language, photography, zoology, and leadership. Campus recreational facilities are available. Hands-on experiences, field trips, and the opportunity to interact with international students are key components of SUMMERSCAPE.

Criteria:	Application; test scores; IQ test (minimum score of 125); invitation to attend state recognition ceremony.
Grade:	Rising 7-10.
Cost:	$160 (per course, tuition); $445 (room and board). Limited need-based financial aid is available.
Contact:	Bob Roach, Director or Mary Potthoff, Program Coordinator SUMMERSCAPE/Drury Leadership Academy Drury University Belle Hall, 900 North Benton Avenue Springfield, MO 65802 (417) 873-7386

Springfield

Drury Leadership Academy (Drury University)
July 6-17

The Drury Leadership Academy is a program for high-achieving high school students who have completed grades 10-12. Courses are available in leadership, science, philosophy, and humanities. Students may take two courses. In addition to academic endeavors, the Drury Leadership Academy is designed to provide appropriate cultural and recreational activities.

Criteria: Application; recommendations.

Grade: Rising 11-12, PG.

Cost: $160 (per course, tuition); $445 (room and board). Limited need-based financial aid is available.

Contact: Bob Roach, Director
or Mary Potthoff, Program Coordinator
SUMMERSCAPE/Drury Leadership Academy
Drury University
Belle Hall, 900 North Benton Avenue
Springfield, MO 65802
(417) 873-7386

MONTANA

STATE DIRECTOR

Kathleen Mollohan, Gifted and Talented State Grants Administrator
Montana Office of Public Instruction
P.O. Box 202501
Helena, MT 59620-2501
(406) 444-4317; Fax: (406) 444-1373
E-mail: kathym@state.mt.us

STATE ASSOCIATION

Montana Association for Gifted and Talented Education, Inc.
Kathie Bailey, President
P.O. Box 39
Coravallis, MT 59828
(406) 961-5159
E-mail: KGBailey52@yahoo.com
Web site: http://www.mtagate.org

REGIONAL TALENT SEARCH

Rocky Mountain Talent Search (University of Denver)
See listing on page 5 for complete information.

LOCTIONS THROUGHOUT MONTANA

Adventure Treks
June 15-August 18

See listing on page 8 for complete information.

NEBRASKA

STATE DIRECTOR

Mary Duffy, State Director
High-Ability Learner Education
Nebraska Department of Education
301 Centennial Mall South, Box 94987
Lincoln, NE 68509-4987
(402) 471-0737; Fax: (402) 471-8850
E-mail: mduffy@nde.state.ne.us

STATE ASSOCIATION

Nebraska Association for the Gifted

NAG's Mission is to promote quality education and opportunities for individuals with high abilities through proactive leadership and advocacy. NAG is a non-profit, statewide, nationally affiliated, organization of parents and educators who are interested in the education of gifted youth.

Linda Engel, Communication Coordinator
1201 Kelland Drive
Norfolk, NE 68701
(402) 644-2500
E-mail: lengel@npsne.org
Web site: http://www.NebraskaGifted.org

REGIONAL TALENT SEARCH

Duke University Talent Identification Program
See listing on page 2 for complete information.

Omaha

Ad Astra (Creighton University)
June 8-14 (Session 1); June 15-21 (Session 2)

Ad Astra, a residential program for gifted and talented students entering grades 7-8, is designed to coordinate a challenging academic program with active, social interchange in a week of living and learning on the Creighton University campus. Each participant takes three of four mini-courses spanning the academic disciplines. Classes are kept small to permit interaction between instructors and students and to allow ample time for appropriate hands-on experiences. Instructors in the program are Creighton professors, master teachers from the metropolitan area, and professionals from the community. Evenings are spent in a variety of social and recreational activities.

Criteria: Application; test scores; nomination.

Grade: Rising 7-8.

Cost: $515 (all-inclusive).
Contact: Mavis Hill
Creighton University
2500 California Plaza
Omaha, NE 68178
(402) 280-2843; Fax: (402) 280-2423
E-mail: mhill@creighton.edu

Arete (Creighton University)
June 22-27

Arete is a residential program on Creighton University campus designed for academically talented students (rising 9-12 grades) to explore the many facets of college life. Students participate in four mini-courses in separate academic fields in a simulation of the college experience. Instructors are Creighton professors, master teachers from the area, and professionals from the community. The academic experience is balanced with social and recreational activities, allowing students to relax and enjoy the company of their peers. Students stay in residence halls, staffed by the director and resident advisors who work together to ensure that each student's experiences on campus are positive.

Criteria: Application; test scores; nomination.

Grade: Rising 9-12.

Cost: $515 (all-inclusive).

Contact: Mavis Hill
Creighton University
2500 California Plaza
Omaha, NE 68178
(402) 280-2843; Fax: (402) 280-2423
E-mail: mhill@creighton.edu

NEVADA

STATE DIRECTOR

Gloria Dopf, Director
Special Education and Diversity
Nevada Department of Education
700 East Fifth Street, Capitol Complex
Carson City, NV 89701
(775) 687-9171; Fax: (775) 687-9123
E-mail: gdopf@nsn.k12.nv.us

STATE ASSOCIATION

Nevada Association of Gifted and Talented

The Nevada Association for Gifted Children (NAGT) is a 501(c)(3) not-for-profit organization of parents, teachers, educators, other professionals, and community leaders who unite to address the unique needs of children and youth with demonstrated gifts and talents as well as those children who may be able to develop their talent potential with appropriate educational experiences.

Mary Greene, President
3931 Leon Avenue
Las Vegas, NV 89130-2816
(702) 870-1794; Fax: (702) 799-5979
Web site: NevadaGT.org

REGIONAL TALENT SEARCH

Rocky Mountain Talent Search (University of Denver)
See listing on page 5 for complete information.

NEW HAMPSHIRE

STATE DIRECTOR

Robert Wells, Consultant
Office of Gifted Education
New Hampshire Department of Education
101 Pleasant Street
Concord, NH 03301
(603) 271-1536; Fax: (603) 271-1953
E-mail: rwells@ed.state.nh.us

STATE ASSOCIATION

New Hampshire Association for Gifted Education
Michelle Munson, President
P.O. Box 6106
Nashua, NH 03063-6106
(603) 882-3512
E-mail: nhaged@yahoo.com

REGIONAL TALENT SEARCH
Center for Talented Youth (The Johns Hopkins University)
See listing on page 4 for complete information.

CANAAN

Cardigan Mountain School
Academic Year and Summer Session

Academic Year (for boys only): Cardigan is a boarding school for boys (grades 6-9) that offers a challenging, family-oriented program to assist each student in reaching his true potential. The curriculum is traditional and demanding, while the multi-track system allows the most accelerated student to proceed at a rapid pace in any and all disciplines. Classes average 13 students, and a daily conference period allows in-depth sharing of ideas and projects with faculty. The school also has outstanding athletic and extracurricular offerings in the heart of New Hampshire's lake and ski country. **Summer Session** (coed, June-August): This program offers talented boys and girls (entering grades 4-8) an opportunity to combine an individualized academic program with the very best of the New England camp experience. Advanced study is available in math, English, environmental science, computer programming, French, Spanish, and Latin in groups of no more than seven students.

Criteria: Application (rolling deadline); $35 application fee ($75 for international applications); transcript; personal essay; recommendations; test scores; interview.

Grade: 6-9 (academic year); rising 4-8 (summer).

Cost: $30,450 (academic year); $6,150 (summer session). Need-based financial aid is available.

Contact: Rich Ryerson, Director of Admissions
Cardigan Mountain School
62 Alumni Drive
Canaan, NH 03741-9307
(603) 523-3548; Fax: (603) 523-3565
E-mail: rryerson@cardigan.org
Web site: http://www.cardigan.org

EXETER

Phillips Exeter Academy
Academic Year

For over 200 years, Exeter has defined its role as a leader in residential education in America. Today, high school students from 44 states and over 26 foreign countries are stimulated to stretch their academic and creative capabilities. Through the school's renowned classroom structure and intensive round-table Harkness discussions between a teacher and twelve students, students develop the maturity, self-discipline and respect necessary to foster and sustain their ongoing development as productive individuals. Located on 471 acres one hour north of Boston, Exeter's campus includes the largest high school library in the nation and its facilities support extensive programs in the arts and in athletics. The faculty of 198 allows students to select from a rich curriculum of over 350 courses and provides the opportunity to participate in 20 different sports at the varsity, junior varsity and club levels. Exeter seeks students with a record of high achievement at their previous schools who possess intellectual curiosity and good character.

Criteria: Application (deadline: January 15); $40 application fee; transcript; personal essays; recommendations; PSAT, SAT, SSAT: dependent upon age; TOEFL for non-native speakers; interview.

Grade: 9-12, PG.

Cost: $28,500 (boarding); $21,700 (day). Financial aid is available.

Contact: Michael Gary, Director of Admissions
Phillips Exeter Academy
20 Main Street
Exeter, NH 03833
(603) 777-3437; Fax: (603) 777-4399
E-mail: admit@exeter.edu
Web site: http://www.exeter.edu

Exeter

Phillips Exeter Academy Summer School
July 6-August 9

Every summer Phillips Exeter Academy welcomes to campus some 590 students for five weeks of academic study, athletics, and exploration that carry participants far beyond the classrooms and the playing fields. Public and private school students come to Exeter from more than 40 states, Puerto Rico, Washington D.C., and several dozen foreign nations. Most reside in campus dormitories; some commute. Together they embody a rich diversity of language, culture, religion, and race. Whether students are from the Upper School or are participants in the Access Exeter program, they have in common a desire to challenge themselves academically and possess an eagerness to live in a richly muticultural community. Classes are small, with students engaged in seminar discussions that promote intellectual inquiry and collaborative discourse. Beyond the classroom, students participate in athletics, sing in choral groups, play musical instruments, or bring dramatic productions to life on stage.

Criteria: Application (and fee); transcript; personal essay; recommendations. International students must also submit a recently graded English paper.

Grade: Rising 8-9 (Access Exeter: Open to U.S. students only); rising 10-12, PG (Upper School).

Cost: $925-$5,575. Limited financial aid is available.

Contact: Douglas G. Rogers, Director
Phillips Exeter Academy Summer School
20 Main Street
Exeter, NH 03833-2460
(603) 777-3488; Fax: (603) 777-4385
E-mail: summer@exeter.edu
Web site: http://www.exeter.edu/summer

NEW JERSEY

State Director

Linda L. Morse, Gifted and Talented Coordinator
Office of Standards and Professional Development
New Jersey Department of Education
100 Riverview Plaza, Box 500
Trenton, NJ 08625
(609) 777-4809; Fax: (609) 292-7276
E-mail: lmorse@doe.state.nj.us

State Association

New Jersey Association for Gifted Children

The New Jersey Association for Gifted Children (NJAGC), a state chapter of the National Association for Gifted Children (NAGC), was incorporated on April 2, 1991 by a small group of interested educators who realized the need to affiliate with a nationally recognized association. Each year their membership has increased dramatically as awareness grows that the needs of gifted children must be served. They serve as a public advocate to disseminate information concerning the needs of gifted and talented children. Membership is open to anyone who is concerned about the needs of gifted children in our schools. Among their ranks are parents, teachers, coordinators/supervisors of gifted programs, administrators, specialists and consultants, school board members and community citizens.

Theodore J. Gourley Jr. Ed.D, President
P.O. Box 667
Mt. Laurel, NJ 08054
(856) 273-7530
E-mail: njagc@yahoo.com

Regional Talent Search

Center for Talented Youth (The Johns Hopkins University)
See listing under Regional Talent Searches for complete information.

Locations throughout New Jersey

The Governor's School of New Jersey
July-August

The Governor's School of New Jersey is a four-week summer program that takes place between the scholars' junior and senior years of high school. Talented high school students, currently in their junior year, are encouraged to apply early in the school year. Applications are available in New Jersey's high schools in the fall. Interested candidates should contact their guidance counselors, vice principals, or principals. Youngsters attending public, private, parochial, out-of-state schools, and those who are home-schooled are eligible to apply. All applicants must be legal residents of New Jersey. Applicants may only apply to one Governor's School program. The number of nominees per high school is based on the size of the current junior class. Nominees' applications and supporting materials are judged by committees or professional judges/evaluators. Approximately 100 scholars are selected for each program every year. The Governor's School of New Jersey is comprised of six programs: Arts, Engineering and Technology, Environment, International Studies, Public Issues, and the Sciences.

Criteria:	All programs: Application; personal essay; recommendations; sample of work; gifted and talented; nomination by New Jersey high school; resident of New Jersey. All programs with the exception of the School of the Arts: Transcript; GPA; PSAT; SAT. School of the Arts only: Sample of work; interview; audition.
Grade:	Rising 12.
Cost:	No cost to participate.
Contact:	Dr. Elaine M. Tryjankowski, Executive Director New Jersey Governor's School The College of New Jersey P.O. Box 7718 Ewing, NJ 08628-0718 (609) 771-3114; Fax: (609) 637-5199 E-mail: njgsa@tcnj.edu Web site: http://www.govschool.org

Hightstown

The Peddie School
Academic Year

The Peddie School is a nationally respected coeducational boarding and day school of 500 students from 21 states and 26 countries. Located on a beautiful 280-acre campus, Peddie challenges students to raise questions, weigh evidence, and communicate ideas effectively. The curriculum is challenging, with a broad spectrum of elective courses. Classes are small, and the teaching style interactive. Peddie is probably best known for the excellence and accessibility of its faculty. Widely published, the faculty has authored major texts in physics, computer science, biology, and history, as well as internationally acclaimed fiction by Peddie's writer-in-residence, Paul Watkins. The strength of Peddie academics is reflected in impressive college placement. Peddie technology, with its campus-wide information system, unrestricted Internet access, and link to the Princeton library, is unsurpassed among secondary schools. Each student receives a laptop computer as part of tuition.

Criteria:	Application (and fee); transcript; personal essay; recommendations; SSAT; interview.
Grade:	8-12, PG.
Cost:	$29,000 (boarding); $21,300 (day). Need-based financial aid is available.
Contact:	Edward de Villafranca, Dean of Admission and College Counseling The Peddie School South Main Street Hightstown, NJ 08520 (609) 490-7501; Fax: (609) 944-7901 E-mail: edevilla@peddie.org Web site: http://www.peddie.org

HOBOKEN

ECOES—Exploring Career Options in Engineering and Science (Stevens Institute of Technology)
July 13-25

Exploring Career Options in Engineering and Science (ECOES) is a two-week residential program for rising juniors and seniors. ECOES gives students the opportunity to explore the diverse fields of engineering and science while experiencing life on a college campus. Students participate in research projects in an engineering discipline of their choice and hands-on laboratories in several disciplines of engineering and science. They compete in a civil engineering design competition. Visits to local industries provide students with an insider's view of what engineers and scientists do on a daily basis. A variety of workshops are offered to inform students about college planning and to develop leadership skills. Recreational activities, including a trip to the New Jersey shore, are planned for free time and weekends.

Criteria:	Application (deadline: May 10); transcript; personal essay; recommendations; ACT; PSAT; SAT.
Grade:	Rising 11-12.
Cost:	$795. Partial scholarships are available.
Contact:	Kathleen W. Hadford, ECOES Director Stevens Institute of Technology Lore-el Center for Women in Engineering and Science Castle Point on Hudson Hoboken, NJ 07030 (201) 216-5245; Fax: (201) 216-5175 E-mail: khadford@stevens-tech.edu Web site: http://www.attila.stevens-tech.edu/lore-el/pre-college/ecoes/index.html

Princeton

The Junior Statesmen Summer School (The Junior Statesmen Foundation)
July 30-July 25

Located on the Princeton University campus, The Junior Statesman Summer School offers a rigorous academic challenge to outstanding high school students. The curriculum features five college-level courses: AP American Government, Speech Communication, United States Foreign Policy, AP Comparative Government, and Political Communication. These courses are enriched by a high-level speakers program on campus and in New York City and nightly sessions of a debate practicum, the Congressional Workshop. The collegiate academic environment stresses substantial reading, research, and writing. Students reside in a Princeton University residence hall and use Princeton dining, classroom, and recreational facilities. Courses are taught by outstanding political scientists and top-ranked speech and debate instructors. Students meet in New York City with guest speakers for an in-depth look at politics, international relations, the media, and business and finance. A cultural trip to New York is also offered. Similar programs are held at Stanford University, Georgetown University, Yale University, and Northwestern University.

Criteria: Application; transcript; personal essay; recommendations; GPA.

Grade: Rising 10-12.

Cost: $3,325 (includes room and board and academic costs). Need- and merit-based scholarships are available.

Contact: Admissions Director
The Junior Statesman Foundation
60 East Third Avenue, Suite 320
San Mateo, CA 94401-4032
(800) 334-5353, (650) 347-1600; Fax: (650) 347-7200
E-mail: jsa@jsa.org
Web site: http://www.jsa.org

NEW MEXICO

STATE DIRECTOR

Sam Howard
Special Education
New Mexico Department of Education
300 Don Gaspar
Santa Fe, NM 87501
(505) 827-6541; Fax: (505) 827-6791

STATE ASSOCIATION

Albuquerque Association for Gifted and Talented Students
Rikki Quintana, President
P.O. Box 94328
Albuquerque, NM 87199-4328
(505) 255-4748

REGIONAL TALENT SEARCH

Rocky Mountain Talent Search (University of Denver)
See listing on page 5 for complete information.

GHOST RANCH

TIP Field Studies (Duke University Talent Identification Program)
June 15-August 6 (two-week programs)

See listing on page 182 for complete information.

Zuni Mountains

Cottonwood Gulch Expeditions (The Cottonwood Gulch Foundation)
June-August (vary with program)

Cottonwood Gulch is a non-profit experiential education organization with an emphasis on the natural sciences and cultural history of the Southwest. The organization maintains 540-acres as an ecological preserve and base camp in the Zuni Mountains for the purposes of environmental education. Students may pursue interests in animal tracking, mapping, forestry, ornithology, geology and archeology, as well as Native American crafts, and history. A challenge course and photography lab are also available. In conjunction with base camp programs, Cottonwood Gulch Foundation sponsors wilderness expeditions for kids age 10-19. During these expeditions, students climb mountains, explore pristine wilderness and investigate ancient Native American dwellings. The program aims to foster the development of positive group dynamics and individual responsibility in an outdoor setting. Expedition members should be open to hard work, new experiences, learning through action, and the responsibility that being part of an expedition group demands.

Criteria:	Application.
Grade:	5-PG (age 10-19).
Cost:	$1,225-$3,795.
Contact:	Adam Schraft, Associate Director
	Cottonwood Gulch Foundation
	P.O. Box 3915
	Albuquerque, NM 87190
	(505) 248-0563; Fax: (505) 248-0563
	E-mail: adam@cottonwoodgulch.org
	Web site: http://www.cottonwoodgulch.org

NEW YORK

STATE DIRECTOR

Mary Daley, Executive Director
New York State Summer Institutes
New York State Education Department
89 Washington Avenue, Room 866 EBA
Albany, NY 12234
(518) 474-8773; Fax: (518) 473-0770
E-mail: mdaley@mail.nysed.gov

STATE ASSOCIATION

Association for Gifted and Talented Education in New York State
Mary-Ellen Seitelman, President
31 Brookline Road
Ballston Spa, NY 12020
E-mail: meseitel@aol.com

REGIONAL TALENT SEARCH

Center for Talented Youth (The Johns Hopkins University)
See listing on page 4 for complete information.

ALBANY

New York State Summer School of the Arts
July-August

The New York State Summer School of the Arts is composed of eight specific schools which run from two to four weeks in cooperation with artistic companies such as the New York City Ballet and the Philadelphia Orchestra, or with nationally-known directors. The schools are designed as intensive, pre-professional experiences in the art form and students actually replicate the daily life of an artist in each form. Specific schools are as follows: Ballet, Choral Studies, Dance, Jazz Studies, Media Arts, Orchestral Studies, Theatre, and Visual Arts. Students are housed on college campuses in various locations in the state.

Criteria: Application; New York State resident; audition or portfolio.

Grade: Rising 8-12 (age 14-18).

Cost: $950-$1,450. Need-based financial aid is available.

Contact: Mary C. Daley, Administrator
NYSSSA, Room 866 EBA
State Education Department
Albany, NY 12234
(518) 474-8773
E-mail: nysssa@mail.nysed.gov
Web site: http://www.emsc.nysed.gov/nysssa

Bronxville

Pre-College Program 2003 (Pratt Institute)
July 7-August 1

Each summer, over 300 high school students from across the country and around the world immerse themselves in art, design, architecture, or creative writing, in Pratt's intensive four-week college-level program. Pratt uniquely combines academic excellence with hands-on studio work. The highly structured Pre-College curriculum, modeled after Pratt's B.F.A. program, includes four types of courses: a foundation course which explores writing or drawing, color, and design; a course in the major of choice in the following disciplines: architecture, fashion design, graphic design, traditional or digital illustration, fine arts/painting and drawing, interior design, photography, sculpture, and creative writing; an art history course; and a portfolio development course to help students prepare a portfolio for college admission. In addition, students participate in weekend social and cultural activities. Students earn four college credits upon completion of the program. The programs are offered at the Manhattan and the Brooklyn campuses.

Criteria: Application (and deposit); personal essay; recommendations; sample of work; gifted and talented.

Grade: Rising 11-12, PG.

Cost: $3,243. Scholarships for tuition are available on a competitive basis.

Contact: Johndell Wilson, Administrative Secretary
            Pre-College Program 2002
            Pratt Institute, Center for Continuing and Professional Studies
            200 Willoughby Avenue
            Brooklyn, NY 11205
            (718) 636-3453; Fax: (718) 399-4410
            E-mail: prostudy@pratt.edu
            Web site: http://www.pratt.edu

Brookville

Long Island University Center for Gifted Youth (C.W. Post Campus)
Fall, Spring, and Summer

The Long Island University Center for Gifted Youth offers Saturday commuter classes in the fall and spring (grades K-6) and an all-day, Monday-Friday program during the month of July (grades 2-8). The specially designed curriculum emphasizes problem solving, critical and creative thinking, and independence in learning. Courses range from science, math, and computers to law, writing, and the social sciences. The combination of extraordinary teachers recruited from leading local schools and university-level facilities gives the program unique strength in producing positive benefits for students. Workshops for parents of enrolled children are an integral part of the program. These special sessions are conducted by psychologists and explore a variety of issues of interest to parents of gifted children.

Criteria: Application ($25 fee); IQ test (minimum score of 130).

Grade: K-6 (Saturday Program); rising 2-8 (Summer Program).

Cost: $935 (Saturday Program); $1,525 (Summer Program).

Contact: Dr. Madelon Solowey, Director
            Center for Gifted Youth
            Long Island University, C.W. Post Campus
            720 Northern Boulevard
            Brookville, NY 11548-1300
            (516) 299-2160; Fax: (516) 299-3323
            E-mail: gifted@cwpost.liu.edu
            Web site: http://www.liu.edu/GiftedYouth

GENEVA

Environmental Studies Summer Youth Program (Hobart and William Smith Colleges)
July 13-16

The Environmental Studies Summer Youth Program is an interdisciplinary residential program for high school students entering their junior and senior years. Explore the scientific, social and humanistic perspectives of environmental issues on our beautiful campus in the heart of the Finger Lakes region. The program is fieldwork-centered including Seneca Lake studies on the 65-foot research vessel the HWS Scandling and a four-day Adirondack research trip. Classes are informal and taught by the college's professors with college credit available. Apply early; space is limited.

Criteria: Application (and $25 fee); teacher recommendations; PSAT; SAT.

Grade: Rising 11-12.

Cost: $1,700. Limited scholarships are available.

Contact: D. Brooks McKinney, Institute Director
            Hobart and William Smith Colleges
            Geneva, NY 14456
            (315) 781-3819; Fax: (315) 781-3860
            E-mail: dbmck@hws.edu
            Web site: http://www.hws.edu/aca/enviro

New York

Barnard's Summer in New York City: A Pre-College Program (Barnard College)
June 22-29 (one-week session); June 22-July 26 (five-week session)

Barnard's Summer in New York City is a coeducational program for students intellectually prepared for college-level work. Program participants choose seminars adapted from Barnard's curriculum, and the city is an important component of the classes. Resources such as the Metropolitan Museum of Art, the United Nations, and "Shakespeare in the Park" are used extensively. Workshops on applying to college and study skills are also offered. During the five-week session, students have the opportunity to shadow professionals in New York businesses and organizations. In the community, students may volunteer to work in hospices, soup kitchens, and housing renovation sites. On evenings and weekends, Barnard and Columbia undergraduate resident assistants lead off-campus excursions to cultural and recreational events. Meeting the cast of a Broadway show, searching for vintage clothing in the Village, and feasting on dim sum in Chinatown are just a few of the activities students will enjoy.

Criteria: Application (and fee); transcript; personal essay; recommendations; GPA.

Grade: Rising 11-12.

Cost: $1,100 (residential; one-week); $700 (commuter; one-week); $3,350 (residential; five-weeks); $2,150 (commuter; five-weeks). A limited number of partial grants are available for the five-week session.

Contact: Director of Pre-College Programs
Barnard College, Columbia University
3009 Broadway
New York, NY 10027-6598
(212) 854-8866; Fax: (212) 854-8867
E-mail: pcp@barnard.edu
Web site: http://www.barnard.edu/pcp

Summer Intensive Studies (Parsons School of Design)
May 27-June 26 (Session 1, college); June 30-July 31 (Session 2, precollege and college)

The Summer Intensive Studies Program is a five-week, full-time program for high school and college-level students at the Parsons New York campus. The curriculum is organized to encourage the interests and to develop the abilities of students who may be considering art or design majors at the college level. Through intensive studio work, discussions, and field trips, students are given a valuable introduction to professional training in their field of interest. Students earn four college credits upon successful completion of one of the following programs: Drawing and Painting, Graphic Design, Animation Design, Photography, Architecture, Fashion Design, Interior Design, Design and Management, Digital Design, and Product Design.

Criteria: Application; hardworking.

Grade: Age 16 -adult.

Cost: $1,800 (tuition); $1,350 (housing); all costs are approximate. Limited tuition-only scholarships are available for highly talented precollege students with financial need (Drawing and Painting only).

Contact: Parsons School of Design
Office of Special Programs
66 Fifth Avenue, Room 819
(212) 229-8925; Fax: (212) 229-5970
E-mail: academy@newschool.edu
Web site: http://www.parsons.edu/sis

OSWEGO

Summer Art Institute and Summer Theatre Institute (Oswego State University of New York)
July 20-August 2

Oswego State Summer Institutes offer intense two-week study programs in both art and theatre. Participants earn three hours of easily transferable college credit. The campus is located on the scenic shores of Lake Ontario in the friendly city of Oswego. A supervised, residential program provides students a total college experience. The **Summer Art Institute** provides studio classes with options in painting, printmaking, photography, sculpture, ceramics, and computer graphic design. Participants take a field trip to visit a number of art galleries and museums. The **Summer Theatre Institute** has workshops in acting, voice and speech, movement, improvisation, auditioning techniques, and unarmed stage combat. Participants take a field trip to the Shaw Festival at Niagara-on-the-Lake, Canada, where they attend several stage productions.

Criteria: Application (and fee); transcript; personal essay; references.

Grade: Rising 11-12.

Cost: $1,995. Partial need-based scholarships are available.

Contact: Thomas Ingram, Coordinator, Summer Sessions
Summer Art and Theatre Institutes
Oswego State University of New York
214 Swetman Hall
Oswego, NY 13126
(315) 312-2270; Fax: (315) 312-3078
E-mail: summer@oswego.edu
Web site: http://www.oswego.edu/conted

Saratoga Springs

Pre-College Program for High School Students (Skidmore College)
June 28-August 1

Since 1978, Skidmore College has been bringing bright high school students to its busy summer campus for an intensive experience of college life and learning. The combination of first-year, college credit-bearing courses; the intellectual, artistic, and social life of Skidmore's summer campus and the summer resort town of Saratoga Springs; and college residence hall living offer high school students a rich and varied experience. Students enroll in two courses selected from among the wide range of Liberal Arts and Science courses taught primarily by full-time Skidmore faculty, known for their attention to students and student learning. Regularly scheduled lectures, readings, and performances offered on campus by the New York State Summer Writers Institute, the Skidmore Jazz Institute, Summer SIX Art Program, and so on, further enhance students' intellectual and cultural life. The numerous off-campus weekend trips and extracurricular activities inject a further element of "pure fun" into the program.

Criteria: Application (and fee); transcript; personal essay; recommendations; GPA.

Grade: Rising 11-12.

Cost: $4,200 (approximate cost for tuition, room, board, and all activities). Financial aid is available.

Contact: Dr. James Chansky, Director
Summer Sessions and Summer Special Programs
Skidmore College
815 North Broadway
Saratoga Springs, NY 12866
(518) 580-5590
E-mail: jchansky@skidmore.edu
Web site: http://www.skidmore.edu/summer

Syracuse

Summer College for High School Students (Syracuse University)
June 29-August 8

Syracuse University Summer College for High School Students offers six-week academic programs in art and design, architecture, acting and musical theater, engineering, fashion and textile design, law, liberal arts, management, and public communications. College-level courses taught by university faculty are credit-bearing, and students earn 6 or 7 college credits. Students can test academic and career interests while starting college early. Many Summer College students live together on campus in a supervised residence hall, while students from the region commute. Students enjoy access to university facilities, including libraries, computer clusters, pools, theatres, and gymnasiums. Summer College students taste a slice of college life through academic offerings and a range of special evening and weekend cultural, social, and recreational activities.

Criteria: Application (deadline: May 15); $50 application fee; transcript; recommendations; test scores; GPA, SAT, or ACT.

Grade: Rising 10-12.

Cost: Approximately $4,900. Partial scholarships are available (deadline: April 15).

Contact: Nance L. Hahn, Associate Director
Syracuse University
Summer College for High School Students
111 Waverly Avenue, Suite 240
Syracuse, NY 13244
(315) 443-5297; Fax: (315) 443-3976
E-mail: sumcoll@syr.edu
Web site: http://www.syr.edu/summer

NORTH CAROLINA

State Director

Valorie Hargett
Academically and Intellectually Gifted Program
North Carolina Department of Public Instruction
301 North Wilmington Street
Raleigh, NC 27601-2825
(919) 807-3987; Fax: (919) 715-1569
E-mail: vhargett@dpi.state.nc.us

State Association

North Carolina Association for the Gifted and Talented

The North Carolina Association for the Gifted and Talented is an organization of teachers, parents, other educators, and community leaders who foster a better understanding of the needs and capabilities of academically/intellectually gifted children. NCAGT promotes and supports the development of academically/intellectually gifted students through dissemination of information and advocate on the behalf of those students. Additionally, they support and foster collaborative efforts between local PAGE organizations and local education agencies that extend advocacy for academically/intellectually gifted students into the local communities.

Dr. Welsey E. Guthrie, Executive Director
P.O. Box 899
Swansboro, NC 28584-0899
(910) 326-8463; Fax: (910) 326-8465
E-mail: guthrie3@coastalnet.com
Web site: http://www.ncagt.org

Regional Talent Search

Duke University Talent Identification Program
See listing on page 2 for complete information.

Arden

Christ School
Academic Year

Christ School is a 102 year-old college preparatory school for boys. Affiliated with the Episcopal Church, the school enrolls approximately 180 boarding and 30 day students. The school's mission is to produce educated men of good character, prepared for both scholastic achievement in college and productive citizenship in society. Boys are challenged academically by outstanding teachers, over 30 of whom live on campus. Honors and Advanced Placement (AP) courses are available in all disciplines, and the school's average class size is 11. Headmaster's Scholarships are merit-based awards available for boys with exceptional academic and leadership ability. All boys participate in athletics and activities, including competitive sports, the outdoor program, drama, and debate. Boys are integrally involved in the care of their campus and with community service. The sustaining value of spiritual growth is gained through regular participation in chapel activities. Located on a beautiful 500 acre campus in the Blue Ridge Mountains, Christ School is ten miles from Asheville, North Carolina.

Criteria: Application (deadline: May 1); $50 application fee; transcript; personal essay; recommendations; test scores; SSAT; interview; male student.

Grade: 8-12.

Cost: $26,975 (seven-day boarding); $25,975 (five-day boarding); $13,450 (day). Financial aid and merit-based scholarships are available ($750,000 for 2002-2003).

Contact: Colin Dunnigan, Director of Admission
Christ School
500 Christ School Road
Arden, NC 28704
(800) 422-3212, (828) 684-6232; Fax: (828) 684-4869
E-mail: admission@christschool.org
Web site: http://www.christschool.org

ASHEVILLE

Asheville School
Academic Year

Asheville School's mission is to prepare students for college and for life by providing an atmosphere that nurtures character and fosters the development of mind, body, and spirit. A leading coeducational, college-preparatory school for approximately 186 boarding and 46 day students, the school attracts a broad geographical representation within the student body. Students of differing ethnic, racial, and socio-economic backgrounds are brought together to appreciate and strive for excellence. A sound, traditional, academic program is enhanced with honors and Advanced Placement courses, offerings in the fine arts, and carefully organized independent study projects. The 300-acre campus, located in the Blue Ridge Mountains, features Tudor-style buildings, complete athletic facilities, an alpine tower, and a newly renovated, state-of-the-art library. Over past years, Asheville students have attended more than 125 colleges and universities including Brown, Cornell, Dartmouth, Davidson, Duke, Emory, Georgetown, Harvard, Kenyon, North Carolina, Oberlin, Penn, Princeton, Stanford, Vanderbilt, Virginia, Washington and Lee, and William and Mary.

Criteria: Application (and fee); transcript; personal essay; GPA; SAT; ACT; SSAT; interview.

Grade: 9-12, PG.

Cost: $27,820 (boarding); $16,175 (day). $1.2 million in grants was awarded last year.

Contact: Charles Baldecchi, Director of Admission
Asheville School
360 Asheville School Road
Asheville, NC 28806
(828) 254-6345; Fax: (828) 252-8666
E-mail: admission@ashevilleschool.org
Web site: http://www.ashevilleschool.org

Asheville

Asheville School Summer Academic Adventures
June 22-July 12 (Session 1); July 13-August 2 (Session 2)

Asheville School Summer Academic Adventures enables students to explore the mountains of North Carolina while participating in a demanding academic enrichment program. The school will offer two 3-week programs in the summer of 2003. The summer program is designed for talented students who are looking for a challenge in math, English, history, science, art, drama, and creative writing. For example, students can paint a landscape, buy stock during investment class, and solve a mystery—all before lunch! Athletic activities such as mountaineering, tennis, soccer, swimming, golf, and white-water rafting; and trips to the Biltmore Estate, Carowinds, and other attractions round out the summer, creating a unique opportunity for talented students from around the world.

Criteria: Application (and fee); transcript; teacher recommendations; essay.

Grade: 7-10.

Cost: $2,500 (three-week session); $4,795 (six-week session). Merit scholarships are awarded (deadline: March 26); limited financial aid is available.

Contact: Erin G. Baldecchi, Director of Summer Programs
Asheville School
360 Asheville School Road
Asheville, NC 28806
(828) 254-6345; Fax: (828) 252-8666
E-mail: saa@ashevilleschool.org
Web site: http://www.ashevilleschool.org

Boone

Summer Enrichment Program for Gifted and Talented Youth at Camp Broadstone (Appalachian State University)
June 15-27; June 29-July 11; July 13-25

The Summer Enrichment Program for Gifted and Talented Youth at Appalachian State University combines academic pursuits with an exciting camping experience at Camp Broadstone. Campers are introduced to many areas of the sciences and creative arts through interactive and individual involvement. Sample topics include computers, mathematics, environmental sciences, creative writing and thinking skills, arts and crafts, drama, and dance. Planned camp activities include rock climbing, canoeing, spelunking, a high ropes course, hiking, an Alpine tower, and a group problem solving course.

Criteria: Application (and fee); test scores.

Grade: 4-9.

Cost: $925. Financial aid is not available.

Contact: Elizabeth DeVivo, CB Summer Enrichment Program
Appalachian State University
Office of Conferences and Institutes
P.O. Box 32042
Boone, NC 28608
(828) 262-2933; Fax: (828) 262-4992
E-mail: devivoej@appstate.edu
Web site: http://www.conferences-camps.appstate.edu

Burnsville

Arthur Morgan School
Academic Year

Arthur Morgan School is a boarding school for 27 boys and girls (grades 7-9), located in the Black Mountains of Western North Carolina. Elizabeth Morgan founded the school in 1962. Her chief models were Maria Montessori, Pestalozzi, Grundtvig, Gandhi, and Arthur Morgan. The philosophy and methods of these educators emphasize the development of the whole person through a combination of study, work, and social interaction in a community. Elizabeth Morgan added her own Quaker values of simple living, consensus decision making, and nonviolent problem solving. Arthur Morgan School is a place where students can experience success in the outdoor hiking program, performing and visual arts, daily work program, and the classroom (6-8 in a class). Three-week field trips in late February offer the opportunity to explore the wilderness areas of the South and participate in community service projects. The program is designed specifically to fit the needs and interests of early adolescents.

Criteria: Application (and fee); personal essay; recommendations; interview.

Grade: 7-9.

Cost: $15,300 (boarding); $7,900 (day). Need-based financial aid is available.

Contact: Tal Galton, Admissions Director
Arthur Morgan School
1901 Hannah Branch Road
Burnsville, NC 28714
(828) 675-4262; Fax: (828) 675-0003
E-mail: info@arthurmorganschool.org
Web site: http://www.arthurmorganschool.org

Cedar Mountain

The Green River Preserve
June 8-August 9 (one-, two-, and three-week sessions)

The Green River Preserve is a magnificent 3,400-acre, private, wildlife preserve in the Blue Ridge Mountains near Brevard, North Carolina. The preserve is also a very special natural science summer camp for gifted students in grades four through eight. The camp is non-profit, coeducational, and purposefully small. Wilderness skills, the arts, and the exhilaration of outdoor fun and discovery are used to inspire young minds. Campers enjoy the social and physical benefits of a nurturing non-competitive summer camp and the joy and wonder of hands-on field studies in natural science. During daily field trips, children taste edible plants, track wild animals, play beneath waterfalls, and "seek the joy of being alive". Recreational skills are developed in such areas as canoeing, rock climbing, archery, and fly-fishing. Creative expression is encouraged in art, pottery, and creative writing. Instructional activities provide intellectual challenge without academic pressure. A teacher-to-student ratio of 1:10 and a staff-to-child ratio of 1:3 assure individual attention, supervision, and guidance. The Green River Preserve offers special expeditions featuring sea kayaking, backpacking, and wilderness arts for rising 9-12 graders.

Criteria: Application; test scores.

Grade: Rising 4-8 (summer camp); rising 9-12 (special backpacking, kayaking, and wilderness arts expeditions).

Cost: $850 (one-week session); $1,690 (two-week session); $2,340 (three-week session). Limited scholarships are available.

Contact: Missy and Sandy Schenck, Directors
Green River Preserve
301 Green River Road
Cedar Mountain, NC 28718
(828) 698-8828; Fax: (828) 698-9201
E-mail: grpreserve@citcom.net
Web site: http://www.greenriverpreserve.com

Charlotte

Kidcollege.com Arts Camps
(Gifted and Talented Development Center at Queens College)
June 8-July 26 (one-week sessions)

Kidcollege.com at Queens College offers a variety of intensive, one-week immersion courses for students who are highly motivated and show exceptional interest and ability in the arts. Students may attend one week or may attend several weeks consecutively. Courses offered at the advanced level include The Actor's Studio and Fine Art Portfolio; appropriate for the student who wishes to attend a fine arts college program. Other courses include Musical Theater, Pre-Med, Forensics, Law, Architecture, Money Management, Creative Writing, and Animation. Instructors are outstanding, working professionals in their fields, who also have strong teaching experience. Classroom-based classes are limited in size to 12-15 students. Spaces fill early. For residential students who choose to live on campus, dorm rooms are double occupancy and air-conditioned. Meals are served cafeteria style. After class, college-age counselors closely supervise social activities.

Criteria:	Application (and fee); recommendations; photos, slides, or CD of three works including one of the human figure; Theater and Musical Theater require resumé and headshot.
Grade:	Rising 6-12.
Cost:	$330 (day); $675 (residential). Limited financial aid is available.
Contact:	Director Kidcollege.com P.O. Box 3129 Matthews, NC 28106 (866) 545-5927, (704) 708-9212; Fax: (704) 708-8973 E-mail: tip@kidcollege.com Web site: http://www.kidcollege.com

CHARLOTTE

Kidcollege.com Technology Camps
(Gifted and Talented Development Center at Queens College)
June 8-July 26 (one-week sessions)

Kidcollege.com at Queens College offers a variety of intensive, one-week immersion courses for middle and high school students with special interests. Classes offered include Computer Programming, Robotics, Computer Flight Simulation, Architecture, Web Page Design, Animation, Computer Animation, and Money Management. Campers may live on campus in supervised dormitory accommodations or they may commute each day. Many campers return each year to stay on campus. Dorm rooms are double occupancy and meals are served cafeteria style. In the late afternoons and evenings, counselors arrange social activities, which may include shopping, movies, games, and parties. The campus of Queens College provides a pleasant, friendly environment with traditional Southern charm. It is located in the heart of "Old Charlotte" with amenities within walking distance. Courses are typically limited to 12-15 students; space is strictly limited; and seats fill early. Instructors are adult professionals. The residential staff is comprised of adult, college-age counselors. The student to staff ratio is no more than 1:10.

Criteria:	Application (and fee); recommendations. For computer- or science-based classes, submit standardized test scores (math: minimum score in the 95th percentile).
Grade:	Rising 6-12.
Cost:	$330 (day); $675 (residential). Limited financial aid is available.
Contact:	Director Kidcollege.com P.O. Box 3129 Matthews, NC 28106 (866) 545-5927, (704) 708-9212; Fax: (704) 708-8973 E-mail: tip@kidcollege.com Web site: http://www.kidcollege.com

Cullowhee

The Cullowhee Experience: A Summer Program for Gifted and Talented Students (Western Carolina University)
June 22-July 5

The Cullowhee Experience state-of-the-art format incorporates the Prudential Youth Leadership Institute's national program to teach leadership and community service skills to youth. Students attending this unique program will participate in modules and field trips that incorporate the latest methodology for teaching key leadership skills while emphasizing the importance and means of applying these skills. All activities will center around the historically rich and beautiful setting of the Appalachian and Great Smoky Mountains. Now in its forty-fifth year, this program is housed on the Western Carolina University campus and shares the facilities of the university.

Criteria: Application (deadline: May 1); $25 application fee; personal essay; recommendations; written verification of gifted and talented status from a local educational agency.

Grade: Rising 8-9.

Cost: $1,150.

Contact: Lena Richie
The Cullowhee Experience
152 University Outreach Center
Western Carolina University
Cullowhee, NC 28723
(828) 227-7249; Fax: (828) 227-7353
E-mail: richie@wcu.edu
Web site: http://www.ceap.wcu.edu/RuralEd/cullex.htm

Davidson

Davidson July Experience (Davidson College)
July 6-26

The 28th annual Davidson July Experience seeks to provide rising high school seniors the opportunity for a unique educational and social three-week program on the campus of Davidson College. Students select two different courses from several liberal arts disciplines: biology, economics, English, mathematics, music, political science, physics, and psychology. Activities may include movies, dances, tennis, sailing, water skiing, swimming, basketball, racquetball, field trips, speakers, a student talent show, concerts, or cultural events as available—even career planning.

Criteria: Application (deadline: April 7); transcript; personal essay; recommendations; PSAT; SAT; GPA.

Grade: Rising 12.

Cost: To be announced. A limited number of minority, need-based scholarships may be available.

Contact: Evelyn Gerdes, Director of Davidson July Experience
          Davidson College
          P.O. Box 7151
          Davidson, NC 28035-7151
          (704) 894-2508; Fax: (704) 894-2645
          E-mail: julyexp@davidson.edu
          Web site: http://www.davidson.edu/academic/education/julyexp.html

Durham

Constructing Your College Experience
(Duke University Office of Continuing Education and Summer Session)
July 27-August 2

Constructing Your College Experience is designed to empower college-bound students to explore their college options and successfully navigate the college application process. Participants will learn to evaluate colleges to find the best fit for them, to understand the various parts of the application process, and to discover the challenges and opportunities that university life may offer. The most distinctive aspect of the program is the individual attention each student will receive from his or her assigned admissions counselor. Each student will be assigned to a counseling group of approximately six students. Throughout the week, students will meet with their counselor for guidance and feedback. At the end of the program, each counselor will send students and parents a letter home discussing what happened during the week and suggesting a list of colleges that the student should seriously consider and investigate.

Criteria: Applicants must have average or above-average academic ability and be interested in exploring the options involved in selecting and attending a university.

Grade: Rising 11-12.

Cost: $1,150.

Contact: Duke Youth Programs
           Constructing Your College Experience
           Duke University
           Box 90702
           Durham, NC 27708
           (919) 684-6259; Fax: (919) 681-8235
           E-mail: learn@acpub.duke.edu
           Web site: http://www.learnmore.duke.edu/youth/

Durham

Duke Action Science Camp for Young Women
(Duke University Office of Continuing Education and Summer Session)
June 15-27

Duke Action's activity-based program engages young women in field and laboratory work in a forest environment. Participants examine ecological and biological principles through explorations of terrestrial and aquatic life; chemical and physical properties of the environment; and the impact of human activities on ecosystems. Learning activities incorporate frequent trips to outdoor field sites, educational games and simulations, and laboratory experiments. To emphasize the impact of science on our daily lives, scientific study is integrated with writing, social studies, and art. Building a community of young women scientists is accomplished through team projects in instructional and recreational activities. Opportunities are provided for students to work with women in careers in the physical, biological, and environmental sciences.

- Criteria: Applicants must have average to above-average academic ability, genuine enthusiasm for science, and curiosity for outdoor exploration of scientific concepts through hands-on activities.
- Grade: Rising 6-8.
- Cost: $1,485 (residential); $795 (day).
- Contact: Duke Youth Programs
  Duke University
  Box 90702
  Durham, NC 27708
  (919) 684-5387; Fax: (919) 681-8235
  E-mail: dukeyouth@duke.edu
  Web site: http://www.learnmore.duke.edu/youth

Duke Creative Writers' Workshop
(Duke University Office of Continuing Education and Summer Session)
June 29- July 11

The Duke Creative Writers' Workshop attracts talented high school juniors and seniors to a unique learning experience. This program provides an intensive creative writing experience for advanced writers who are committed to refining their skills and building a community of writers. The interactive "workshop" format gives participants the opportunity to share their work in small groups and to provide feedback to one another in a supportive environment. The peer review and critique process is combined with extensive one-on-one conferencing with instructors to help writers identify the strengths and weaknesses in their work and sharpen their critical thinking skills. Instructional and recreational activities are offered in the afternoons and evenings.

- Criteria: Applicants must have average to above-average academic ability, proficiency in reading and writing, and a genuine interest in critiquing and refining their writing.
- Grade: Rising 11-12.

Cost: $1,475 (residential only).

Contact: Duke Youth Programs
Duke University
Box 90702
Durham, NC 27708
(919) 684-5387; Fax: (919) 681-8235
E-mail: dukeyouth@duke.edu
Web site: http://www.learnmore.duke.edu/youth

Durham

The Duke Drama Workshop (Duke University Office of Continuing Education and Summer Session)
July 13-25

Now entering its eighth year, the Duke Drama Workshop is an exciting program designed to offer high school sophomores, juniors, and seniors an intense experience in drama. The workshop provides a supportive environment for students who are committed to refining their skills and building a community of actors. Master Craft seminars offer opportunities to explore related topics such as playwriting, movement, and voice. Instructional and recreational activities are offered in the afternoons and evenings. The small class size enhances the intensity of the experience, which ends with a final performance and celebration.

Criteria: Applicants must have average to above-average academic ability, proficiency in reading and writing, and a genuine interest in exploring drama and theater techniques.

Grade: Rising 10-12.

Cost: $1,475 (residential only).

Contact: Duke Youth Programs
Duke University
Box 90702
Durham, NC 27708
(919) 684-5387; Fax: (919) 681-8235
E-mail: dukeyouth@duke.edu
Web site: http://www.learnmore.duke.edu/youth

Durham

Duke Young Writers' Camp
(Duke University Continuing Education and Summer Session)
June 15-27 (Session I); June 29- July 11 (Session II); July 13-25 (Session III)

Now in its twentieth year, the Duke Young Writers' Camp attracts talented young people from across the nation for stimulating and lively classes in creative and expository writing. The program blends the traditional fun of a summer camp with the intellectual challenges of a specialized writing program. The camp offers quality instruction, a supportive environment, and the opportunity for young writers to develop confidence in their writing. The curriculum focuses on the creative and analytical processes of writing. More than a dozen courses are offered each session and campers select from those courses which are appropriate to their grade level. Recent courses have included Writing Fiction, Whodunit? Mystery Writing, The Art of Journal Writing, Dramatic Poetry, Playwriting, The Art of Writing Reviews, Science Fiction and Fantasy, Write Your Own Ticket: The College Application Essay, and The Camp Newspaper.

Criteria:	Applicants must have average to above-average academic ability, proficiency in reading and writing, and a genuine interest in exploring writing styles and techniques.
Grade:	Rising 7-12.
Cost:	$1,475 (residential); $725 (day).
Contact:	Duke Youth Programs
Duke University
Box 90702
Durham, NC 27708
(919) 684-5387; Fax: (919) 681-8235
E-mail: dukeyouth@duke.edu
Web site: http://www.learnmore.duke.edu/youth

North Carolina School of Science and Mathematics
Academic Year

The North Carolina School of Science and Mathematics (NCSSM), an affiliate school of the University of North Carolina, is the nation's first state-supported, residential high school for students with talent and interest in science and mathematics. It is the model for numerous other state schools. Opened in 1980, NCSSM offers students in grades 11 and 12 a rigorous and diverse program designed to prepare leaders in science, mathematics, and technology. Students also have the opportunity to participate in the Mentorship Program where they are paired with professionals to provide firsthand experience in a career field of their choice. Independent research in science courses is also available. Other unusual aspects include Mini-Term in the spring where students spend two weeks researching and exploring a topic of personal interest instead of attending class. Students must complete sixty hours of community service in their hometowns as a graduation requirement.

Criteria:	Application; transcript; recommendations; GPA; SAT; personal essay; interview; aptitude tests; interest in science and mathematics; North Carolina resident.

Grade: 11-12.

Cost: There is no cost for tuition, room, and board. NCSSM is funded by the state of North Carolina, and attendance is limited to students whose parents are legal residents of North Carolina.

Contact: Sandra Jackson, Office of Admissions
North Carolina School of Science and Mathematics
P.O. Box 2418
Durham, NC 27715
(919) 416-2850
E-mail: jackson@ncssm.edu
Web site: http://www.ncssm.edu

Durham

Summer Ventures in Science and Mathematics
(North Carolina School of Science and Mathematics)
June 16-July 27 (four-week sessions)

Summer Ventures in Science and Mathematics (SVSM) supplements high school and university courses, taking students beyond the traditional boundaries of high school science and mathematics. A distinguished faculty of university professors and master high school teachers, working in cooperation with science and mathematics professionals from other institutions, government, and industry, guide students through an academic program specially designed to provide experience in scientific inquiry and mathematical problem solving. Specifically, students learn experimental design, laboratory skills, instrumentation, mathematical modeling, strategies in mathematical problem solving, and exploratory data analysis. Moreover, the students learn these basics while engaged in specific scientific and mathematical topics of interest. Students live in dormitories under the supervision of qualified residential advisors who provide guidance and plan social, athletic, cultural, and co-curricular activities.

Criteria: Application (deadline: January 31); transcript; personal essay; test scores; GPA; North Carolina resident.

Grade: Rising 11-12.

Cost: There is no cost for tuition, room, and board. Students must provide transportation. Limited need-based financial aid is available.

Contact: Dr. Sally M. Adkin, State Coordinator
Summer Ventures in Science and Mathematics
North Carolina School of Science and Mathematics
P.O. Box 2976
Durham, NC 27715
(919) 416-2876
Web site: http://www.ncssm.edu/outreach/svsm.html

Durham

TIP Field Studies (Duke University Talent Identification Program)
June 15-August 6 (two-week programs)

A TIP Field Study Program is much more than just a science or humanities class. Each is an authentic academic experience, providing students with opportunities for hands-on development of their skills and interests. Scientific courses place students in research environments alongside instructors who are experienced in the field. Courses in the humanities encourage students to foster their creative talents in an inspiring environment. In each course, a variety of teaching styles are employed to help students benefit most from their coursework while enjoying the beauty of each site. Students work in cooperation to excel beyond their own self-perceived limits. The **International Field Studies** programs allow students to study a variety of topics in the context of a specific culture. 2002 domestic and international programs include Radio Astronomy in the Smoky Mountains (June 15-28); Filmmaking in Orange, California (June 28-July 12); Creative Writing at Ghost Ranch, NM (June 16-30); Ecology, Biology, and Geology at Mountain Lake, VA (July 13-27); Tropical Medicine and Ethnobiology in Costa Rica (June 15-29); Tropical Ecology in Costa Rica (July 1-22); France (June 21-August 6); Greece (June 12-June 30); and Italy (June 24-July12).

Criteria: Application (deadline March 21); PSAT, SAT, or ACT.

Grade: Rising 10-12, PG.

Costs: $1,600-$2,950 (includes tuition, room, board, and activities). Airfare not included. Limited financial aid is available.

Contact: Duke University Talent Identification Program
Box 90747
Durham, NC 27708-0747
(919) 684-3847; Fax: (919) 681-7921
E-mail: info@tip.duke.edu
Web site: http://www.tip.duke.edu

TIP Global Dialogues Institute: International Politics and Law (Duke University Talent Identification Program)
June 22-July 5

At Duke University TIP's Global Dialogues Institute, students study and learn to understand the complex and urgent challenges facing the world today. Each year, gifted students, educators, and speakers from around the world gather together at prestigious Wake Forest University to explore critical current issues that will affect the future. Working in an interdisciplinary manner, participants study fields such as law, international relations, economics, politics, religion, history, and philosophy to understand how they relate to the current world situation.

Criteria: Application (deadline: March 21); PSAT, SAT, or ACT.

Grade: Rising 10-12, PG.

Costs: $2,100. Limited financial aid is available.

Contact: Duke University Talent Identification Program
Box 90747
Durham, NC 27708-0747
(919) 684-3847; Fax: (919) 681-7921
E-mail: info@tip.duke.edu
Web site: http://www.tip.duke.edu

Durham

TIP Independent Learning (Duke University Talent Identification Program)
Year-round

TIP Independent Learning offers academically gifted students an opportunity to pursue accelerated studies any time, anywhere. Course materials are designed to serve as resources for challenging independent study and to provide students of various grade levels with unique and rewarding learning experiences. Independent Learning study courses are intended for enrichment learning, not course credit. If academic or elective credit for these courses is desired, parents should negotiate with their local school officials. TIP also does not assign grades for completed courses. Successful completion of a course will be acknowledged with a Duke TIP certificate. Courses currently available: **MAPack**: MathPack: Quest (grade 4-6), and Word Power (grade 4-6); **Learn on Your Own**: Discovering King Arthur: Medieval Mystery and Meaning (grade 5-9), Algebra I (grade 7-9), Algebra II (grade 8-11), Reflective and Persuasive Writing (grade 7-12), and Writing with Power (grade 7-12); **CD-ROM Enrichment Courses**: Switched on Sound: Movements in 20th Century Music, Clues in Crime: The Role of Forensic Science in Criminal Investigations, and Peace and Protest: The Turbulent Sixties.

Criteria: Gifted and talented student; a mentor in the content area (Learn on Your Own and MAPack); supplemental texts (Learn on Your Own and MAPack).

Grade: 4-12.

Cost: $29.95-$79.99 (plus shipping and handling).

Contact: TIP Independent Learning
Duke University Talent Identification Program
Box 90780
Durham, NC 27708-0780
(919) 683-1400 (Learn on Your Own and MAPack);
(888) 825-3643 (CD-ROM Enrichment Courses)
E-mail: info@duke.edu
Web site: http://www.tip.duke.edu

Durham

TIP Leadership Institute (Duke University Talent Identification Program)
July 10-26

The Duke University TIP Leadership Institute allows students to discover their own leadership potential through study, discussion, and service experience. Through a diverse combination of methodologies—traditional coursework, research, case studies, team-building, service-learning, and writing—students will learn skills to help them become excellent leaders. The cumulative goal of the program is to allow students to find their own personal style of leadership while designing a service project to be implemented in their local school or community.

Criteria: Application (deadline: March 21); PSAT, SAT, or ACT.

Grade: Rising 10-12, PG.

Costs: $2,300. Limited financial aid is available.

Contact: Duke University Talent Identification Program
Box 90747
Duke University
Durham, NC 27708-0747
(919) 684-3847; Fax: (919) 681-7921
E-mail: info@tip.duke.edu
Web site: http://www.tip.duke.edu

TIP PreCollege Program (Duke University Talent Identification Program)
June 28-August 10 (six-week program)

The Duke University PreCollege Program provides intellectually rigorous college courses to highly motivated students who are capable and willing to meet the demands of study at a selective university. Students may choose two courses from nearly all departments in Duke University's Trinity College of Arts and Sciences—including math, natural sciences, computer science, social science, languages, and the humanities. PreCollege participants study alongside undergraduates in lectures, laboratories, and seminars led by Duke faculty members and guest instructors. Students earn Duke University course credit while they rise to the challenges of the college experience and to the demands of higher learning.

Criteria: Application (deadline: March 21); high school transcript; personal essay; PSAT, SAT, or ACT; resumé; school recommendation.

Grade: Rising 12.

Costs: $5,295 (includes housing, fees, tuition for two courses, meal plan). $150 (books and supplies). Costs are approximate. Need-based financial aid is available.

Contact: Duke University Talent Identification Program
           Box 90747
           Duke University
           Durham, NC 27708-0747
           (919) 684-3847; Fax: (919) 681-7921
           E-mail: info@tip.duke.edu
           Web site: http://www.tip.duke.edu

DURHAM

TIP Scholar Weekends (Duke University Talent Identification Program)
Spring and Fall

TIP Scholar Weekends provide opportunities for academically talented students in grades 7-12 to take short courses during a weekend at Duke University. These courses introduce topics that might not be available in high schools, as well as provide enrichment, sharpen skills, and help students define pathways to college and careers. TIP Scholar Weekends provide a glimpse into the collegiate experience and an opportunity for students to interact with similarly motivated students. Previously, courses have been offered in law, philosophy, business, science, politics, environmental issues, medicine, writing, and drama. The program is not intended to provide high school or college credit.

Criteria: Gifted and talented or a Duke University TIP Seventh Grade Talent Search participant; $25 application fee.

Grade: 7-12.

Cost: $350 (tuition, room, and board; cost is approximate). Day student rates are available. Limited, need-based financial aid is available.

Contact: TIP Scholar Weekends
          Duke University Talent Identification Program
          Box 90747
          Durham, NC 27708-0747
          (919) 684-3847
          Web site: http://www.tip.duke.edu

Durham

TIP Summer Studies Programs (Duke University Talent Identification Program)
June-July (three-week sessions)

TIP Summer Studies Programs offer intensive, fast-paced courses for academically talented students. Participants enroll in one class during a three-week session, and generally complete the equivalent of a year of high school or a semester of college-level work. Classes meet seven hours per day, Monday through Friday, and three hours on Saturday. The instructors are a talented and diverse group that include university faculty, outstanding teachers from secondary schools, experienced professionals, and advanced graduate students. Each class also has a teaching assistant who is with demonstrated proficiency in the subject. Depending on test scores, TIP Summer Studies students may attend either the Center for Summer Studies or the Academy for Summer Studies. Center programs are held at Duke the Duke University Marine Lab, University of Kansas, and Davidson College. Academy programs are held at the Duke University Marine Lab, Appalachian State University, and the University of Kansas. A complete listing of courses and detailed admissions criteria are published in the *TIP Summer Studies Bulletin* (available upon request), and on the TIP Web site.

Criteria: Center: Application and rating scale completed by school official; test scores (minimum scores: SAT: Math 570 or Verbal 570; ACT: Math 20, English 27, Science Reasoning 24, or Reading 25; or combined SAT Math 520 and Verbal 520; ACT Math 19, English 25 for grade 7; higher scores are required for grades 8-10). Academy: Application and rating scale completed by school official; test scores; (minimum scores: SAT: Math 500 or Verbal 500; ACT: Math 18, English 25, Science Reasoning 24, or Reading 25 for grade 7; higher scores are required for grades 8-10).

Grade: Rising 8-11.

Cost: Call or see Web site for costs. Need-based financial aid is available.

Contact: Admissions Officer for Educational Programs
Duke University Talent Identification Program
Box 90747
Durham, NC 27708-0747
(919) 684-3847; Fax: (919) 681-7921
Web site: http://www.tip.duke.edu

Greensboro

**All-Arts and Sciences Camp
(University of North Carolina at Greensboro)**
June 29-July 4; July 27-August 1 (one-week sessions)

The All-Arts and Sciences Camp is a weeklong, residential, summer camp for youth, age 7-15. Designed to give quality instruction in the arts and sciences, the camp also includes recreation, values exploration, and citizenship components. Each camper selects two courses lasting two hours a day from over twenty science and art courses ranging from anthropology to chemistry and creative writing to sculpture. Campers are divided into age groups for academic coursework and other activities. The camp design and curriculum have grown from the conviction that the creativity in youth will blossom in a climate of exploration, challenge, and instruction. The program also believes that becoming an artist and a scientist are related creative developments. The All-Arts and Sciences Camp sees the goal of education as the creation of a person fully actualized in mind, body, and imagination. A similar program is offered at the College of William and Mary in Williamsburg, Virginia; George Mason University in Fairfax, Virginia; North Carolina State University in Raleigh, North Carolina; and Virginia Tech in Blacksburg, Virginia.

Criteria: Application (and fee).

Grade: 2-9.

Cost: $550-$625 per week (dependent upon location).

Contact: Robert Prout, Director of Youth Programs
All-Arts and Sciences Camp
University of North Carolina at Greensboro
P.O. Box 26170
Greensboro, NC 27402-6170
(866) 334-2255, (336) 256-2255; Fax: (336) 334-5628
E-mail: allarts@uncg.edu
Web site: http://allarts.uncg.edu

OAK RIDGE

Oak Ridge Military Academy
Academic Year and Summer Programs (June/July)

Oak Ridge Military Academy is a coeducational, college preparatory school with both boarding and day programs. The philosophy of Oak Ridge is to stress the importance of preparing students for college and life by teaching them the attitudes, information, and skills they will need to successfully meet the requirements of a college curriculum. The Oak Ridge curriculum is designed for the average to above average student and emphasizes reading, writing, and speaking skills. The average SAT score for 2001 was 1100+ and for the past eleven years 100% of the graduating seniors have been accepted to a college, university, or service academy of their choice. Special provisions within the curriculum are made for the gifted and talented. College courses are available through the University of North Carolina at Greensboro's Fast Forward Program in addition to eight Advanced Placement courses. Oak Ridge is "The Official Military School of North Carolina." Academic Excellence Since 1852.

Criteria: Application (and fee); transcript; personal essay; test scores; interview.

Grade: 7-12 (academic year); 6-12 (summer programs).

Cost: Varies. Merit-based scholarships are available.

Contact: Oak Ridge Military Academy
P.O. Box 498
Oak Ridge, NC 27310
(336) 643-4131; Fax: (336) 643-1797
E-mail: rwilson@oakridgemilitary.com
Web site: http://www.oakridgemilitary.com

Raleigh

All-Arts and Sciences Camp
(University of North Carolina at Greensboro)
June 29-July 4; July 27-August 1 (one-week sessions)

See listing under Greensboro, North Carolina for complete information.

Governor's School of North Carolina
June-July

The Governor's School of North Carolina is the oldest statewide summer residential program for academically or intellectually gifted high school students in the nation. The program, which is open to rising seniors only, with exceptions made for rising juniors in the performing/visual arts area, is located on two campuses: Governor's School West at Salem College in Winston-Salem and Governor's School East at Meredith College in Raleigh. Funded annually by the General Assembly of North Carolina, the program is administered by the Department of Public Instruction through the Exceptional Children Division. The program offers a non-credit curriculum for 800 students in academics and performing/visual arts, with additional study of philosophy, epistemology, ethics, aesthetics, values, morals, thinking processes, and social and personal development. Contemporary theories, as they relate to the past and future, are emphasized throughout the curriculum.

Criteria:	School nomination; audition (performing/visual arts); North Carolina resident.
Grade:	Rising 12 (exceptions for rising junior nominations are made in the performing/visual arts area if seniors are not available).
Cost:	No cost to students.
Contact:	Special Assistant Governor's School of North Carolina Exceptional Children Division, N.C. Department of Public Instruction 6356 Mail Service Center Raleigh, NC 27699-6356 (919) 807-3986 Web site: http://www.ncpublicschools.org/ec/

Summer Science Programs (The Science House, North Carolina State University)
Summer

The Science House at North Carolina State University sponsors several science and mathematics research camps for high school and middle school students across the state. Both commuter and residential camps are available. Past programs include Science of Sports, EnviroTech and Imhotep Academy. Visit their Web site or call for details on programs offered this summer.

Criteria:	Transcript; personal essay; recommendations.
Grade:	6-12.
Cost:	TBA.

Contact: Mike Smith
Summer Science Programs
The Science House
NCSU Box 8211
Raleigh, NC 27695
(919) 515-6118; Fax: (919) 515-7545
E-mail: science_house@ncsu.edu
Web site: http://www.science-house.org

WILMINGTON

MarineQuest (University of North Carolina at Wilmington)
June-August (one-week sessions)

MarineQuest, the marine and environmental outreach education component of UNCW, is located ten minutes from Wrightsville Beach and offers a wide variety of hands-on, feet-wet educational enrichment programs for age 11 and up. Twenty-four hour supervision is provided for all programs. **Coast Trek** and **OceanLab** are weeklong, residential outdoor and laboratory programs for highly motivated and academically gifted students. Programs include unique, diverse activities in local marine habitats with lab enhancement. Structured recreation insures socialization with peers from across the United States. **Biology of the Sea** is a college course offering 3 transferable college credits. **The Real Hawaii: O'ahu** explores the bountiful ecological environment with snorkeling and visits to the Polynesian Cultural Center and other attractions. **Marine Biology Camp for Teens** offers coral reef snorkeling, wild dolphin observations, manta ray studies, and dolphin swims. **Ocean Chemotion** is a weeklong, residential, outdoor and lab studies with focus on the chemistry of the ocean. Visit their Web site for additional information on all MarineQuest programs.

Criteria: Application (deadline: varies with program); recommendations; highly motivated or academically gifted.

Grade: Age 11-17 (varies with program)

Cost: $565-$1,750 (varies with program).

Contact: Nancy Elden
MarineQuest
University of North Carolina at Wilmington
601 College Road
Wilmington, NC 28403
(910) 962-2460; Fax: (910) 962-2410
E-mail: marinequest@uncw.edu
Web site: http://www.uncwil.edu/dpsee/marinequest/

WINSTON-SALEM

Governor's School of North Carolina
June - July

See listing under Raleigh, North Carolina for complete information.

Winston-Salem

North Carolina School of the Arts
Academic Year and Summer

An arts conservatory of international renown, the North Carolina School of the Arts (NCSA) was established by the N.C. General Assembly in 1963 and became part of the University of North Carolina in 1972. NCSA offers professional training for careers in the arts through its five professional schools: Dance; Design & Production; Drama; Filmmaking; and Music. More than 1,000 students are enrolled annually; half come from North Carolina. Because the school encompasses middle school through graduate school, students have the opportunity to earn a North Carolina high school diploma, a college Arts Diploma, a Professional Artist Certificate, and bachelor's and master's degrees. Concentrated arts studies, plus a full academic program through the Division of General Studies, prepare students for a professional career, entrance into college, and/or advanced studies. Residence halls are available for students in grades 9-12; grade 8 students must live within commuting distance. A five-week summer session is also offered.

Criteria: Application; $45 application fee ($90 for international applications); audition and/or interview; recommendations; transcripts; SAT or ACT (for applicants to undergraduate program); photograph (for identification); resumé.

Grade: 8-12 (dance: ballet); 11-12 (dance: contemporary); 12 (drama); 9-12 (music); 11-12 (visual arts).

Cost: Varies.

Contact: Sheeler Lawson, Director of Admissions
North Carolina School of the Arts
1533 S. Main Street
Winston-Salem, NC 27127-2188
(336) 770-3290; Fax: (336) 770-3370
E-mail: admissions@ncarts.edu
Web site: http://www.ncarts.edu

WINSTON-SALEM

Salem Academy
Academic Year

Salem Academy seeks to enroll female students of above average ability who have personal integrity; a positive attitude toward work; potential for developing self-discipline, self-confidence, and self-esteem; and a strong desire to broaden their intellectual and cultural horizons. The curriculum includes Advanced Placement courses in each discipline with the opportunity to take courses for credit at Salem College. The January mini-term provides each student an opportunity to choose her own educational experience. Internships and independent studies in teaching, music, medicine, banking, and other fields may be pursued under faculty supervision. A school-sponsored trip is offered during the January Term each year to such places as England, Greece, Canada, Australia, Mexico, and Egypt. On campus, teachers conduct intensive tutorials as well as a variety of elective courses. Salem Academy graduates attend colleges across the country including such institutions as Columbia, Duke, Stanford, MIT, Northwestern, Harvard, Wake Forest, Sewanee, Yale, and the Universities of North Carolina and Virginia.

Criteria:	Application (and $35 fee); transcript; personal essay; recommendations; SSAT; interview; female student.
Grade:	9-12.
Cost:	$23,650 (boarding); $14,000 (day). Financial aid and merit scholarships are available.
Contact:	Lucia Uldrick, Director of Admissions Salem Academy 500 Salem Avenue Winston-Salem, NC 27108 (336) 721-2643; Fax: (336) 917-5340 E-mail: academy@salem.edu Web site: http://www.salemacademy.com

SuperCamp®
July-August

See listing on page 13 for complete information.

NORTH DAKOTA

STATE DIRECTOR

Jeanette Kolberg, Assistant Director of Special Education
North Dakota Department of Public Instruction
State University Station, Box 5036
Fargo, ND 58105-5036
(701) 328-2277
E-mail: jkolberg@state.nd.us

REGIONAL TALENT SEARCH

Center for Talent Development (Northwestern University)
See listing on page 3 for complete information.

FARGO

North Dakota Governor's Schools in Business/Entrepreneurship, Mathematics and Science (North Dakota State University)
June 8-July 19

The North Dakota Governor's Schools in Business/Entrepreneurship, Mathematics and Science is a six-week residential program hosted by North Dakota State University. Besides emphasis in individual disciplines, there are sessions on personal and social development, the fine arts, and ethics. Students in business/entrepreneurship attend lectures on business and entrepreneurship and participate against each other via a software package on starting a company. The students spend afternoons at selected area businesses. Students studying the mathematical sciences have three 1.5-hour daily sessions in discrete math, computer science, and math theory. The students in the laboratory sciences have one week of introduction into laboratory skills where quantitative skills are stressed, plus an introduction to microscopy and data collection. They then work in a research laboratory conducting their own research program. Weekend trips introduce other topics in science, careers, and team building.

Criteria: Application; transcript; personal essay; recommendations; test scores; GPA; PSAT; ACT; SSAT; resident of North Dakota attending a ND high school.

Grade: Rising 11-12.

Cost: No cost to participants.

Contact: Lonnie Hass, Director
North Dakota's Governor's School
North Dakota State University
Stevens Hall
Fargo, ND 58105
(701) 231-7411; Fax: (701) 231-6507
E-mail: lonnie.hass@ndsu.nodak.edu
Web site: http://www.ndsu.nodak.edu/govschool/

OHIO

STATE DIRECTOR
Mark Lentz, Gifted Education Consultant
Division of Exceptional Children
Ohio Department of Education
65 South Front
Columbus, OH 43215
(614) 466-2650; Fax: (614) 752-1492
E-mail: mark.lentz@ode.state.oh.us

Dr. Jeanie Goertz, Gifted Education Consultant
Division of Exceptional Children
Ohio Department of Education
65 South Front
Columbus, OH 43215
(614) 752-1221; Fax: (614) 752-1429
E-mail: jean.goertz@ode.state.oh.us

STATE ASSOCIATION

Ohio Association of Gifted Children
Ce Ann Chalker, President
P.O. Box 30801
Gahanna, OH 43230
E-mail: president@oagc.com
Web site: http://www.oagc.org

REGIONAL TALENT SEARCH

Center for Talent Development (Northwestern Univeristy)
See listing on page 3 for complete information.

CLEVELAND

National Computer Camps
June-August

See listing on page 10 for complete information.

Columbus

Ross Mathematics Program (The Ohio State University)
June 23-August 15

The Ross Program is an eight-week experience in discovery learning, employing mathematical immersion at a deep level. The objective is to train students to think mathematically, a skill essential for research in many scientific fields. Students acquire a wide array of problem solving tools and discover new insights into the nature of mathematics and science. The basic course in number theory provides an ideal avenue for young participants to perform their own investigations with number systems, to make their own discoveries about the patterns that they observe, and to explain their discoveries clearly and logically. Participants are encouraged to ask why things work the way they do. This independence of thought and questioning attitude is what the Ross Program strives to nurture. Students are encouraged to return for subsequent summers, taking more advanced courses, and inspiring the younger participants.

Criteria:	Personal essay; transcript; recommendations; solutions to problems presented on the application form.
Grade:	9-12.
Cost:	$2,600. Limited financial aid is available.
Contact:	Professor Daniel Shapiro, Director Department of Mathematics The Ohio State University 231 West 18th Avenue Columbus, OH 43210 (614) 292-5101; Fax: (614) 292-0167 E-mail: ross@math.ohio-state.edu Web site: http://www.math.ohio-state.edu/ross

Dayton

Women in Engineering Summer Camp (University of Dayton)
July 13-18

The Women in Engineering Summer Camp is a weeklong residential summer program sponsored by the University of Dayton School of Engineering. The program introduces high school girls to career opportunities in engineering. Participants experience a total immersion into the world of engineering with 18 hours of classroom activities taught by School of Engineering faculty and practicing engineers. Participants also observe and interact with many practicing engineers and engineering students. Throughout the week, participants gain an understanding of chemical, civil, electrical, environmental, industrial, manufacturing, and mechanical engineering as well as an understanding of the wide range of career opportunities these fields have available to them. The participants also attend challenging evening sessions in areas such as inventions, rockets, computer-aid design, and optics. One day of the camp is spent at a sponsoring industry observing engineers on the job. The 2003 program will mark the program's thirtieth anniversary.

Criteria:	Application (deadline: June 15); teacher/counselor recommendation signature on the application; female student.
Grade:	Rising 10-12.
Cost:	$325. Scholarships are available.
Contact:	Karen Updyke, Program Coordinator Women in Engineering Summer Camp University of Dayton 300 College Park Dayton, OH 45469-0228 (937) 229-3296; Fax: (937) 229-2756 E-mail: wie@engr.udayton.edu Web site: http://engineering.udayton.edu/wie

DAYTON

Pre-College Summer Enrichment Programs (Wright State University)
June-August

The Office of Pre-College Programs offers students entering grades 7-12 the opportunity to expand their educational and personal horizons by attending one- and two-week summer residential camps. Programs are offered on the following topics: art, aviation, creative writing, leadership, mathematics, science, space, television, and theatre. Each program is comprised of a variety of learning experiences including lectures, hands-on projects, small group discussions, and field trips. The programs are taught by university faculty, staff, and experts from the local community. Applications are accepted on a first-come, first-served basis. Each program has a limited enrollment.

Criteria:	Application; school nomination.
Grade:	Rising 7-12.
Cost:	$600-$1,400 (varies by program).
Contact:	Chris Hoffman, Special Program Coordinator Pre-College Programs Wright State University 120 Millett Hall Dayton, OH 45435 (937) 775-3135; Fax: (937) 775-4883 E-mail: precollege@wright.edu Web site: http://www.wright.edu/academics/precollege

Hudson

Western Reserve Academy
Academic Year

Western Reserve Academy (WRA) is a medium sized (375 students) coeducational boarding and day school for college-bound students. The challenging curriculum features 19 AP courses with approximately 90% receiving a score of 3 or better. The school provides a 12:1 student-to-teacher ratio in the classroom. Academy students score 1230 combined average SAT. WRA places in the top third in the Junior Engineering Talent Search Competition each year. All graduates from the Academy are placed in competitive colleges. The school also has a direct connection with the Internet, and fiber optics provide school wide networking to all school buildings including dormitory rooms. Superb fine arts offerings (teachers in vocal and instrumental music are members of the Cleveland Orchestra, the Akron Symphony, or the faculty at Cleveland Institute of Music) and required daily athletics for all students complement the academic curriculum.

Criteria: Application (and fee); transcript; personal essay; parent statement; recommendations; test scores; GPA; PSAT; SAT; SSAT; interview.

Grade: 9-12.

Cost: $25,200 (boarding); $18,600 (day). Financial aid is available; approximately $2.3 million in aid was awarded to approximatley 30% of the students in 2002-2003.

Contact: Britt Flanagan, Dean of Admissions
or Marshall Murdough, Director of Enrollment and Financial Aid
Western Reserve Academy
115 College Street
Hudson, OH 44236-2999
(330) 650-9717; Fax: (330) 650-9788
E-mail: admission@wra.net
Web site: http://www.wra.net

Millersburg

The Country School Farm
June-July (five-day sessions)

Established in 1976, The Country School Farm provides children with the opportunity to actually live through the meaning of the agricultural revolution and come away understanding what makes civilization possible. As Montessori teachers, the Barkers have designed the farm so that children have direct access to its essence. Animal lovers do well, as do children who are comfortable with mixed ages. Participants come away with a twinkle in the eye that reflects both the intrinsic satisfaction and fun of farm life. Although the 42-acre farm is located in the heart of the world's largest settlement of Amish people, the Barkers are not Amish themselves and this program has no religious affiliation. The consistency yet variety of the experience brings children back year after year. Request references by writing or e-mailing the school.

Criteria:	Application (no deadline, but 98% full by the date of their Open House: May 18).
Grade:	Age 6-12.
Cost:	$600.
Contact:	The Barkers The Country School Farm 3516 Township Road 124 Millersburg, OH 44654 E-mail: barkers@thecountryschool.com Web site: http://www.thecountryschool.com

SHAKER HEIGHTS

Hathaway Brown School
Academic Year

Hathaway Brown School, founded in 1876, is Ohio's oldest independent preparatory school for girls in grades K-12. Current enrollment is 810, with a student to faculty ratio of 8:1. The school's motto "We Learn Not For School, But For Life," is reflected in the Student Research Program. Students conduct projects in areas representing a cross-section of the cutting-edge research and technology at Case Western Reserve University, the NASA Glenn Research Center, the Cleveland Clinic Foundation, University Hospitals, and the Cleveland Museum of Art. Students have worked with sensors that detect and remove pollution, in-body drug delivery systems, and electrical stimulation systems that help paralyzed spinal cord injury patients to regain movement. There is also the opportunity for medical and genetic research seeking cures or prevention of cancer, strokes, cystic fibrosis, multiple sclerosis, and heart disease. These and other non-science related activities are available in one- to four-year programs that can be conducted during the school year or the summer.

Criteria:	Application (deadlines: December 10 and March 4); $35 application fee; transcript; personal essay; recommendations; test scores; ISEE; interview.
Grade:	K-12.
Cost:	$2,800-$16,880. Financial Aid is available.
Contact:	Sarah Johnston, Director of Admission and Financial Aid Hathaway Brown School 19600 North Park Boulevard Shaker Heights, OH 44122 (216) 320-8767; Fax: (216) 397-0992 E-mail: admissions@hb.edu Web site: http:// www.hb.edu

Springfield

WISE Academic Camp (Wittenberg University)
June 15-20

Academic enrichment is the hallmark of the WISE Academic Camp. WISE has assembled a faculty team that is experienced with high-achieving middle school students. Each camper attends five classes daily and chooses one discipline as a "major." Recent majors have been biology, drama, geology, music, and photography. WISE seeks campers who are curious about the "what" and "why" of their subjects. The residential program offers structured recreational and social programs. Experienced professional and student staff members strive to create a supportive community so each camper has the opportunity to develop independence and self-reliance. Student counselors are selected from Wittenberg's most talented undergraduates, and are with campers 24 hours a day to give the "real scoop" on college life. Counselors report to a professional head counselor. An activities coordinator plans the recreational activities combining non-intense sports and group games.

Criteria: Application (deadline: April 15); $30 application fee; recommendations; test scores; GPA; nomination; class rank.

Grade: Rising 6-8.

Cost: $460. Partial need-based scholarships aid qualified youngsters regardless of economic circumstances.

Contact: Dr. Barb Mackey, Director of Community Programs
WISE Academic Camp
Wittenberg University
P.O. Box 720
Springfield, OH 45501
(937) 327-7050; Fax: (937) 327-7014
Email: bmackey@wittenberg.edu
Web site: http://www.wittenberg.edu

OKLAHOMA

State Director

Dr. Kristy Ehlers, State Director
Gifted and Talented Education Section
Oklahoma Department of Education
2500 North Lincoln Boulevard, Suite 316
Oklahoma City, OK 73105-4599
(405) 521-4287; Fax: (405) 521-2971
E-mail: Kristy_Ehlers@mail.sde.state.ok.us

Rebecca McLaughlin, State Coordinator
Gifted and Talented Education Office
Oklahoma Department of Education
2500 North Lincoln Boulevard
Oklahoma City, OK 73105-4599
(405) 521-4287; Fax: (405) 521-6205
E-mail: Rebecca_McLaughlin@mail.sde.state.ok.us

State Association

Oklahoma Association of Gifted, Creative, and Talented

OAGCT was founded to bring together concerned professionals and other persons interested in gifted, creative, and talented youth for their mutual support and growth; to support appropriate educational opportunities; to encourage the improvement of educational services to all youth, specifically those who are gifted, creative, and talented; to inform the general public of the needs of gifted, creative, talented youth; to disseminate news and information of interest and concern to parents, teachers, administrators, and other persons interested in gifted, creative, and talented youth; to foster professional growth of educators so that they may better serve the needs of gifted, creative, and talented youth; to support legislation and funding for programs that benefit gifted, creative and talented youth; to work in cooperation with and support of the philosophy and goals of the National Association for Gifted Children; and to provide a forum for the exchange of information and ideas among the membership.

Donna Walker, President
810 Southwest 23rd Street
El Reno, OK 73036
(405) 262-2765
E-mail: Donnaw@norman.k12.ok.us
Web site: http://www.oagct.org

Regional Talent Search

Duke University Talent Identification Program
See listing on page 2 for complete information.

ADA

Gifted and Talented Lyceum (East Central University)
June 15-20

A week of learning and discoveries awaits students at East Central University's 24th Annual Gifted and Talented Lyceum. ECU's tradition of fun learning experiences continues to join curious learners from across the country to share ideas and adventures in four classes from a selection of more than twenty. Classes include art, computer technology, creative writing, dramatics, languages, and environmental sciences. In addition, supervised recreation is planned throughout the week. From Sunday evening to Friday morning, students will have the opportunity to explore the worlds of art, technology and friendship. This residential program is for students age 11-14. It has a counselor-to-student ratio of 1:12. A brochure and an application are available in late April.

Criteria: Recommendations or participation in gifted and talented program.

Grade: Age 11-14.

Cost: $265 per student. Financial aid is not available.

Contact: Domenica Carsten, Coordinator
East Central University
ECU Box E-3
Ada, OK 74820
(580) 332-8000, ext. 456; Fax: (580) 310-9007
E-mail: dcarsten@mailclerk.ecok.edu

NORMAN

Horizons Unlimited Gifted and Talented Academy (University of Oklahoma)
July 6-11

The University of Oklahoma will offer a one-week intensive program for academically gifted and talented youth (rising grades 6-8). The goal is to stimulate academically superior students with intellectual challenges and exciting learning experiences. Students will discover new concepts, philosophies, and perspectives as they enjoy a preview of the riches on a major college campus. Classes offered in the past include geography, meteorology, chemistry, algebra, theatre arts, biology survey, architecture, geology, microworld exploration, history, art, television commercial production, and Web page design. Students select two classes, which will be instructed by University of Oklahoma faculty or staff. Classes are limited to 12-15 students. Students may live on campus in a university residence hall or commute. Evening activities are planned and commuter students are invited to participate.

Criteria: Application (deadline: June 13); personal essay; recommendations; test scores.

Grade: Rising 6-8.

Cost: $450 (residential); $400 (commuter).

Contact: Amy Logan, Academy Director
Horizons Unlimited
University of Oklahoma
1700 Asp Avenue
Norman, OK 73072
(405) 325-6897; Fax: (405) 325-7679
E-mail: alogan@ou.edu

OKLAHOMA CITY

International Aerospace Academy
(Aerospace Science and Technology Education Center)

May-July

The Aerospace Science and Technology Education Center (ASTEC) in Oklahoma City presents the historic eighteenth summer of the International Aerospace Academy (IAA). ASTEC space camps educate, excite, and motivate children age 8-18. The IAA uses interdisciplinary, hands-on activities as well as an exciting curriculum based on content, character, competency, and community to teach students not only about science, math, and technology, but also communication, teamwork, critical/creative thinking, and responsible decision making. **Day Camp** is a five-day commuter program for students age 8-10. Five-day, four night residential sessions include a simulated shuttle mission involving a full-scale shuttle simulator and cutting edge computerized mission control. IAA also offers the high-flying wild **Blue Wonders Aviation Camp**. The International Aerospace Academy excites children about education and launches them into the twenty-first century!

Criteria: Personal essay; recommendations.

Grade: 3-12.

Cost: $300 (day); $600 (residential). All costs are approximate. Scholarships are available.

Contact: Gail Huneryager, COO/Public Relations Officer
ASTEC, Inc.
2401 NW 23rd Street, Suite 3
Oklahoma City, OK 73107
(405) 947-6272; Fax: (405) 947-0035
E-mail: ghuneryager@astec-inc.org
Web site: http://www.astec-inc.org

Oklahoma City

Oklahoma School of Science and Mathematics (State of Oklahoma)
Academic Year

OSSM is Oklahoma's public, tuition-free, residential high school for juniors and seniors with exceptional ability and interest in mathematics and science. While in residence at OSSM, students must successfully complete four and one-half units of science, two units of mathematics, one-half unit of computer science, two units of English, two of social science, two units of a foreign language, one unit of fine arts, and two units of physical education. Each science class features a two-or-three hour laboratory experience. Students receive five and one-half days of academic instruction weekly. They must also receive satisfactory participation reports in campus and community service. The Mentorship Program provides concentrated research opportunities in specialized fields under the direction of professionals in the scientific and technological community. Doctorate degrees are held by 65% of the faculty, and all faculty members have extensive teaching experience.

Criteria: Application; transcript; personal essay; recommendations; parent statement; test scores; ACT; interview; Oklahoma resident.

Grade: 11-12.

Cost: No cost for tuition, room, and board.

Contact: Dr. Edna McDuffie Manning, President
Oklahoma School of Science and Mathematics
1141 North Lincoln Boulevard
Oklahoma City, OK 73104
(405) 521-6436; Fax: (405) 521-6442
E-mail: emanning@ossm.edu
Web site: http://www.ossm.edu

OREGON

STATE DIRECTOR

Dr. Laura Pehkonen, Consultant
Talented and Gifted Programs
Oregon Department of Education
255 Capitol Street Northeast
Salem, OR 97310
(503) 378-3600 ext 2313; Fax: (503) 378-5156
E-mail: laura.pehkonen@state.or.us

STATE ASSOCIATION
Oregon Association for Talented and Gifted

The Oregon Association for Talented and Gifted (OATAG) is a non-profit, non-discriminatory, statewide organization of educators and parents interested in promoting growth opportunities for talented and gifted children in Oregon. OATAG is the state affiliate for the National Association of Gifted Children. OATAG's mission is to advocate for the needs of talented and gifted children; serve as a resource for families, educators, and communities; and provide direction for excellencies in education.

Betty Palmer, President
P.O. Box 1703
Beaverton, OR 97075
(541) 663-3227; Fax: (541) 663-3211
E-mail: board@oatag.org
Web site: http://www.oatag.org

REGIONAL TALENT SEARCH

Center for Talented Youth (The Johns Hopkins University)
See listing on page 4 for complete information.

LOCTIONS THROUGHOUT OREGON

Adventure Treks
June 15-August 18

See listing on page 8 for complete information.

Portland

Challenge Program (Portland State University)
Academic Year

The Challenge Program is a cooperative program between Portland State University (PSU) and metropolitan area high schools. It provides seniors an opportunity to take regular college courses on their own campuses. Students who have a cumulative GPA of 3.0 or above after the completion of six high school semesters (or the equivalent in high school credits) are eligible to enroll in the Challenge Program. The Challenge Program currently offers introductory college courses in computer science, English, foreign languages, history, and mathematics. Carefully selected high school instructors teach Challenge Program courses as part of their regular teaching loads. Students who successfully complete their Challenge Program coursework are entitled to a Portland State University transcript. The credit earned by the student can be transferred to all Oregon state colleges and universities and to many other institutions nationally.

Criteria:	GPA; faculty recommendation; Oregon resident.
Grade:	12.
Cost:	$117 (1 class); $198 (2 classes). Financial aid is available from some participating districts.
Contact:	Karen Tosi, Challenge Program Director Portland State University P.O. Box 751 Portland, OR 97207 (503) 725-3430, (503) 725-5255; Fax: (503) 725-3693 E-mail: tosik@pdx.edu Web site: http://www.clas.pdx.edu/challink.html

LINK Program (Portland State University)
Academic Year

Portland State University is committed to serving the needs of the metropolitan area by providing an academic environment for intellectually gifted students. The LINK program makes it possible for selected gifted high school students to attend Portland State University for part-time advanced study in a particular academic discipline. To qualify for the program, students must be recommended to the university by their school district and complete the LINK admissions process. First opportunity goes to high school seniors. Accepted students meet with a Portland State University advisor regarding course selection. Each student will be limited to one course per quarter, for which Portland State University credit will be granted. Students receive a partial tuition remission for their undergraduate part-time credits. Students are responsible for the purchase of books and materials, as well as for arranging transportation to and from the university.

Criteria:	Transcript; personal essay; recommendations; sample of work; PSAT; SAT; interview; Oregon resident.
Grade:	11-12.
Cost:	Varies.

Contact: Karen Tosi, LINK Program Director
Portland State University
P.O. Box 751
Portland, OR 97207
(503) 725-3430, (503) 725-5255; Fax: (503) 725-3693
E-mail: tosik@pdx.edu
Web site: http://www.clas.pdx.edu/challink.html

PORTLAND

OMSI Science Camps (Oregon Museum of Science and Industry)
Summer

OMSI Science Camps provide exploratory science education for students (grades 3-12) in geology, paleontology, marine biology, astronomy, and arid lands ecology in residential and field settings in Oregon, Washington, and California. Programs are one to three weeks in length and some include rafting, canoeing, and backpacking. High School research teams in marine biology, paleontology, archaeology, volcanic geology will team students with university professors and government agency professionals. High school students are encouraged to work on individual research projects. Base camps are at a mountain lodge in the Cascade Mountains near Bend, Oregon; at Wolf Creek Education Center in Redwoods National Park, California, at Hancock Field Station inside the John Day Fossil Beds National Monument in Central Oregon, and on San Juan Island, Washington. Instructors are professional science educators with undergraduate or graduate degrees in one of the natural sciences and are certified in Wilderness First Responder, life guarding, and school bus driving.

Criteria: Application and personal letter.

Grade: 3-12.

Cost: $790 (three weeks); $580 (two weeks); $410 (one week); $385 (one week; OMSI members). Financial aid is available.

Contact: Registrar
OMSI Science Camps
1941 SE Water Avenue
Portland, OR 97214
(503) 797-4662
E-mail: camps@omsi.edu
Web site: http://www.omsi.edu

SHERIDAN

The Delphian School
Academic Year and Summer (June 4-August 2)

The Delphian School (Delphi) is a coeducational, college preparatory day and boarding school. The school has over 700 acres of wooded hills, meadows, and fields overlooking the Willamette Valley near coastal Oregon. Delphi's program fosters self-esteem, integrity, honesty, and true enthusiasm for learning in each student by using a unique study technology developed by author and educator, L. Ron Hubbard. This allows each and every student to receive not only one-on-one attention but also an academic program specifically tailored for the individual's needs and strengths. Summer at Delphi provides an exciting mix of individualized academics, exciting activities, and trips. Rafting, camping, horseback riding, tennis, volleyball, soccer, and computer camps are all available, challenging, and just plain fun. Students can brush up on weak areas (at any level), excel in advanced subjects, or simply explore new interests. Delphi prepares students for any educational setting by supplying them with a challenging academic program and a summer full of exciting and productive activities. English-as-a-Second-Language (ESL) is also offered. The Delphian School is licensed to use Applied Scholastics ™ Educational Services.

Criteria: Application (and $50 fee); admissions and placement testing.

Grade: 3-12.

Cost: Academic Year: $28,325 (middle school boarding); $28,750 (upper school boarding); $16,275 (day, cost depends on age of student). Summer at Delphi: $5,052-$5,190 (six-week, residential, cost depends on age of student); $2,164 (six-week, day). Prices are subject to change. Financial aid is available (academic year only).

Contact: Donetta Phelps, Director of Admissions
The Delphian School
20950 SW Rock Creek Road
Sheridan, OR 97378
(800) 626-6610; Fax: (503) 843-4158
E-mail: info@delphian.org
Web site: http://www.delphian.org

PENNSYLVANIA

STATE DIRECTOR

Barbara Thrush, Special Education Advisor
Bureau of Special Education
Pennsylvania Department of Education
333 Market Street, 7th floor
Harrisburg, PA 17126-0333
(717) 783-6881
E-mail: bthrush@state.pa.us

STATE ASSOCIATION

Pennsylvania Association for Gifted Education
3026 Potshop Road
Norristown, PA 19403
(215) 616-0470

REGIONAL TALENT SEARCH

Center for Talented Youth (The Johns Hopkins University)
See listing on page 4 for complete information.

HAWLEY

Science Camp Watonka (Camp Watonka, Incorporated)
June 21-August 16; June 21-July 19; July 19-August 16

Camp Watonka is a small camp of 120 boys supervised by a staff of about 60. In addition to the traditional camp activities, Camp Watonka offers daily laboratory experiences in such subjects as chemistry, biology, computer science, electronics, astronomy, robotics, photography, physics, earth science, ham radio, and rocketry. Well-equipped laboratories, along with qualified instructors, make this a worthwhile experience for all boys who are interested in science. Camp Watonka is not a summer school, but it does offer a hands-on program that is both educational and fun. In addition to the sciences, Camp Watonka offers a wide range of other activities that include mini-bike riding, climbing, riflery, sailing, sports, trips, woodworking, crafts, windsurfing, and ARC swimming. Campers select their own program and they are given individual instruction in all activities. High standards are maintained in all areas of the camp operation. There are no charges beyond the camp fee.

Criteria: Application (and fee); male student.

Grade: Rising 2-10.

Cost: $5,195 (eight weeks); $3,195 (four weeks).

Contact: Donald Wacker, Director
Science Camp Watonka
P.O. Box 356
Paupack, PA 18451
(570) 857-1401; Fax: (570) 857-9653
E-mail: donwackr@voicenet.com
Web site: http://www.watonka.com

Mercersburg

Mercersburg Academy
Academic Year

Only 90 minutes from Washington, D.C., and Baltimore, Md., Mercersburg offers extensive opportunities in fine/performing arts, athletics (including nationally ranked swimming), 18 Advanced Placement courses, and students from 29 states and 20 countries. Drawing talented youth from around the world, Mercersburg has long served students who wish to be participants in the educational arena and not mere spectators. A thorough admission process that seeks to gauge a student's strengths and needs is followed by a program of careful placement testing that accelerates able students in all areas regardless of age or grade level. Thus, a ninth grader who is ready for third-year French or a tenth grader who needs calculus may take those courses in classes that average 12 students. Following an accelerated program, a student may do honors and Advanced Placement works in almost every curricular area.

Criteria: Application (deadline: February 1); $50 application fee; transcript; personal essay; recommendations; sample of work; test scores; GPA; PSAT; SAT; SSAT; interview.

Grade: 9-12, PG.

Cost: $28,700 (boarding); $20,900 (day). $3.2 million in need-based financial aid was awarded to over 45% of student body in 2002-2003.

Contact: Director of Admission and Financial Aid
Mercersburg Academy
300 E. Seminary Street
Mercersburg, PA 17236
(717) 328-6173; Fax: (717) 328-6319
E-mail: admission@mercersburg.edu
Web site: http://www.mercersburg.edu

Mercersburg Adventure Camps (Mercersburg Academy)
June 22-August 1 (one-, two-, four-, and six-week sessions)

Mercersburg Academy's Adventure Camp series offers diverse opportunities for the development of every camper's mind, body, and spirit. Junior Adventure Camp, Adventure Camp, and Teen Adventure Camp offer sessions ranging from one week to six weeks. Contemporary camps with a traditional flavor, the unique structures blend enrichment activities, varied sports, outdoor activities, trips, and traditional camp experiences. Energetic counselors encourage each camper to embark on quests of discovery, learn teamwork, develop independence and leadership, and build friendships. Campers enjoy adventures in diverse enrichment activities that range from robotics to the visual and performing arts, utilizing Mercersburg's modern academic facilities. Campers engage in various outdoor adventures that range from Civil War battlefield excursions to kayaking to horseback riding, and many other choices. Each camp travels, with trips that include amusement parks, overnight campouts, baseball games, and river rafting. Program enrollments range from 40 to 70 and feature a 3:1 camper-to-staff ratio.

Criteria: Application.

Grade:	1-3 (Junior Adventure Camp); 3-8 (Adventure Camp); 8-11 (Teen Adventure Camp).
Cost:	$650-$4,150. Financial aid is not available.
Contact:	Rick Hendrickson, Director of Summer and Extended Programs Mercersburg Adventure Camps Mercersburg Academy 300 E. Seminary Street Mercersburg, PA 17236 (717) 328-6225; Fax: (717) 328-9072 E-mail: summerprograms@mercersburg.edu Web site: http://www.mercersburg.edu/open-sumprog.cfm

NEWTOWN

George School
Academic Year

Established in 1893 by the Religious Society of Friends, George School is committed to cultivating respect for differences by affirming the Light of God in everyone and to meeting the intellectual, social, and development needs of students. A coeducational boarding and day school of 540 students in grades 9-12, George School offers a comprehensive college preparatory curriculum including Advanced Placement courses and the International Baccalaureate Program. Internationally renowned, the IB Diploma Program is an academically rigorous two-year course of study, which often culminates in a full-year of college credit. George School is conveniently located in Bucks County, PA, 30 miles from Philadelphia and 70 miles from New York City. Nearly 40% of the student body receives $4.0 million of financial assistance, including four $10,000 merit-based Anderson Scholarships. Quaker values such as tolerance, equality, and social justice create a diverse community where academics, sports, arts, and service share emphasis.

Criteria:	Application (and fee); transcript; personal essay; recommendations; test scores; SSAT; interview.
Grade:	9-12.
Cost:	$28,650 (boarding); $20,000 (day). Scholarships and need-based financial aid are available.
Contact:	Karen Hallowell, Director of Admission George School Box 4000 Newtown, PA 18940 (215) 579-6547; Fax (215) 579-6549 E-mail: admissions@georgeschool.org Web site: http://www.georgeschool.org

Pennsburg

Perkiomen School
Academic Year

Perkiomen School is a traditional, coeducational, college preparatory boarding and day school, located on a 165-acre campus. With a diverse student population from 15 states and 11 countries, the school seeks to create an appreciation for and an understanding of the role of the individual in helping create a viable, productive, and supportive community. Within a structured and traditional environment, the staff endeavors to develop an inquisitive student who can work independently after goals have been established and procedures outlined. The school seeks to expand horizons and challenge the mind in a manner that will promote priorities and ideals which are purposeful, reasonable, in tune with traditional values, spiritually balanced, and flexible enough to handle arising emergencies in a complicated and confusing world. In this challenge, the staff at Perkiomen seeks to nurture common sense, the growth of a sense of justice, a sense of honor, a sense of responsibility, and a sense of humor.

Criteria: Application (and fee); transcript; personal essay; recommendations; interview.

Grade: 5-12, PG (day); 7-12, PG (boarding).

Cost: $17,300 (day); $29,500 (boarding). Financial aid is available ($1.1 million grants awarded in 2002-2003).

Contact: Carol Dougherty, Assistant Head of School
Perkiomen School
200 Seminary Avenue, P.O. Box 130
Pennsburg, PA 18073
(215) 679-9511; Fax: (215) 679-1146
E-mail: cdougherty@perkiomen.org
Web site: http://www.perkiomen.org

Philadelphia

Pre-College Summer Institute (The University of the Arts)
July 7-August 1

The Pre-College Summer Institute at The University of the Arts offers gifted and talented high school sophomores, juniors, and seniors the opportunity to study the arts in an exciting urban setting. **Performing arts** offerings include four-week intensive program in Musical Theater (acting, coaching, voice, and movement) and Drama (stage combat, movement, mask, speech, and acting), and a two-week instrumental and voice Jazz Performance Workshop (big band, ensemble, improvisation, large and small groups, private lessons, and theory). **Visual arts** students in the four-week intensive Art Smart Program take drawing as well as a contemporary art history seminar. Students also choose two from the following elective choices: computer games and animation, mixed media sculpture, painting, figurative sculpture, comic book illustration, industrial design, digital photography workshop, painting from the figurer, jewelry and small metals, black and white photography, graphic design, and ceramics. Intensive four-week workshops are offered in writing for television and film, animation, video production, screen directing, and photography.

Criteria: Registration deposit.

Grade: Rising 9-12.

Cost: $1,100 (Jazz Performance Workshop); $1,770 (four-week programs). Prices are for tuition only. Housing is $175 per week. Talent and merit-based scholarships are available.

Contact: Erin Elman, Director, or Melissa DiGiacomo, Assistant Director
Pre-College Summer Institute
The University of the Arts
320 South Broad Street
Philadelphia, PA 19102
(215) 717-6430; Fax: (215) 717-6433
E-mail: precollege@uarts.edu
Web site: http://www.uarts.edu/precol

PITTSBURGH

National Computer Camps
June-August

See listing under Multiple Locations for complete information.

Pre-College Program (Carnegie Mellon University)
June 29-August 7

The Carnegie Mellon Pre-College Program is a six-week residential program for academically and artistically motivated students. Rising high school juniors and seniors can participate in three available programs. **Summer Academy for Minority Students** is an engineering, science and computer science program, designed for underrepresented minority high school students (African American, Hispanic American, and Native American) who are considering careers in engineering, science, and computer science. **Advance Placement/Early Admission** (APEA) is a program that offers college credit for courses in engineering, science, computer science, and humanities. The **Pre-College Program** in the Department of Fine Arts offers non-credit courses in architecture, art, design, drama, and music. All expose students to a college-level, professional program. In addition to the academic and artistic programs, students live in the residence halls (Note: students must be age 16 or older to live on campus), eat on campus, and participate in a wide variety of events and activities.

Criteria: Application (deadline: May 1); $30 application fee; transcript; personal essay; recommendations; test scores; PSAT; PACT; ACT; SAT I.

Grade: 11-12.

Cost: $3,930-$5,403.

Contact: Pre-College Programs
Carnegie Mellon University
5000 Forbes Avenue
Pittsburgh, PA 15213-3890
(412) 268-2082; Fax: (412) 268-7838
E-mail: precollege@andrew.cmu.edu
Web site: http://www.cmu.edu/enrollment/pre-college

PITTSBURGH

The Pennsylvania Governor's School for the Sciences
(Pennsylvania Department of Education and Carnegie Mellon University)
June 29-August 2

The Pennsylvania Governor's School for the Sciences (PGSS) is an upgraded summer enrichment program, which is in session for five weeks, seven days per week. All students are required to live on the Carnegie Mellon University campus in college dormitories. It is an intense program in which students take lecture courses in biology, chemistry, physics, mathematics and computer science. In addition, they are expected to participate in their choice of one laboratory course in either biology, chemistry, physics, or computer science, and to engage in team research projects in one of the above five major discipline areas. The students also have the opportunity to take elective courses which may vary from year to year, to participate in several field trips, and to be further enriched by a distinguished guest lecture series and special seminars on leadership and college selection. Only residents of the Commonwealth of Pennsylvania are eligible to apply.

Criteria: Application; transcript; personal essay; recommendations; test scores; PSAT; SAT; strong interest in science or mathematics; Pennsylvania resident.

Grade: Rising 12.

Cost: None.

Contact: Barry Luokkala, PGSS Director
Carnegie Mellon University
5000 Forbes Avenue
Pittsburgh, PA 15213
(412) 268-6669; Fax: (412) 681-0648
E-mail: pgss@cmu.edu
Web site: http://www-pgss.mcs.cmu.edu

SALTSBURG

The Kiski School
Academic year

Located on 370 acres in western Pennsylvania, The Kiski School has offered a superb academic and athletic program for high school boys since 1888. All 220 students board, as do most of the teachers and administrators, creating a classic boarding school environment. Boys are required to participate in athletic pursuits each afternoon, whether on a competitive team, or in another structured physical endeavor. All students are supplied with a laptop computer, which they take to class and study halls. Athletic facilities include a golf course, five tennis courts, two swimming pools, lighted athletic fields, a cross-country course, venues for wrestling and basketball, and two weight rooms. The program features family-style meals, and students wear coat and tie to classes. The John A. Pidgeon Library won recognition as the best school library in the state of Pennsylvania in the spring of 2001. Numerous weekend activities and clubs are available.

Criteria:	Application (and $35 application fee); transcript; personal essay; recommendations; test scores; SSAT; interview.
Grade:	Rising 9-12.
Cost:	$26,250. Financial aid is available.
Contact:	Lawrence J. Jensen The Kiski School 1888 Brett Lane Saltsburg, PA 15681 (724) 639-3586; Fax: (724) 639-8596 E-mail: admissions@kiski.org Web site: http://www.kiski.org

SCRANTON

PATHWAYS (Marywood University School of Continuing Education)
July 14-25

PATHWAYS is a two-week residential or commuter program which provides qualified high school students with the opportunity to explore and experience college life, fields of study, skill enhancement, and social activities. The program is open to students (rising grades 9-12). Juniors and seniors are eligible to earn college credit. Course offerings include: the arts, business, communication arts, dietetics, computers, education, psychology, social sciences, English, history, science, fitness, SAT review, and many more.

Criteria:	Application (deadline: June 30); transcript; recommendations.
Grade:	Rising 9-12.
Cost:	$750 (estimated for full-time resident). Need-based scholarships are available.
Contact:	Meg Cullen-Brown, Program Director PATHWAYS Marywood University, SCE 2300 Adams Avenue Scranton, PA 18509 (800) 724-0399, (570) 348-6237; Fax: (570) 961-4776 E-mail: brownm@marywood.edu Web site: http://www.marywood.edu

RHODE ISLAND

STATE DIRECTOR

Ina S. Woolman, Coordinator
Gifted and Talented Programs
Rhode Island Department of Elementary & Secondary Education
255 Westminister Street, Room 400
Providence, RI 02903-3400
(401) 222-4600, ext. 2318; Fax: (401) 222-6030
E-mail: iwoolman@ride.ri.net

STATE ASSOCIATION

Rhode Island State Advisory Committee on Gifted and Talented Education
Dr. Dianne McAulay
150 Half Moon Trail
Wakefield, RI 02879
(410) 783-8052

REGIONAL TALENT SEARCH

Center for Talented Youth (The Johns Hopkins UNiversity)
See listing on page 4 for complete information.

SOUTH CAROLINA

STATE DIRECTOR

Wayne Lord, Education Associate
Office of Curriculum & Standards
South Carolina Department of Education
1429 Senate Street, Room 801
Columbia, SC 29201
(803) 734-8335; Fax: (803) 734-6142
E-mail: wlord@sde.state.sc.us

STATE ASSOCIATION

South Carolina Consortium for Gifted Education
Anna Pruitt, President
1301 Dubose Court
Camden, SC 29020
(803) 432-8416; Fax: (803) 425-8919
E-mail: annapruitt@anderson5.net

REGIONAL TALENT SEARCH

Duke University Talent Identification Program
See listing on page 2 for complete information.

BEAUFORT

Beaufort Academy
Academic Year

Beaufort Academy (BA) is a coeducational, independent, college preparatory school of 340 students in grades PreK-12. For over 35 years, it has been the premier independent school in Beaufort County. BA graduates distinguish themselves in major colleges and universities throughout the country. The college preparatory curriculum is designed to enhance each student's education by tailoring it to fit his or her academic needs within the traditional classroom structure. The Upper School provides honors and Advanced Placement courses in all disciplines. Students at Beaufort Academy lead incredibly busy and rewarding lives. Over 70 percent of Upper School students participate in inter-scholastic sports and benefit from the campus and community service opportunities provided by the BA Student Government and the Interact Club. Other extra-curricular organizations include the National Honor Society and National Junior Honor Society, the French, Spanish, and Latin Honor Societies, the Fellowship of Christian Athletes, the Chess Club, the Math Club, the Upper and Middle School Quiz Bowl teams, and the *Aquila* (yearbook) and *Herald* (student newspaper).

Criteria: Application; $60 application fee; transcript; writing sample; test scores; GPA; PSAT; OLSAT; CTP II; SAT.

Grade: PreK-12.

Cost: $4,420-$6,490. Financial aid is available.

Contact: William D. Dalton, Director of Admissions
Beaufort Academy
240 Sams Point Road
Beaufort, SC 29907
(843) 524-3343; Fax: (843) 524-1171
E-mail: bdalton@beaufortacademy.org
Web site: http://beaufortacademy.org

CHARLESTON

The Governor's School of South Carolina (The College of Charleston)
June 8-July 5

Established in 1976, the Governor's School of South Carolina at the College of Charleston provides special academic opportunities at the college level for high school students who have demonstrated exceptional academic achievement and intellectual potential. Governor's Scholars receive intensive instruction in two courses: a subject concentration class from a variety of academic subjects and a seminar on contemporary global issues. Supplementing the academic program are numerous enrichment activities including concerts, lectures, films, sports, and social activities.

Criteria: Application (deadline: January 15); $25 application fee; personal essay; recommendations; SAT; nomination; student in a South Carolina public or private school.

Grade: Rising 12.

Cost:	$625. Need-based financial aid is available.
Contact:	Dr. John H. Newell, Director or Maria Mansfield Richardson, Associate Director The Governor's School of South Carolina The College of Charleston 66 George Street Charleston, SC 29424 (843) 953-6592; Fax: (843) 953-1824 E-mail: guvie@cofc.edu Web site: http://www.guvie.cofc.edu

CLEMSON

Summer Science, Engineering, and Architecture Enrichment Program (Clemson University)

June 1-July 26 (one-, two-, and three-week sessions)

The Summer Science, Engineering, and Architecture Enrichment Program at Clemson University is a residential course/research enrichment program for motivated, gifted and talented junior and senior high school students (rising grades 7-12). The program challenges students through a concentrated study of selected concepts and principles. Students experience college life by living and eating in residence halls. Clemson University faculty instruct all classes in the university science buildings and laboratories. University materials and equipment will be used to conduct scientific investigations. Students have access to all recreational and medical facilities. Subject areas include: architecture, basic electronics, biology, chemistry, creativity and engineering design, computer science, physics, astronomy/earth science, psychology/physiology, and math. Evening and weekend activities are planned around the social, intellectual, cultural, and athletic needs and interests of the students.

Criteria:	Application (deadline: May 15); recommendations; PSAT.
Grade:	Rising 7-12.
Cost:	$550 (one-week session); $950 (two-week session); $975 (two-week architecture session); $1,550 (three-week session).
Contact:	Nell Coffey, Student Services Coordinator II Summer Science, Engineering, and Architecture Enrichment Programs Clemson University 101 Sikes Hall Clemson, SC 29634 (864) 656-5849; Fax: (864) 656-1480 E-mail: cnell@clemson.edu Web site: http://www.clemson.edu/summerscience

COLUMBIA

Hammond School
Academic Year

Hammond School offers a college preparatory education to 870 students in grades PreK–12. The Hammond curriculum emphasizes classical academic tradition with a creative focus on global education. Students are grounded with a mastery of basic skills in the progression and style of learning that is appropriate for each individual. Exceptional faculty and small classes provide students the opportunity to accelerate while remaining within the student's own age group. The Advanced Placement and Honors programs encompass all disciplines and offer Upper School students an even greater academic challenge. All graduates attend college. Hammond tends to matters of the heart as well as of the mind, encouraging students to serve not only the school community but also the larger communities in which they live. The physical well being and competitive spirit of the students are fostered by a full interscholastic athletic program in the Middle and Upper Schools. Other extracurricular activities include clubs, student government, admission guides, school newspaper, yearbook, theater, field studies, and international travel.

Criteria: Application (and $50 fee); transcript; personal essay; work and writing samples; recommendations; test scores; GPA; PSAT; SAT; SSAT; ERB; interview.

Grade: PreK–12.

Cost: $4,800 (PreK–K); $7,575 (grades 1-4); $8,275 (grades 6-8); $8,950 (grades 9-12).

Contact: Julia S. Moore, Director of Admission
Hammond School
854 Galway Lane
Columbia, SC 29209
(803) 776-0295; Fax: (803) 776-0122
E-mail: hammond4@usit.net
Web site: http://www.hammondschool.org

Heathwood Hall Episcopal School
Academic Year

Celebrating more than 50 years, Heathwood Hall Episcopal School is dedicated to fostering the spiritual growth of its students. Accredited by the Southern Association of Colleges and Schools, Heathwood is a three-time National Blue Ribbon School—the only college preparatory school in the state so honored by the U.S. Department of Education. A Heathwood Hall education challenges students to achieve in the classroom and beyond, helping them to grow in mind, body, and spirit. The school currently enrolls more than 750 boys and girls from all ethnic, social, and religious heritages. Student accomplishments spring from a rigorous curriculum that includes honors and Advanced Placement courses, extensive use of computer technology, and early and sustained exposure to fine arts, foreign languages, and the award-winning faculty. Daily devotionals, weekly chapels, a nationally recognized outdoor adventure/education program, championship athletic teams, and a host of other extracurricular offerings complement the academic program. 100 percent of seniors are accepted to undergraduate programs each year. Each year, seniors qualify for national distinction by the College Board as AP Scholars and average SAT scores have surpassed 1200, with one quarter of the senior class scoring 1370 or higher.

Criteria: Application (and fee); transcript; recommendations; sample of work; test scores; GPS; PSAT; SAT; interview.

Grade: PreK-12.

Cost: $5,250-$10,590. Need-based financial aid is available. Academic scholarships are available for grades 7-11.

Contact: Lindsey F. Smith, Jr., Director of Admission
Heathwood Hall Episcopal School
3000 South Beltline Boulevard
Columbia, SC 29201
(803) 765-2309; Fax: (803) 343-0437
E-mail: hhes2@heathwood.org
Web site: http://www.heathwood.org

COLUMBIA

Carolina Master Scholars Adventures Series (University of South Carolina)
June-July (one-week sessions)

Become a Carolina Master Scholar (CMS) by attending the invigorating, academically challenging Carolina Master Scholars Adventures Program. Students gather on the campus of the University of South Carolina (USC) for a weeklong academic exploration of the arts and sciences featuring two off-site excursions including travel to some of our nation's historic cities. The program exposes participants in greater depth to a subject area and encourages independent thinking. Each one-week course is taught by a university faculty member, a community educator, or a professional. Courses are available in air and space, science, theatre, law and criminology, medicine, music, the arts, testing skills, and the architecture and history of our nation's capital. Students attend class in the mornings, and in the afternoon, residential staff members lead students in recreational activities such as swimming, craft workshops, movies, barbecues, and field trips to local events. At the end of the week, students participate in a closing ceremony and make short presentations to parents, staff, teachers, and friends. CMS students who participate in three adventures programs over a six-year period receive special admissions tracking to USC and special alumni status.

Criteria: Application; recommendations; GPA; PSAT, SAT, or ACT.

Grade: Rising 7-12.

Cost: $500-$1,050. Partial need-based scholarships are available.

Contact: Continuing Education
University of South Carolina
Columbia, SC 29208
(803) 777-9444; Fax: (803) 777-2663
E-mail: confs@gwm.sc.edu
Web site: http://www.rcce.sc.edu/adventures

Columbia

Summer Academic Programs (University of South Carolina)
June-August

Summer Academic Programs at the University of South Carolina (USC) offer a diverse array of educational enrichment opportunities in a fun, safe, environment. The programs are specifically designed for students ages 11 through 17. Whether students are interested in becoming a journalist, a lawyer, a physician, or an artist, they can gear up for it at USC. Residential and day programs are offered from June through August. Programs range from **Adventures in Creativity**, a two-week interdisciplinary program for junior scholars, to the **Carolina Master Scholars Adventure Series**, which weaves academic disciplines with hands-on experience. The **Carolina Journalism Institute** is an intensive workshop that focuses on editing, writing, design, and production of scholastic publications. The **Center for Coastal Ecology** offers a multitude of summer programs at Pritchard's Island facility. Students can even explore the dazzling world of fine and performing arts with the **Summer Dance Conservatory, Drama Conservatory, Music Camp**, or the **String Project Summer Camp**. It's all at the University of South Carolina. So stretch those knowledge-thirsty tentacles. Turn into a colossal adventure-seeking sponge. Soak up an invigorating summer of excitement at the University of South Carolina.

Criteria: Application; some programs require recommendations.

Grade: 7-12.

Cost: Varies.

Contact: Continuing Education
University Of South Carolina
Columbia, SC 29208
(803) 777-9444; Fax: (803) 777-2663
E-mail: confs@gwm.sc.edu
Web site: http://www.rcce.sc.edu/sap

Summer Math and Computer Science Camp (Columbia College)
July 21-25

The Summer Math and Computer Science Camp at Columbia College is a day camp for motivated rising seventh, eighth, and ninth grade girls who have demonstrated competence in math or computer science. Students participate in hands-on activities designed to challenge girls to see the beauty, power, and usefulness of math and computer science. Problem-solving, collaboration, and career information are woven throughout the courses. College faculty teach all classes. Students learn about programming, mathematical modeling, and the history of these fields; interact with women in these fields; and enjoy the computer lab, pool, and physical education facilities on campus. The camp meets Monday through Friday, 9 a.m. until 4 p.m. Lunch and two snacks will be served each day. Visit their Web site and click on "Summer Programs" for additional information.

Criteria: Application (deadline: May 31); $10 non-refundable application fee; recommendations; test scores.

Grade: Rising 7-9.

Cost: $225.

Contact: Dr. Lucy Carpenter Snead
Department of Mathematics and Computing
Columbia College
1301 Columbia College Drive
Columbia, SC 29203
(803) 786-3775; Fax: (803) 786-3809
E-mail: lsnead@colacoll.edu
Web site: http://www.columbiacollegesc.edu

GREENVILLE

Furman University Summer Scholars Program
June 15- July 12

During the summer of 2003, the Furman University Summer Scholars Program will offer one-week and two-week programs of academic enrichment for talented rising juniors and seniors. Each program provides an opportunity for students to experience campus life, explore an area of academic interest and meet students with similar interests. Topics include computing, French, graphic art, mock trial, leadership, psychology, theater arts, and writing. Directed by Furman faculty members with the assistance of Furman students, each program emphasizes engaged learning, a hands-on, problem solving, and collaborative educational philosophy that encourages students to put into practice the theories and methods learned from texts or lectures. Participants will be housed in Lakeside Housing, one of Furman's residential complexes. Summer Scholars Program participants have access to campus amenities such as the James B. Duke library, tennis courts, jogging and fitness trails, swimming pool, the university center and campus dining facilities.

Criteria: Application (deadline: May 31); GPA; ACT; PSAT or SAT.

Grade: 10-12.

Cost: $750-$1,250.

Contact: Anne Chubb, Manager
Summer Scholars
Furman University
3300 Poinsett Highway
Greenville, SC 29613
(864) 294-2155; Fax: (864) 294-3378
E-mail: continuingeducation@furman.edu
Web site: http://www.furman.edu/summerscholars

Hartsville

South Carolina Governor's School for Science and Mathematics
Academic Year

Acknowledged for its "commitment to intellectual growth" and as a school that will "graduate tomorrow's leaders," the South Carolina Governor's School for Science and Mathematics (GSSM) was again chosen as one of the best secondary schools in the nation for overall excellence. GSSM is a two-year, residential high school that provides an enriched and balanced curriculum with special focus on science, math, and research. Located on Coker College campus, GSSM has excellent facilities and one of the best teaching faculties anywhere. All have master's degrees; with 70% holding doctorates. Instructors are committed to the development and well-being of the students and encourage student input and discussion. The 10:1 student-to-teacher ratio assures GSSM students significant individual attention and the chance to engage in meaningful independent research projects.

Criteria: Transcript; personal essay; recommendations; test scores; PSAT; GPA; South Carolina resident.

Grade: 11-12.

Cost: $250 (activity and room deposit fee); no cost for tuition, room, and board.

Contact: William Perkins, Director of Admissions
South Carolina Governor's School for Science and Mathematics
306 E. Home Avenue
Hartsville, SC 29550
(843) 383-3944; Fax: (843) 383-3903
E-mail: perkins@gssm.k12.sc.us
Web site: http://www.gssm.k12.sc.us

Summer Program for Research Interns
(South Carolina Governor's School for Science and Mathematics)
June 9-July 18

South Carolina Governor's School for Science and Mathematics (GSSM) is a leading institution in promoting and coordinating scientific research by high school students through the Summer Program for Research Interns (SPRI). Students conduct research in university and individual laboratories for six weeks during the summer with professional scientists serving as mentors. Most placements are within driving distance of the students' homes. Room and board are provided at universities for some who do not live near a mentor. Participants submit an abstract and present their work at the annual GSSM Winter Research Colloquium (February 7, 2004). Students are encouraged to present their work at professional society meetings through their mentors and the South Carolina Junior Academy of Science (SCJAS). Many students have won local, regional, and national honors. The SPRI program depends on dedicated mentors who volunteer to work with students. (To date, over 425 mentors have worked with SPRI.)

Criteria: Application; transcript; personal essay; recommendations; GPA; SAT or other standardized test; South Carolina resident.

Grade: Rising 12 (must be at least age 16 by June 1, 2003).

Cost: None. A small stipend is offered.

Contact: Dr. Carolyn F. Randolph, Vice President of Outreach and Research
          SPRI Program
          South Carolina Governor's School for Science and Mathematics
          306 E. Home Avenue
          Hartsville, SC 29550
          (843) 383-3916; Fax: (843) 383-3950
          E-mail: randolph@gssm.k12.sc.us
          Web site: http://www.gssm.k12.sc.us

SUMTER

Wilson Hall
Academic Year

Wilson Hall offers a superior academic program with dedicated faculty directing a student-oriented education. It is a coeducational, college preparatory day school where students are nurtured and encouraged to grow to their potential. Accredited by the Southern Association of Colleges and Schools, Wilson Hall's mission is to prepare students for success in college. This is accomplished by providing a challenging curriculum in a structured, safe and nurturing atmosphere that promotes learning and growth at all levels of instruction. Wilson Hall also holds membership in the South Carolina Independent School Association, the Palmetto Association of Independent Schools, and the Southern Association of Independent Schools. Because Wilson Hall is a college preparatory school, all courses in grades 6-12 are taught at an advanced level. Specially trained faculty members teach the twelve Advanced Placement courses that are offered. The average SAT score is well above state and national averages, and 100 percent of Wilson Hall graduates matriculate to college.

Criteria: Application; $150 application fee; transcript; personal essay; interview; test scores; GPA; PSAT; SAT.

Grade: PreK-12.

Cost: $3,410 (PreK-K); $3,720 (1-5); $3,800 (6-8); $3,920 (9-12).

Contact: Sean P. Hoskins, Director of Admissions and Public Relations
           Wilson Hall
           2801 South Wise Drive
           Sumter, SC 29150
           (803) 469-3475; Fax: (803) 469-3477
           E-mail: sean_hoskins@hotmail.com
           Web site: http://www.wilsonhall.org

SOUTH DAKOTA

STATE DIRECTOR

Terri Cordrey, Education Program Representative
South Dakota Department of Education
700 Governors Drive
Pierre, SD 57501-2291
(605) 773-4662; Fax: (605) 773-3782
E-mail: terri.cordrey@state.sd.us

STATE ASSOCIATION

South Dakota Association for Gifted Children
Dr. Donna Silver-Miller, President
2006 Buena Vista Drive
Rapid City, SD 57702
605/394-4031; Fax:
silverman@rapidnet.com

REGIONAL TALENT SEARCH

Center for Talent Development (Northwestern University)
See listing on page 3 for complete information.

TENNESSEE

State Director

Coordinator, Special Education Assessment and Gifted
Tennessee Department of Education
Division of Special Educucation
710 James Robertson Parkway, 5th floor, Andrew Johnson Tower
Nashville, TN 37243-0380
(888) 212-3162; Fax: (615) 532-9412

STATE ASSOCIATION

Tennessee Association for the Gifted
Martha McCarley, President
605 Whispering Way
Kingsport, TN 37663
(423) 239-1370
E-mail: mcmccarley1@juno.com

REGIONAL TALENT SEARCH

Duke University Talent Identification Program
See listing on page 2 for complete information.

Bell Buckle

The Webb School
Academic Year

Since its founding in 1870, the Webb School has been recognized both nationally and internationally for its highly challenging liberal arts curriculum, offering honors classes at every level, as well as many Advanced Placement courses. Tennessee's oldest boarding school, Webb is also the South's leading producer of Rhodes Scholars. A coeducational, college preparatory school for 292 boarding and day students, it draws from both traditional and innovative philosophies to create a learning environment that fosters academic excellence and honor. As a small school, Webb offers students the chance to be an individual, a luxury often unavailable at larger institutions. Although the members of the Webb community are a diverse group, one unifying characteristic is evident: Webb students have a strong desire to meet the school's academic requirements and its high standard for personal integrity. Graduates of Webb continue to be active scholars and responsible citizens throughout their lives.

Criteria: Application (and $30 application fee); transcript; personal essay; recommendations; test scores; interview.

Grade: 6-12.

Cost: $25,700 (boarding); $10,400 (day). Financial aid is available (over $900,000 in financial aid was awarded in 2002).

Contact: Matt Radtke, Director of Admissions
The Webb School
Highway 82
Bell Buckle, TN 37020
(931) 389-6003; Fax: (931) 389-6657
E-mail: admissions@webbschool.com
Web site: http://www.thewebbschool.com

Chattanooga

Baylor School
Academic Year

For more than 100 years, Baylor School has been one of the leading college-preparatory boarding schools in the South. Located on a spectacular 670-acre campus, Baylor provides a challenging academic program featuring small classes (13 students on average), outstanding teaching, and 19 Advanced Placement courses. Over half of the teaching faculty have masters and doctoral degrees. Each year, Baylor graduates are accepted into some of America's top universities. Last year, 48 percent of graduates earned $3 million in college merit scholarships. Academic support includes college counseling, a writing center, study halls, and academic advisors. Fine arts include dance, drama, music, and studio arts. Students participate in more than 30 extracurricular activities, including an extensive outdoor program, and a championship athletic program featuring 74 teams in 17 sports. Baylor's mission is to instill in students the desire and ability to make a positive difference in the world.

Criteria: Application (and fee); transcript; recommendations; test scores; GPA; PSAT; SSAT; ISEE; interview.

Grade:	9-12 (boarding); 6-12 (day).
Cost:	$26,780 (boarding); $13,755 (day). More than $1.5 million is available in need-based financial aid. A competitive merit scholarship program is available for qualifying 9-10 grade boarding students.
Contact:	Dale Hanson, Director of Boarding Admissions Baylor School P.O. Box 1337 Chattanooga, TN 37405 (423) 267-8505; Fax: (423) 265-4276 E-mail: dhanson@baylor.chattanooga.net Web site: http://www.baylorschool.org

CHATTANOOGA

Camp Baylor (The Baylor School)

July 13-19 (1-week session); June 15-27 and June 29-July11 (2-week sessions); June 15-July 11 (4-week session)

A residential program with one-, two-, and four-week sessions, Camp Baylor offers students (rising grades 3-9) the opportunity to explore enrichment classes in video production, multimedia computers, drama, environmental studies, studio art, woodworking, journalism, and the Civil War, while also enjoying a full range of sports and wilderness activities. Campers experience a slate of morning enrichment opportunities and in the afternoon may choose three specialty areas in various sports, art, and wilderness activities. Campers also participate in several sports clinics, including clinics in fencing, tennis, basketball, and soccer. Camp Baylor boasts an extensive outdoors program in which campers enjoy SCUBA, kayaking, mountain biking, rock climbing, canoeing, caving, and backpacking trips. Baylor's 670-acre campus is comprised of 300 acres of woodlands, a lake, a wetlands area, and a border on the Tennessee River, all of which create the ideal experiential laboratory for classes in science, art, wilderness skills, video, computers, and the environment. Campers at Baylor are well supervised with a staff-to-camper ratio of 1:4.

Criteria:	Application.
Grade:	Rising 3-9.
Cost:	$775 (one-week session); $1,500 (two-week sessions); $2,900 (4-week session).
Contact:	Steve Margio, Director of Camp Baylor Camp Baylor The Baylor School P.O. Box 1337 Chattanooga, TN 37401 (423) 757-2824; Fax: (423) 756-2314 E-mail: summer@baylor.chattanooga.net Web site: http://www.baylorschool.org

Chattanooga

The McCallie School
Academic Year

Founded in 1905, McCallie is an all-boys boarding and day school offering a nationally recognized academic program to students. The school offers five endowed chairs of teaching excellence, an extensive college counseling program, a writing center where the past president of the National Writing Center Association counsels students, and an Academic Dean who directs the school's Learning Center. Recently, McCallie introduced the merit-based Honors Scholarship, an $11 million endowed program modeled after the Morehead Program at UNC-Chapel Hill. Each year McCallie will select and award 17 merit-based scholarships from a pool of nominated finalists. McCallie offers a "Coordinate Program" with the Chattanooga Girls Preparatory School; an extensive weekend activities program; music, theater, and art departments; an athletic program featuring 14 varsity sports; and a $13 million sports and activities center. McCallie offers several summer programs, including academic and sports camps.

Criteria: Application (and $50 fee); transcript; recommendations; test scores; SSAT; GPA; interview; male student.

Grade: 6-12 (day); 9-12 (boarding).

Cost: $14,000 (day); $27,615 (boarding). $1.6 million in need-based and academic financial aid is available.

Contact: David Hughes, Director of Boarding Admissions
The McCallie School
500 Dodds Avenue
Chattanooga, TN 37404
(800) 234-2163; Fax: (423) 629-2852
E-mail: boardingadmissions@mccallie.org
Web site: http://www.mccallie.org

Cookeville

PRIME (Tennessee Technological University)
Summer (six-week program)

The Pre-College Initiative for Minorities in Engineering (PRIME) is an opportunity for students whose goal is to earn a degree in engineering. Individuals pursue an intense summer program of study that includes regular academic classroom work integrated with seminars, tutorials, and other social activities. PRIME students may earn credits toward the bachelor of science degree in engineering. Some students may earn advanced placement in mathematics or English for the freshman year, depending on their performance on diagnostic tests. Students selected to participate in PRIME have a head start in earning credits toward their B.S. degree. PRIME students build a strong foundation upon which to be successful in the transition from high school or community college to a university experience and will be strongly encouraged to consider one of the many facets of the career of engineering. All students who complete the six-week program receive a $1,200 scholarship.

Criteria: Application (deadline: May 1); $15 application fee; acceptance into Tennessee Technological University; recommendations; transcript (applicants must have completed four semesters of math); GPA; ACT or SAT.

Grade: PG.

Cost: Tuition scholarships will be provided to selected students as funds are available. Room and board, books, supplies, and other materials are the responsibility of the students.

Contact: Tony Marable, Program Director
Introduction to Engineering
Tennessee Technological University
P.O. Box 5005
Cookeville, TN 38505
(931) 372-3172; Fax: (931) 372-6172
E-mail: tmarable@tntech.edu

KNOXVILLE

Appalachian Institute for Creative Learning: Summer Enrichment Session (Emory and Henry College)
July 13-26 (one- or two-week programs)

See listing on page 256 for complete information.

MEMPHIS

Rhodes Summer Writing Institute (Rhodes College)
June 15-27

Rhodes College, located on a beautiful campus in the heart of Memphis, offers the Rhodes Summer Writing Institute as a two-week, residential program that introduces talented high school students to college-level, writing-intensive coursework. Participants choose one course from offerings in creative writing or academic subjects such as literature, history, political science, or psychology. Classes are small (not more than 15 students), taught by Rhodes' professors, and are worth two hours of transferable college credit upon successful completion.

Criteria: Application; $25 non-refundable application fee; transcript; personal essay; recommendation.

Grade: Rising 11-12.

Cost: $1,275. Limited financial aid is available; contact the director for additional information.

Contact: Dr. Rebecca Finlayson, Director
Rhodes Summer Writing Institute
Rhodes College
2000 North Parkway
Memphis, TN 38112
(901) 843-3794; Fax: (901) 843-3728
E-mail: finlayson@rhodes.edu
Web site: http://www.rhodes.edu/writinginstitute

Nashville

Science Motivation Program
(Meharry Medical College, School of Graduate Studies and Research)
Mid June-late July

The Meharry Medical College Science Motivation Program is a cooperative venture between Meharry Medical College and Nashville high schools. The program was established to encourage qualified African American students to consider a career in the sciences. The goal of the program is to spark students' interest and motivation in science careers. Nashville-area high school students are selected based on interview, grades, counselor recommendation, and economic background. They will be invited to participate in a six-week, nonresidential summer program where they will conduct research in various biomedical laboratories. Preference is given to high school sophomores and juniors. The students will be involved in science projects where they will learn research techniques and develop their skills of critical thinking and analytical reasoning. As part of this experience, research papers will be presented, and there will be opportunities to visit various special facilities for exposure to state-of-the-art biotechnology.

Criteria: Application (deadline: April 30); transcript; personal essay; recommendations; interview; African American student; interest in science.

Grade: Rising 10-12.

Cost: No cost for program. Participants receive a stipend.

Contact: Fredrick H. Hamilton, Assistant Dean
School of Graduate Studies and Research
Meharry Medical College
1005 D. B. Todd, Jr. Boulevard
Nashville, TN 37208
(615) 327-6533; Fax: (615) 321-2933
E-mail: fhamilton@mail.mmc.edu

Vanderbilt Program for Talented Youth (Vanderbilt University)
June 8-28 (Session 1); July 6-26 (Session 2)

Vanderbilt University offers an intensive, enriched three-week summer residential program for academically talented youth. The goal of Vandy PTY is to provide a highly stimulating and challenging intellectual environment, while allowing students to have lots of fun and form lasting friendships. Each student will enroll in one course—mathematics, computer science, creative writing, American history, chemistry, genetics, theatre arts, statistics, or environmental science—for nearly 100 hours of instructional contact. The courses are taught by instructors with experience in teaching gifted students. Full-time teaching assistants help the instructors provide individual attention to each student. Students will reside in air-conditioned housing under the supervision of resident staff. They will eat all meals in Vanderbilt dining halls and will have access to Vanderbilt recreational facilities as well as learning facilities such as the libraries and computer labs.

Criteria: Application (and fee); ACT, SAT, PSAT, or PLAN.

Grade: 7-11.

Cost: $2,300. Limited need-based financial aid is available.

Contact: Laura Montgomery, Program Coordinator
Vanderbilt Program for Talented Youth
Vanderbilt University, GPC 506
Nashville, TN 37203
(615) 322-8261; Fax: (615) 322-3457
E-mail: pty.peabody@vanderbilt.edu
Web site: http://peabody.vanderbilt.edu/pty

SEWANEE

Sewanee Young Writers' Conference (University of the South)
June 29-July 13

The Sewanee Young Writers' Conference offers intensive workshops in fiction and poetry to serious high school-aged writers. Drawing upon the resources of the well-known Sewanee Writers' Conference (for adults), the Young Writers' Conference is able to recruit a distinguished faculty of workshop leaders, who have in recent years included Daniel Anderson, A. Manette Ansay, Tony Earley, Kerry Madden-Lunsford, Ellen Slezak, and Philip Stephens. Enrollment is limited to 40 students, each of whom spends most of each morning in one of four workshops. Other activities include readings by distinguished visiting writers (Ernest Gaines, Horton Foote, Andrew Hudgins, Alice McDermott, and Ann Patchett have attended recently) and lectures by members of the University of the South English faculty. The 10,000-acre university domain also offers ample recreational opportunity, including hiking, swimming, and access to the new Fowler Sports and Fitness Center.

Criteria: Application; recommendations; sample of work.

Grade: 9-12.

Cost: $1,350.

Contact: Elizabeth Grammer, Co-Director
Sewanee Young Writers' Conference
University of the South
735 University Avenue
Sewanee, TN 37383
(931) 598-1541; Fax: (931) 598-1145
E-mail: egrammer@sewanee.edu

Sewanee

St. Andrew's-Sewanee School
Academic Year

St. Andrew's-Sewanee School (SAS) is one of the oldest Episcopal boarding schools in the country. The school is coeducational with boarding in grades 9-12 and a day program for grades 7-12. Located on a scenic, 550-acre campus adjoining the University of the South (Sewanee), where qualified students may take college courses for credit, SAS offers an academic program for highly motivated students in an environment known for its commitment to the values of community and family. Students from 10 countries (including Jamaica, Germany, and Korea) and 19 states (including California, Michigan, Washington, North Carolina, and Georgia) make up the student body of 250. In addition to an extensive academic curriculum, SAS also prides itself on their afternoon programs. Students improve their skills through participation in a variety of activities such as mountain biking, outing/wilderness, yearbook, community service, drama, and eleven varsity sports.

Criteria: Application (and fee); transcript; teacher recommendations; test scores; interview.

Grade: 7-12.

Cost: $26,760 (boarding); $10,575 (day).

Contact: Brian Chatterley, Director of Admission and Financial Aid
St. Andrew's-Sewanee School
290 Quintard Road
Sewanee, TN 37375-3000
(866) 513-8290, (931) 598-5651; Fax: (931) 598-0039
E-mail: admissions@sasweb.org
Web site: http://www.sasweb.org

TEXAS

Linda Phemister, Director, Gifted and Talented Education
Advanced Academic Services
Texas Education Agency
1701 North Congress Avenue
Austin, TX 78701-1494
(512) 463-9455; Fax: (512) 305-8920
E-mail: lphemist@tmail.tea.state.tx.us

Ann Wink, Director, Elementary Gifted Programs
Advanced Academic Services
Texas Education Agency
1701 North Congress Avenue
Austin, TX 78701-1494
(512) 463-9455; Fax: (512) 305-8920
E-mail: awink@tea.state.tx.us

STATE ASSOCIATION

Texas Association for the Gifted and Talented
Jay McIntire, Executive Director
406 East 11th Street, Suite 310
Austin, TX 78701-2617
(512) 499-8248; Fax: (512) 499-8264
E-mail: txgifted_jmcintire@yahoo.com
Web site: http://www.txgifted.org

REGIONAL TALENT SEARCH

Duke University Talent Identification Program
See listing on page 2 for complete information.

Cooperative Program

TAG—Talented and Gifted Program
(Gifted Students Institute, Southern Methodist University)
July

TAG is open to students entering grades 8-10. During this three-week program, students participate in two stimulating classes chosen from a wide selection of SMU credit and non-credit courses. Cultural enrichment activities are provided for all TAG students. Three-hour credit courses include Mathematical Sciences, Economics, Political Science, Electronic Technologies, Psychology, Philosophy, and Ethics. Non-credit courses include Literature and Writing, Computer Science, Engineering, Shakespeare, Theater Arts, Film, Economics, Leadership, Public Discourse, Mathematics, Painting and Drawing, Physics, Geography, and Paleontology. **This program is offered through cooperative efforts with the Duke University Talent Identification Program.**

Criteria: Application (and fee); transcript; teacher recommendation; GPA; SAT or ACT; gifted and talented. Enrollment is limited each session to 150; apply as soon as possible.

Grade: Rising 8-10.

Cost: $1,390 (estimated tuition), $850 (estimated room and board). Need-based scholarships are available.

Contact: Marilyn Swanson, Assistant Director
Gifted Students Institute -TAG
Southern Methodist University
P.O. Box 750383
Dallas, TX 75275-0383
(214) 768-5437
E-mail: gifted@mail.smu.edu

Arlington

CATS SUMMERSTARS '03: Comprehensive Theatre Workshop
(Creative Arts Theatre & School, Inc.)
July 12-26

CATS SUMMERSTARS '03 is a two-week residential and commuter program that provides a laboratory where students work and learn with professionals in many aspects of the theatre, specifically acting, singing, and dancing. CATS provides the stage, studio and shop space, tools, costumes, and professional guidance needed to create a performance. Students provide the talent. In the mornings, students (rising 7-12) rotate among classes in acting styles and techniques, music, and movement. Afternoons are devoted to production rehearsals, set and prop building, costuming, and choreography. The production focus is a major musical. The workday is 9:00 a.m. to 5:30 p.m. On the final Saturday, a full-fledged production (with two performances) will be presented for family, friends, and the public. Local families house out-of-town students. A field trip to a professional theatre performance is included.

Criteria: Application; personal essay; teacher recommendation; test scores.

Grade: Rising 7-12.

Cost: $850 (residential); $650 (commuters); $250 (host family). Limited financial aid is available.

Contact: Kathey Ward, Artistic Director
           CATS SUMMERSTARS '03
           Creative Arts Theatre & School, Inc.
           1100 West Randol Mill Road
           Arlington, TX 76012
           (817) 861-CATS, (817) 265-8512; Fax: (817) 274-0793
           E-mail: cats@creativearts.org
           Web site: http://www.creativearts.org

ARLINGTON

Honors Academy
(University of Texas at Arlington Honors College)
Year-round

The University of Texas at Arlington Honors College offers an outstanding program of study for exceptionally motivated high school students. While meeting high school graduation requirements, students may earn up to 13 college credit hours during the summer, or 6 credit hours during fall and spring semesters. They may choose from a diverse selection of college courses. Students are challenged to investigate new ideas from a variety of disciplinary perspectives and while interacting with top research faculty. Students taking six or more hours prior to high school graduation and making a "B" or better in their university coursework will be awarded a $1,500 per year scholarship upon their acceptance as entering freshmen at UTA Honors College.

Criteria: Application ($25 application fee); SAT, ACT, or PSAT (minimum scores: 120 PSAT, 1200 SAT, 27 ACT).

Grade: 9-12.

Cost: $250 per 3 credit hour course (price reflects student fee waivers and scholarship for qualified students). Cost is approximate.

Contact: Sandra K. Campbell, Assistant Dean
           Honors College
           University of Texas at Arlington
           P.O. Box 19222
           Arlington, TX 76019
           (817) 272-7215; Fax: (817) 272-7217
           E-mail: honorsacademy@honors.uta.edu
           Web site: http://honors.uta.edu

BEAUMONT

Texas Academy of Leadership in the Humanities (Lamar University)
Academic Year

The Texas Academy of Leadership in the Humanities is a nationally recognized residential honors program that allows juniors and seniors in high school to complete their last two years of high school credits and their first two years of college requirements concurrently. Successfully completing university classes, Academy students leave the program with a high school diploma and 60 or more college hours. Because the program is tuition-free, students save not only valuable time but also thousands of dollars in college expenses.

Criteria: Application; transcript; personal essay; recommendations; test scores; GPA; SAT; interview.

Grade: 11-12.

Cost: Tuition-free. Financial aid is available for books and housing.

Contact: Dr. Mary Gagné, Director
Texas Academy of Leadership in the Humanities
Lamar University
P.O. Box 10062
Beaumont, TX 77710
(409) 839-2995; Fax: (409) 839-2991
E-mail: talh@hal.lamar.edu
Web site: http://hal.lamar.edu/~talh

COLLEGE STATION

Youth Adventure Program (Texas A&M University)
June 15-July 19 (one-week sessions)

The Youth Adventure Program is a series of one-week "unique topic" courses of study directed by university faculty. Students select one course per week and attend class sessions twice daily. In the afternoons and evenings, the campers are able to participate in social activities, innovative events, and interactive games. Students have access to the Texas A&M Recreation Center and also compete in the "Wacky Olympic" competition. The camp is residential, and all students are housed in a luxury dorm with adult supervision. Courses under consideration for 2003 include: Law School, Veterinary Medicine, Computer Design, Advanced Graphics and Animation, Journalism, Psychology, Architecture: Designing Cities of the Future, Medical School, Interpreting Music, Television Communication, Astronomy/Space Science, Creative Writing, Photography, and Theater Arts. Visit their Web site for additional information.

Criteria: Application (and fee).

Grade: Rising 6-12.

Cost: $699 (each session).

Contact: Jay Woodward, Director of the Youth Adventure Program
Institute for the Gifted and Talented
4225 TAMU
College Station, TX 77843-4225
(979) 845-1802; Fax: (979) 862-1256
E-mail: gifted@coe.tamu.edu
Web site: http://www.globalnets.com/yap

DALLAS

Episcopal School of Dallas
Academic Year

The Episcopal School of Dallas (ESD) in Dallas, Texas is a coeducational, college preparatory day school enrolling students from pre-elementary through twelfth grade. As an independent, faith-centered school, ESD strives to enhance the intellectual, physical, spiritual, and social growth of its students. Open to students of all faiths and backgrounds, the school seeks to provide a flexible, traditional curriculum that is complimented by chapel attendance, studies in religion, an extensive community service program, and an outstanding program in outdoor education. Students at ESD enjoy small classes, averaging sixteen students per class, led by a talented and experienced faculty. Over sixty percent of the school's 180 faculty and staff members hold advanced degrees. The school regularly places one hundred percent of its graduating seniors at four-year colleges and universities. Over fifty percent of the Class of 2001 received scholarships and awards totaling more than $3,000,000, and twenty-one percent of the class was recognized by the National Merit Scholarship Corporation.

Criteria: Application (deadline: January 10); $175 application fee; transcript; personal essay; recommendations; test scores; ISEE; interview.

Grade: PreK-12.

Cost: $5,600-$16,300. More than $900,000 in financial aid is available.

Contact: Ruth Burke, Director of Admission and Financial Aid
Episcopal School of Dallas
4100 Merrell Road
Dallas, TX 75229
(214) 358-4368; Fax: (214) 353-5872
E-mail: burker@esdallas.org
Web site: http://www.esdallas.org/esd/

DALLAS

College Experience (Southern Methodist University)
June 29-July 31

Academically talented high school students can get a head start on college and a taste of campus life during this exciting five-week summer program at SMU. The selection of college-credit subjects for morning classes includes philosophy, English, math, psychology, history, and government. In the afternoon, all College Experience students will participate in a "core" class or humanities overview class for three hours of college credit. Students who elect to live in the CE residence hall will participate in special cultural, educational, and recreational activities. Southern Methodist University is a private coeducational institute located in Dallas, Texas. The 164-acre campus, replete with Georgian architecture, is home to numerous theaters, concert halls, and a library collection of over two million volumes. Enrollment is limited to sixty students. Applications are available on their Web site after January 1.

Criteria: Application; transcript; recommendations; academic ability and motivation; GPA; SAT or ACT.

Grade: Rising 11-12.

Cost: $1,710 (estimated tuition); $1,250 (estimated fee for room and board; 2002 costs). Limited need-based financial aid is available (early application is highly recommended).

Contact: Marilyn Swanson, Assistant Director
Gifted Students Institute - College Experience
Southern Methodist University
P.O. Box 750383
Dallas, TX 75275-0383
(214) 768-5437; Fax: (214) 768-3147
E-mail: gifted@smu.edu
Web site: http://www.smu.edu/ce

DENTON

Access to the Careers in the Sciences (ACES, Texas Woman's University)
June 10-27 (Session 1); June 15-27 (Session 2); July 20-August 1 (Session 3)

The Access to the Careers in the Sciences (ACES) Camps focus on career opportunities for women in the mathematics and science fields. While providing the information and the hands-on experiences needed to make realistic career choices, the residential camps also introduce girls to women who have already established themselves in these careers. These women give ACES participants an accurate picture of what each job entails and how to prepare for this job in terms of education and experience. The camps enable young women to see, hear, and experience what a career in a mathematics or science field might be like while they can still choose the paths that might lead them to one of these careers. Possible courses for ACES 2003 may include Anatomy and Physiology, Aquatic Science, Chemistry, Engineering, Forensic Science, Genetics, Health Care, Marine Biology, Microbiology, Movement Science, Neuroscience, Physics, and Physical Therapy. Girls attending Session 1 will receive college credit. Check the Web site for more information.

Criteria:	Application (deadline: April 25); $30 application fee; transcript; personal essay; recommendations.
Grade:	6-12.
Cost:	$1,500 ($2,000 for non-Texans; session 1). $850 (sessions 2 and 3).
Contact:	Catherine Banks, Director of ACES Texas Woman's University P.O. Box 425846 Denton, TX 76204-5846 (800) 860-2237, (940) 898-2769; Fax: (940) 898-2767 E-mail: ACES@twu.edu Web site: http://www.twu.edu/smcw

DENTON

Summer Math Institute
(Texas Academy of Mathematics and Science, University of North Texas)
July 6-26

SMI is an intensive program for highly motivated students who wish to accelerate their mathematics education. Students will attend daily classes taught by experienced mathematics teachers in Algebra I, Algebra II, Geometry, or Precalculus. The classroom setting is highly interactive and easily adapted to each individual student's ability and pace. Students will live in a residence hall at the University of North Texas and be supervised by experienced residence life personnel. During free time in the evenings and on weekends, participants will have the opportunity to interact with other academically driven peers in fun, educational recreational activities and field trips.

Criteria:	Application; transcript; recommendations; GPA.
Grade:	Rising 7-10.
Cost:	$2,000 (includes room and board, classroom supplies, and recreational activities).
Contact:	Wendy Boyd-Brown, Academic Counselor Texas Academy of Mathematics and Science The University of North Texas P.O. Box 305309 Denton, TX 76203 (940) 565-4033; Fax: (940) 369-8796 E-mail: smi@tamsadmn.unt.edu Web site: http://www.tams.unt.edu

DENTON

Texas Academy of Mathematics and Science (University of North Texas)
Academic Year

The Texas Academy of Mathematics and Science is a statewide, coeducational, residential, early admissions program at the University of North Texas for high-ability students with demonstrated talent and aptitude in science and mathematics. Texas students are eligible to enter the Academy following the tenth grade. They complete the final two years of high school and the first two years of college concurrently by taking college courses taught by full-time faculty members of the University of North Texas. Those who successfully complete this program receive their high school diplomas from Texas Academy and are eligible to transfer to most universities with junior-level college standing.

Criteria: Application; personal essay; SAT; transcript; parent statement; recommendations; GPA; interview; Texas resident.

Grade: 11.

Cost: $4,096 (approximate cost per academic year for room and board). Scholarships provide for tuition, fees, and books for a reasonable course load. Financial aid is available.

Contact: Dr. Brent M. Jones, Director of Admissions
Texas Academy of Mathematics and Science
The University of North Texas
P.O. Box 305309
Denton, TX 76203-5309
(800) 241-TAMS, (940) 565-4369; Fax: (940) 369-8796
E-mail: jones@tams.unt.edu

GALVESTON

Sea Camp (Texas A & M University at Galveston)
June 1-August 2 (one-week sessions)

Sea Camp offers weeklong adventure exploring the wonders of the marine environment. At **Sea Camp I**, campers live on campus and have access to research vessels, oceanographic equipment, laboratory facilities, and a professional staff, enabling them to learn about the ocean through firsthand experiences. Students trawl from the Earl L. Milan, seine in the marsh, visit a sea turtle lab, and attend a marine mammal workshop. Evening activities include a poolside pizza party as well as a beach cookout. **Sea Camp II** is a continuation of Sea Camp I. **Sea Camp III** teaches marine biology/ecology through fishing. **Sea Camp IV** is an intense workshop on marine mammals. **Sea Camp V** camps out along the Texas coast. **Sea Camp VI** studies mangroves and coral reefs in Belize. **Sea Camp VII** explores the Quintana Roo Peninsula of Mexico to study Mayan culture and marine life. Other camps focus on careers, marine chemistry, and coastal photography.

Criteria: Application (and $125 application fee).

Grade: Rising 5-12.

Cost: $725-$775 (inside U.S.); $1,800 (outside U.S.); (scholarship packets available upon request).

Contact: Daisy Duerson, Registrar
           Sea Camp
           Texas A & M University at Galveston
           P.O. Box 1675
           Galveston, TX 77553
           (409) 740-4525; Fax: (409) 740-4894
           E-mail: seacamp@tamug.tamu.edu
           Web site: http://www.tamug.tamu.edu/~seacamp

GALVESTON

TAG—Talented and Gifted Distinguished Achievement Summer Program (Texas A&M University at Galveston)
June 14-22 (Session 1); July 5-13 (Session 2)

Texas A&M University at Galveston will offer the twenty-third annual Talented and Gifted Distinguished Achievement Summer Program for gifted students. Participation in these academically advanced courses allows each student the opportunity to complete requirements necessary to graduate from high school with the Distinguished Achievement Degree (DAD). First session courses: Marine Biology, Veterinary Medicine, and Scuba/Research Diving. Second session courses: Marine Biology, Advanced Skills Diving, and Commercial Web Design. Instructors are university faculty, industry professionals and graduate students. Classroom teachers receive professional development hours for their participation as mentor/counselors. Evidence of high academic ability must be submitted with the application.

Criteria: Application (and fee); GPA.

Grade: Rising 8-12.

Cost: $850 (Non-DAD: 8 nights); $975 (DAD: 10 nights)

Contact: Kyle Jackson, Director
           TAG Distinguished Achievement
           Texas A&M University-Galveston
           P.O. Box 1675
           Galveston, TX 77553-1675
           (409) 740-4924; Fax: (409) 740-4994
           E-mail: jacksonk@tamug.edu
           Web site: http://www.tamug.edu/tag

Houston

Rice University Summer School for Grades 8-12 (Rice University)
June 9-July 17

Each summer for the past 38 years, students in grades 8 through 12 have spent six weeks on the Rice campus participating in a wide variety of learning activities. Most students indicate they came to Rice because of a special interest in certain courses that are not offered in their schools, to review a difficult subject, or to prepare for future schoolwork. At this six-week, commuter program, students take courses in painting and sculpture, creative writing, and dramatics. They become absorbed in laboratory work, debates on social issues, and earnest attempts at conversing in foreign languages. Students take field trips to complement some courses and become involved in sports and the intricacies of operating a computer. The summer school seeks to create an academically serious program that aspires to give students an intellectual advantage in their academic work.

Criteria: Application; commuter only.

Grade: Rising 8-12.

Cost: $700 (approximate cost).

Contact: Olga Trejo, Program Coordinator
Summer School for Grades 8-12
Rice University
6100 Main Street MS-145
Houston, TX 77005
(713) 348-4967; Fax: (713) 348-5459
E-mail: edsumsch@rice.edu
Web site: http://www.ruf.rice.edu/~edsumsch/

Lubbock

Science: It's a Girl Thing (Texas Tech University)
June 23-26 (Session 1); July 21-24 (Session 2)

This residential camp is co-sponsored by the Texas Tech Women's Studies Organization. The goals of the program are to provide girls with strong role models, spark interest in the pursuit of scientific study and to introduce economically disadvantaged girls to a collegiate experience. Apply early; the camp fills quickly.

Criteria: Application; personal essay; teacher nomination.

Grade: Rising 6-7.

Cost: $245. Financial aid is available.

Contact: Martha Hise, Director
Science: It's a Girl Thing
Texas Tech University
P.O. Box 41008
Lubbock, TX 79409
(806) 742-2420; Fax: (906) 742-0480
E-mail: m.hise@ttu.edu
Web site: http://www.ttu.edu/ideal

Lubbock

Shake Hands With Your Future
(Institute for the Development and Enrichment of Advanced Learners, Texas Tech University)
June 8-20 (Session 1); July 6-11 (Session 2)

Shake Hands With Your Future presents opportunities for gifted and talented youth to experience extraordinary academic offerings. Students choose to attend two classes that meet Monday through Friday. Some class choices include theatre, animal science, chemistry, engineering, photography, and journalism. Faculty guide students through investigations of complex, diverse subject matter and the research process. In the evenings and on weekends, campers participate in a variety of activities including films, sports, field trips, and a talent show.

Criteria: Application; personal essay; recommendations; test scores.

Grade: Rising 8-11 (Session 1); rising 4-7 (Session 2).

Cost: $935 (Session 1: residential); $530 (Session 2: residential); $395 (Session 2: commuter); $450 (Session 2: commuter with participation in evening recreation).

Contact: Martha Hise, Director
Shake Hands With Your Future
Texas Tech University
P.O. Box 41008
Lubbock, TX 79409
(806) 742-2420; Fax: (806) 742-0480
E-mail: m.hise@ttu.edu
Web site: http://www.ttu.edu/ideal

San Antonio

Saint Mary's Hall
Academic Year

Saint Mary's Hall, Texas' oldest boarding school, has been educating young men and women for over 120 years. Located on 60 acres in San Antonio, the school is committed to the intellectual growth and personal development of each student. Saint Mary's Hall offers a Montessori preschool, a traditional kindergarten, grades 1-12, English as a Second Language, and a postgraduate year. In Upper School, a college preparatory curriculum (including honors and 23 AP courses) is enriched with fine art offerings and 15 Upper School varsity sports, and 11 Middle School sports. One hundred percent of Saint Mary's Hall graduates are accepted at selective colleges across the nation. Recent graduates were accepted at Trinity, the University of Texas at Austin, Southern Methodist, Vanderbilt, Texas A&M, University of the Incarnate Word, University of Southern California, Duke, Georgetown, and the University of Colorado at Boulder.

Criteria: Application (and fee); transcript; personal essay; recommendations; ISEE; interview.

Grade: PreK-12, PG.

Cost: $5,330-$13,650. Merit-based scholarships for rising grade 9 students and need-based financial aid are available.

Contact: Elena D. Hicks, Director of Admission
Saint Mary's Hall
9401 Starcrest Drive
San Antonio, TX 78217
(210) 483-9234; Fax: (210) 655-5211
E-mail: admissions@smhall.org
Web site: http://www.smhall.org

SeaWorld/Busch Gardens Adventure Camps (SeaWorld San Antonio)
Year-round

Junior Expedition Camp (grade 4-6) and **Expedition Camp** (grades 6-8) allow campers to explore the marvels of marine live at SeaWorld and at the beaches and wetlands along the Texas Coast. **Eco-Oddysea** (grade 6-9) is an adventure that blends the excitement and wonder of SeaWorld and its animals with a trip to experience the history and ecosystems of the Trinity River, Galveston Bay. **Career Camp** (grade 9-12), **Advanced Careers Camp** (grade 10-12), and **Marine Zoological Careers** (college) are provide experiences for students to discover, first-hand, if a career working with animals is in their future. Other camps at SeaWorld include **Teacher Camps** for educators, **Adventure Camp for Families** (children age 8-18, with parents) and **Adventure Camp for Adults** (adults age 19+).

Criteria: Transcript; personal essay; interview; recommendations.

Grade: 4-adult.

Cost: $300-$1,350.

Contact: Ann Quinn, Education Manager
           SeaWorld/Busch Gardens Adventure Camps
           SeaWorld San Antonio
           10500 SeaWorld Drive
           San Antonio, TX 78251-3002
           (210) 523-3608; Fax: (210) 523-3898
           E-mail: ann.quinn@seaworld.com
           Web site: http://www.seaworld.org

San Marcos

14th Annual SWT Honors Summer Math Camp (Southwest Texas State University)
June 15 - July 26

The goal of the SWT Honors Summer Math Camp is to excite talented young students about doing mathematics, to teach students to reason rigorously and precisely, and to develop questioning minds. The focus on number theory is modeled after the Ross Summer Program at Ohio State, teaching students to "think deeply of simple things" (Arnold Ross). Students work together exploring new ideas and share in the excitement of finding the simple mathematical ideas which underline and explain seemingly complex problems. First year students take courses in elementary number theory, Mathematica computer programming, and an honors seminar. Returning students study combinatorics, analysis, and abstract algebra. Students may also work on a supervised Siemens Competition research project. Extracurricular activities include weekly seminars by guest speakers, picnics, recreation each afternoon including aerobics, volleyball, basketball, or tennis, and weekend excursions which give the participants a chance to relax and enjoy the local surroundings.

Criteria: Application; transcript; personal essay; recommendations; test scores; PSAT; SAT; GPA.

Grade: Rising 10-12.

Cost: $1,750. Includes room, board, books, supplies, and activities. Scholarships are available based on need.

Contact: Professor Max Warshauer
            SWT Honors Summer Math Camp
            Southwest Texas State University
            601 University Drive
            San Marcos, TX 78666
            (512) 245-3439; Fax: (512) 245-1469
            E-mail: max@swt.edu
            Web site: http://www.swt.edu/mathworks

Seguin

Lone Star Scholars Academy (Texas Lutheran University)
June 15-28

The Lone Star Scholars Academy (LSSA) is a two-week residential opportunity on the Texas Lutheran University campus for academically talented high school students. Participants take two college credit courses from various disciplines that are designed specifically for the Academy. Past representative courses include American Sign Language, All the World's a Stage, Aquatic and Marine Ecosystems, Understanding Our Differences: The DNA Way, and Protest and Patriotism. In addition to the classroom experience, students build relationships, venture on field trips, utilize state-of-the-art fitness equipment, engage in friendly competition, and produce a talent show. The LSSA faculty includes Texas Lutheran University faculty, area educators, and visiting faculty from throughout the United States.

Criteria: Application (deadline: June 1); transcript; recommendations; test scores; class rank.

Grade: 10-12.

Cost: $1,195. Financial aid is available.

Contact: Steve Vrooman, LSSA Director
Lone Star Scholars Academy
Texas Lutheran University
1000 W. Court Street
Seguin, TX 78155
(830) 372-8050; Fax: (830) 372-8096
E-mail: admissions@tlu.edu
Web site: http://www.tlu.edu

Waco

High School Summer Science Research Fellowship Program (Baylor University)
May 26-June 27

The High School Summer Science Research Fellowship Program at Baylor University offers superior high school students hands-on research experience by working with university science professors in many disciplines. Approximately ten students who have completed their junior year will be selected for this research summer program which allows each student to earn one semester hour of college credit. Students will be involved in exciting research projects with Baylor professors and their research groups. They will gain familiarity with the operation of instruments and interpretation of data obtained by techniques not usually available in high school laboratories. Participants will develop effective working relationships with scientists, enhancing specific interests in and across scientific disciplines. They will have the opportunity to associate with other exceptional students having similar interests and will take part in science and technology seminars and group social activities.

Criteria: Application (deadline: April 1); transcript; personal essay; recommendations; PSAT.

Grade: Rising 12.

Cost: $535 (room, board, and student fee; approximate costs). Limited financial aid is available.

Contact: Bernice Helpert, Administrative Associate
High School Summer Science Research Fellowship Program
Baylor University
P.O. Box 97344
Waco, TX 76798
(254) 710-4288; Fax: (254) 710-3639
E-mail: bernice_helpert@baylor.edu
Web site: http://www.baylor.edu/~Research/high_school.html

WACO

Interdisciplinary Creative Problem Solving Conference (Baylor University)
February 28-March 1

The Interdisciplinary Creative Problem Solving Conference (ICPSC) at Baylor University is an exciting conference designed for gifted students in grades eight through twelve. Teams of students are led by exceptional master teachers of the gifted in the process of Creative Problem Solving to address a critical problem. Students debate important issues, solve a crisis, and work as a team toward the goal of presenting their solution to the problem. Students must have a designated educator, parent, or guardian in attendance at the conference as their sponsor. Attending educators receive 12 hours of gifted professional development credit along with timesaving lesson plans and a comprehensive training packet.

Criteria: Application (deadline: February 10); gifted and talented student with an accompanying sponsor.

Grade: Rising 8-12.

Cost: $75 (students); $90 (teachers).

Contact: Dr. Mary M. Witte, Director
Baylor University
P.O. Box 97282
Waco, TX 76798-7282
(254) 710-2171; Fax: (254) 710-4909
E-mail: k-12andProfDev@baylor.edu
Web site: http://www.baylor.edu/SOE/CCLE

Waco

University for Young People (Baylor University)
June 3-28

The University for Young People (UYP) at Baylor University is now in its nineteenth year. This commuter program, designed for gifted students, consists of two, two-week sessions for students entering grades one through twelve. Students in grades four through twelve choose 1-4 classes that meet one and one-half hours per day. Outstanding professors on the Baylor faculty and other exceptional teachers of the gifted teach the students. Students may select from courses in art, biology, chemistry, communications, computers, creative writing, drama, foreign languages, geology, leadership, mathematics, and social studies. Average class size is 14. Younger UYP students entering grades one through four participate in an interdisciplinary, thematic curriculum simulation. During the session, students meet to discover archaeological treasures, recreate diverse environments, or develop international space stations, or explore the fine arts.

Criteria: Application (and fee); teacher report; parent statement; sample of work; test scores.

Grade: Rising 1-12.

Cost: $75 (per 1.5-hour class). Some classes require additional lab or supply fees.

Contact: Dr. Mary M. Witte, Director
Baylor University
P.O. Box 97282
Waco, TX 76798-7282
(254) 710-2171; Fax: (254) 710-4909
E-mail: k-12andProfDev@baylor.edu
Web site: http://www.baylor.edu/SOE/CCLE

UTAH

STATE DIRECTOR

Connie Amos, Gifted and Talented Education Specialist
Utah Office of Education
250 East 500 South
Salt Lake City, UT 84111
(801) 538-7743; Fax: (801) 538-7769

STATE ASSOCIATION

Utah Association for Gifted Children

The Utah Association for Gifted Children is a nonprofit organization established in 1985 to improve the opportunities for gifted and talented students in the state of Utah. Local groups of parents, teachers, and administrators serve as public advocates for gifted children and also disseminate information concerning gifted and talented education to educators, parents, and other interested persons. The mission of the Utah Association for Gifted Children is to bring together the many groups and individuals who care about the education of the gifted and talented students in the state. The association accomplishes this by networking with state and district coordinators of gifted programs, principals, teachers, affiliate members, and others interested in gifted education to provide up-to-date information, to discuss issues and concerns and to advocate for continued support and development of gifted/talented programs.

Dr. Scott Hunsaker, President
P.O. Box 9332
Salt Lake City, UT 84109
801/461-9002
E-mail: scotth@coe.usu.edu

REGIONAL TALENT SEARCH

Rocky Mountain Talent Search (University of Denver)
See listing on page 5 for complete information.

VERMONT

State Director

Dr. Carol Story, Consultant, Gifted Education
Vermont Department of Education
c/o Johnson State College
337 College Hill
Johnson, VT 05656
(802) 635-1321; E-mail: storyc@badger.jsc.vsc.edu

State Association

Vermont Council for Gifted Education

The Vermont Council for Gifted Education (VCGE) is a non-profit organization of educators, parents, and others who recognize the need to provide appropriate education and support for gifted and talented students. VCGE works actively on the local, state, and national levels to help educators and parents foster the growth and development of children and youth who have exceptional abilities, talents, and needs.

Ellen Koier, President
337 College Hill
Johnson, VT 05656
E-mail: ekoier@cambridge.k12.vt.us

Regional Talent Search

Center for Talented Youth (The Johns Hopkins University)
See listing on page 4 for complete information.

BENNINGTON

Excel at Bennington College (Putney Student Travel)
June-August (Three-, four-, and seven-week programs)

See listing on page 9 for complete information.

BURLINGTON

Engineering, Mathematics, and Computer Sciences Summer Institute (University of Vermont, College of Engineering and Mathematics)
June 21-29

Students explore aerospace, biomedical, civil, mechanical, and electrical engineering disciplines as well as statistics, mathematics, and computer applications through hands-on activities and presentations by professional guest speakers and university faculty. Tours include the IBM facility which features state-of-the-art computer-related technology, the Burlington waste water facility, the Chittenden solid waste district, and the Ben & Jerry's Homemade plant in Waterbury. Students build robots and participate in a robot war competition, as well as write poems for a poetry contest, and compose an oath for the Technocratic Oath Competition. Prizes and trophies are given to the winners in each category at the closing ceremony. Students are housed in campus dorms. The program includes presentations on college survival strategies and information regarding financial aid. Students gain insight into career opportunities and develop a first-hand awareness of the nature of college life.

Criteria: Application (and fee); transcript; PSAT; SAT; GPA.

Grade: Rising 10-11.

Cost: $925. Multicultural students may qualify for financial assistance.

Contact: Dawn Densmore, Director
UVM, College of Engineering and Mathematics
109 Votey, 33 Colchester Avenue
Burlington, VT 05405
(802) 656-8748; Fax: (802) 656-8802
E-mail: densmore@emba.uvm.edu
Web site: http://www.emba.uvm.edu/summer/2002/index/html

Santa Barbara

Summer Discovery Pre-College Enrichment Programs
June-August (three- to six-week programs)

See listing on page 12 for complete information.

St. Johnsbury

St. Johnsbury Academy
Academic Year

Named one of the nation's exemplary schools by the United States Department of Education and described by The Wall Street Journal as "hardly your ordinary high school", St. Johnsbury combines the best features of a large independent school—extraordinary facilities, experienced faculty, and extensive curriculum—with the personal attention, close community, and nurturing environment of a small boarding school. Students enjoy myriad opportunities in the fine and performing arts, a strong athletic program, a pre-engineering curriculum, and challenging academics. One of the nation's only tuition voucher systems ensures an extremely diverse student body. St. Johnsbury Academy is attractive to students seeking an outstanding educational opportunity in a safe, small-town environment.

Criteria: Application (and fee); transcript; personal essay; recommendations; test scores.

Grade: 9-12, PG.

Cost: $25,469 (boarding: 2002-2003 academic year); $8,655 (day: 2002-2003). Financial aid is available.

Contact: John J. Cummings, Director of Admission
St. Johnsbury Academy
1000 Main Street
St. Johnsbury, VT 05819
(802) 751-2130; Fax: (802) 748-5463
E-mail: admissions@stj.k12.vt.us
Web site: http://www.stjohnsburyacademy.org

VIRGINIA

State Director

Dr. Barbara McGonagill, Specialist
Governor's Schools and Gifted Education
Virginia Department of Education
Office. of Elementary & Middle School
P.O. Box 2120
Richmond, VA 23218-2120
(804) 225-2884; Fax: (804) 786-1703
E-mail: bmcgonag@pen.k12.va.us

State Association

Virginia Association for the Gifted
Elissa Brown, President
P.O. Box 26212
Richmond, VA 23260
(804) 355-5945; Fax: (804) 355-5137
E-mail: vagifted@attbi.com
Web site: http://www.vagifted.org

Regional Talent Search

Center for Talented Youth (The Johns Hopkins University)
See listing on page 4 for complete information.

Locations Throughout Virginia

Virginia Governor's Schools (Virginia Department of Education)
Academic Year

Initiated in 1973, Virginia now has a network of 16 Academic-Year Governor's Schools (AYGS) serving high school students across the Commonwealth. While most programs emphasize mathematics, science, and technology, some have established alternative focuses. Students identified as gifted in the local school districts are eligible to apply for the AYGS in which their school divisions participate. Three schools function as stand alone high schools from which students receive diplomas. Others are half-day schools with students returning to their home schools for the completion of certain courses required in Virginia Standards of Accreditation. All are funded through state and local money. While most serve juniors and seniors, some serve freshmen and sophomores as well. Several schools use technology as the mode of instruction, with one school's program operating at more than 40 sites through the Internet and ITV.

Criteria:	Vary according to the specific program.
Grade:	9-12.
Cost:	None.
Contact:	Local gifted program administrator or see Web site: http://www.pen.k12.va.us/VDOE/Instruction/Govschools/

Locations throughout Virginia

Summer Regional Governor's Schools
Summer dates vary with location

The Commonwealth of Virginia and local school divisions offer a variety of summer regional programs for public, private, and home-schooled students. The twenty programs have been developed by regional boards to provide specific opportunities to students in the localities. Programs range in length from five days to one month. All, with the exception of one, are day programs that serve a variety of ages and offer programs with a variety of focuses.

Criteria: Based on the application process of the localities involved; Virginia resident.

Grade: Varies with location.

Cost: None.

Contact: Local gifted education coordinator, headmaster or see Web site: http://www.pen.k12.va.us/VDOE/Instruction/Govschools/

Summer Residential Governor's Schools
Summer dates vary with location

The Commonwealth of Virginia sponsors seven Summer Residential Governor's Schools serving the needs of gifted rising juniors and seniors. The programs are open to public school, private school, and home-schooled students who are residents of the Commonwealth. Nominations for these programs are made by the public school divisions or through the private school regional system. Those interested should contact their local gifted education coordinator or their headmaster. Program information and applications are accessible at the Web site: http://www.pen.k12.va.us/VDOE/Instruction/Govschools/SRGS/. Applications are submitted to the Virginia Department of Education.

Criteria: Application (deadline: February 13); nomination; test scores; recommendations; adjudication (VPA); honors; recognitions; essays; Virginia resident.

Grade: Rising 11-12.

Cost: None except transportation to and from residential sites.

Contact: Local gifted education coordinator, headmaster or see Web site: http://www.pen.k12.va.us/VDOE/Instruction/Govschools/

Alexandria

Episcopal High School
Academic Year

Episcopal High School (EHS) is a college preparatory boarding school serving 410 boys and girls in grades nine through twelve, all of whom board. Located in suburban Alexandria, Virginia, the 130-acre campus is just minutes from a vast array of opportunities and experiences available to students in Washington, D.C. Renowned for challenging and dynamic academics, the school offers AP and honors courses in all disciplines. Nearly 90 percent of the full-time faculty of 70 men and women live on campus with their families and are available to teach and guide students while promoting community. Since its founding in 1839, EHS has maintained a commitment to the development of the intellectual, physical, and spiritual life of each student. EHS's students come from 32 states, the District of Columbia, and 12 international locations. The average class size is 12 students; the student-to-faculty ratio is 6:1.

Criteria: Application (and $50 fee); transcript; personal essay; teacher report; parent statement; recommendations; test scores (PSAT, SAT, SSAT, or TOEFL); GPA; interview; school profile (if available).

Grade: 9-12.

Cost: $27,600 (2002-2003 school year). $2.1 million in financial aid is available.

Contact: Douglas C. Price, Director of Admissions
Episcopal High School
1200 North Quaker Lane
Alexandria, VA 22302
(877) 933-4EHS (toll-free); (703) 933-4062; Fax: (703) 933-3016
E-mail: admissions@episcopalhighschool.org
Web site: http://www.episcopalhighschool.org

Blacksburg

All-Arts and Sciences Camp
(University of North Carolina at Greensboro)
June 29-July 4; July 27-August 1 (one-week sessions)

See listing on page 186 for complete information.

Charlottesville

St. Anne's-Belfield School
Academic Year

A school of 830 students in grades PreK through 12, St. Anne's-Belfield is located on two campuses in Charlottesville, Virginia. A rigorous curriculum and caring teachers prepare the students for the nation's finest colleges and universities. Students enjoy varied fine arts offerings, complete an inclusive interscholastic athletic program, and hold fast to the school's revered honor code and a weekly chapel service. Limited five- and seven-day boarding is available; an ESL program with students from twelve countries is in its seventh year. Ninety-eight percent of the Class of 2002 matriculated to college. The graduating class achieved a median score of 1290 on the SAT, and ninety-three percent of the students sitting for AP exams scored 3 or better.

Criteria: Application (and fee); transcript; personal essay; test scores; GPA; SAT; SSAT; interview.

Grade: PreK-12 (boarding for grades 9-12 only).

Cost: $6,900-11,978 (tuition plus boarding fee). Need-based financial aid is available.

Contact: Jean Craig, Director of Admission
St. Anne's-Belfield School
2132 Ivy Road
Charlottesville, VA 22903
(434) 296-5106; Fax: (434) 979-1486
E-mail: jcraig@stab.org
Web site: http://www.stab.org

CHARLOTTESVILLE

Summer Enrichment Program
(University of Virginia, Curry School of Education)
June 29-July 10; July 13-24; July 27-August 7

For the 24th consecutive summer, The University of Virginia is offering a two-week, residential program for gifted/highly capable students interested in the particular fields of mathematics, social science, science and technology, and arts and humanities. Residing on the grounds of the historic University and utilizing various resources in our community, students conduct an in-depth and concept-based investigation of their topic. The curriculum emphasis is on the process of developing skills such as problem solving, critical inquiry, academic risk-taking, critical evaluation, and creativity through the use of innovative, hands-on group investigations and independent research techniques. The faculty includes gifted educators, university teachers, and discipline experts from our community and beyond. To complement the academic setting, students receive a well-rounded camp experience under the guidance and supervision of our trained residential staff. Recreation, evening activities, and social interactions help students to create a non-competitive, educational atmosphere.

Criteria: Application (deadline: February 15); test scores; four short essays.

Grade: Rising 5-11.

Cost: $840 (per session; 2002). Need-based financial aid is available.

Contact: Karen Lelli Austin, Director, or Barbara Rogers, Secretary
Summer Enrichment Program
405 Emmet Street South, P.O. Box 400264
Charlottesville, VA 22904-4264
(434) 924-3182; Fax: (434) 924-0747
E-mail: curry-sep@virginia.edu
Web site: http://curry.edschool.virginia.edu/go/enrich

Chatham

Chatham Hall
Academic Year

An all-girls college preparatory boarding school, Chatham Hall offers students a structured academic environment, a rich extracurricular program, and a beautiful 362-acre campus. A 5:1 student-to-faculty ratio, a highly qualified faculty, and a curriculum that includes 17 Advanced Placement classes and numerous electives prepare students for college. Recent graduates have attended UNC-Chapel Hill, University of Richmond, University of Virginia, William and Mary, and Davidson. Students participate fully in academics, sports, art, riding, drama, music, and dance. Chatham Hall has the highest percentage of boarding students among peer girls' schools.

Criteria:	Application (deadline: February 14); $45 application fee; transcript; personal essay; recommendations; test scores; SSAT; interview; female student.
Grade:	9-12.
Cost:	$27,195 (boarding); $9,800 (day). Need-based financial aid is available.
Contact:	Alexis Weiner, Director of Admission Chatham Hall 800 Chatham Hall Circle Chatham, VA 24531 (434) 432-2941; Fax: (434) 432-2405 E-mail: admission@chathamhall.com Web site: http://www.chathamhall.com

Emory

Appalachian Institute for Creative Learning: Summer Enrichment Session (Emory and Henry College)
July 13-26 (one- or two-week programs)

Founded in 1982, as the Summer Institute for Gifted Children, AICL's Summer Enrichment Session is a residential, coeducational, non-sectarian, one- or two-week program held in the Knoxville, Tennessee area at Emory and Henry College in Emory, Virginia. Students choose four classes a week from topics such as physics, philosophy, theater, math, creative writing, video production, problem solving, music, visual art, computer science, rocketry, French, chemistry, and leadership training. The curriculum offers over forty classes and a schedule of recreational and evening activities. Encouraging the importance of experience to the gifted child, the program philosophy is: "Learning is fun and should be ongoing."

Criteria:	Application (deadline: June 14); parent statement.
Grade:	Rising 3-12.
Cost:	$515 (one week); $990 (two weeks).

Contact: Chad Watson
Appalachian Institute for Creative Learning
P.O. Box 9027
Knoxville, TN 37940-0027
Phone/Fax: (800) 951-SIGC
E-mail: info@appalachianinstitute.org
Web site: http://www.appalachianinstitute.org

Fairfax

All-Arts and Sciences Camp
(University of North Carolina at Greensboro)
June 29-July 4; July 27-August 1 (one-week sessions)

See listing on page 187 for complete information.

Lexington

Summer Scholars (Washington and Lee University)
June 29-July 25

This well-established, four-week educational program gives college-bound students the opportunity to experience college life. The program is for rising high school seniors who are academically motivated, are self-disciplined, and are strong students. Participants choose an area of study from eight curriculum groups: Brain and Behavioral Sciences, Business, Environmental Studies, Humanities, Journalism, Law and Society, Premedical Studies, and Politics. Students may participate in chorus, art classes, a writing lab, and field trips to local attractions. Secondary schools and parents are informed of satisfactory completion of coursework.

Criteria: Application (deadline: April 30); transcript; recommendations; test scores; GPA; PSAT; SAT; ACT.

Grade: Rising 12.

Cost: $2,200. Financial aid is available.

Contact: Dr. Mimi Milner Elrod, Director
Summer Scholars
Washington and Lee University
Hill House
Lexington, VA 24450
(540) 458-8727 or (540) 458-8722; Fax: (540) 458-8113
E-mail: summerscholars@wlu.edu
Web site: http://summerscholars.wlu.edu

Lynchburg

Virginia Episcopal School
Academic Year

Virginia Episcopal School (VES) is located on a beautiful 160-acre campus in the foothills of the Blue Ridge Mountains. Founded in 1916 by the Reverend Dr. Robert Carter Jett, VES is a coeducational boarding and day, college-preparatory school, serving 245 young men and women in grades 9-12. With a structured and rigorous liberal arts based curriculum and an average class size of 12 students, VES offers a challenging but nurturing academic environment where average to superior students can thrive. Small classes and energizing teachers provide students with an exciting and interactive environment. The addition of individual Internet connections in each dorm room, has allowed our students to continue learning long after the class period is over.

Criteria: Application (and fee); transcript; personal essay; recommendations; test scores; GPA; PSAT; ACT; SSAT; interview.

Grade: 9-12.

Cost: $25,650 (boarding); $13,000 (day). 25% of the student body received a total of $610,000 of merit and need-based financial aid.

Contact: Richard Beaugh, Director of Admissions
Virginia Episcopal School
400 VES Road
Lynchburg, VA 24503
(434) 385-3607; Fax (434) 385-3603
E-mail: admissions@ves.org
Web site: http://www.ves.org

Middleburg

Foxcroft School
Academic Year

Foxcroft School combines a demand for academic excellence with the development of a strong character, a well-defined moral code, and a responsibility for service. Eighty percent of its faculty and administrators live on campus. These families are the hub of a caring community, where girls develop the self-esteem, confidence and sense of purpose essential to their future success. Learning takes place in small, challenging, college preparatory classes where faculty use collaborative learning techniques and students work in small groups to develop skills and formulate ideas. The curriculum includes approximately 100 courses, including Advanced Placement offerings in every discipline. Annual events such as the Goodyear Fellow Program, a two-week Interim Term, and the Poetry Festival enrich the rigorous curriculum. Outstanding extracurricular opportunities include the Leadership Program, Senior Projects, the Senior Thesis, extensive community service, and nine interscholastic sports teams. The 500-acre campus is located just 50 miles from the cultural and educational resources of Washington, D.C.

Criteria: Application (and fee); transcript; personal essay; parent questionnaire; SSAT; teacher recommendations (math and English); interview; female student.

Grade:	9-12, PG.
Cost:	$29,750 (boarding); $19,750 (day). Need-based financial aid is available.
Contact:	Eileen Polachek, Associate Director of Admission Foxcroft School P. O. Box 5555 Middleburg, VA 20118-5555 (800) 858-2364, (540) 687-4340; Fax: (540) 687-3627 E-mail: admissions@foxcroft.org Web site: http://www.foxcroft.org

MOUNTAIN LAKE

TIP Field Studies (Duke University Talent Identification Program)
June 15-August 6 (two-week programs)

See listing on page 182 for complete information.

RICHMOND

St. Catherine's School
Academic Year

St. Catherine's School is an Episcopal diocesan day and boarding school for girls which provides a rigorous, college preparatory curriculum in grades junior kindergarten through twelve. The school's mission is to develop in students the desire and means to attain knowledge, a sense of personal worth and integrity, and an acceptance of responsibility in society. Students may choose from a diverse and challenging academic program. AP and honors courses are offered in English, history, mathematics, biology, chemistry, physics, Mandarin Chinese, Russian, French, Spanish, Latin, art, computer science, and music. Additional courses are available in religion, theater, and dance. The student-to-faculty ratio is 6:1. A full athletic program invites students to participate in 11 team sports with more than 30 varsity and junior varsity teams. The school's metropolitan location provides many cultural and historical experiences, and opportunities for study-travel are available through minimester programs. An Honor Code enhances the community's unusually strong sense of trust and caring for one another.

Criteria:	Application (and fee); transcript; personal essay; recommendations; test scores; GPA; PSAT; SSAT; interview; female student.
Grade:	JK-12 (day); 9-12 (boarding).
Cost:	$10,140 (JK-K); $11,055 (grades 1-5); $12,070 (grades 6-8); $12,920 (grades 9-12, day); $25,850 (grades 9-12, boarding). Financial aid is available.
Contact:	Katherine S. Wallmeyer, Director of Admissions St. Catherine's School 6001 Grove Avenue Richmond, VA 23226 (800) 648-4982, (804) 288-2804; Fax: (804) 285-8169 E-mail: admissions@st.catherines.org Web site: http://www.st.catherines.org

Staunton

Program for the Exceptionally Gifted (Mary Baldwin College)
Academic Year

The Program for the Exceptionally Gifted (PEG) is a unique, residential program that offers academically talented, young women the opportunity to begin college one to four years early while living with their peers. Eligible students may enter the program at any point after completing the eighth grade. PEG students are full-time college students and generally receive their BA or BS degrees within four years. All PEG students begin their experience in a supervised residence hall where they receive the support necessary to adjust to college life. A full-time, professional staff provides supervision, guidance, and programming. Age-appropriate activities are planned around students' interests. Eventually, PEG students live independently on campus; the number of independent years varies according to the age and maturity of each student.

Criteria: Application (and $35 application fee); transcript; personal essays; recommendations; test scores; PSAT, SAT, or ACT; interview; female student.

Grade: Rising 9-12.

Cost: $24,140 (includes tuition, room, board, and activity/technology fees). Need-based financial aid is available.

Contact: Jill Urquhart, Associate Director of Admissions
Program for the Exceptionally Gifted
Mary Baldwin College
Frederick and New Streets
Staunton, VA 24401
(540) 887-7039; Fax: (540) 887-7187
E-mail: peg@mbc.edu
Web site: http://www.mbc.edu

Wallops Island

Marine Science Pre-College Summer Program (Marine Science Consortium, Inc.)
June-August (five one-week sessions)

Marine Science Pre-College Summer Program is a one-week, residential program for students in grades 8-12 interested in discovering more about the wonders of marine biology, ocean studies, experimental ecology, animal behavior, fishes of the Atlantic, shark biology, dolphin behavior, and sea kayaking. Minimum enrollment age: Ocean Studies (15), Sea Kayaking (15), and all other courses (13). Courses such as Wetland Ecology, Marine Invertebrates, Experimental Ecology, and Advanced Marine Science expand on other class topics; therefore students must have completed the prerequisite before enrolling in them. All courses offer students a hands-on experience through beach and forest hikes, marsh mucks, and research cruises in tidal creeks and offshore. Dolphin Behavior, Fishes of the Atlantic, and Shark Biology courses include a trip to the National Aquarium. Ocean Studies students travel to the Virginia Marine Science Museum. For the Sea Kayaking Program, experience is preferred but not required.

Criteria: Application (and $150 application fee); sincere interest in marine science.

Grade: Rising 8-12.

Cost: $440 (approximate cost; some courses have additional fees). Financial aid is not available.

Contact: Cynthia Sheppard, Treasurer
Marine Science Pre-College Summer Program
Marine Science Consortium, Inc.
7278 Enterprise Street
Wallops Island, VA 23337
(757) 824-5636; Fax: (757) 824-5638
E-mail: mscva@msconsortium.org
Web site: http://msconsortium.org

WILLIAMSBURG

All-Arts and Sciences Camp
(University of North Carolina at Greensboro)
June 29-July 4; July 27-August 1 (one-week sessions)

See listing on page 186 for complete information.

Pre-Collegiate Summer Program in Early American History (The National Institute of American History and Democracy, The College of William and Mary)
June 29-July 26

The Pre-Collegiate Summer Program in Early American History is a residential program in which students earn four hours of academic credit at The College of William and Mary. Sponsored by the National Institute of American History and Democracy, a partnership between the College and The Colonial Williamsburg Foundation, the summer program teaches early American history through the use of historic places, archaeology sites, and museums. Under the general supervision of Dr. James Whittenburg of the College of William and Mary's History faculty, students work in seminars of 8-10 students "on-site" at Colonial Williamsburg, Jamestown, Yorktown, and many other historic places in Virginia. Within these small seminars, each with its own instructor, students discuss political, social, familial, cultural, religious, and economic themes of colonial America. Reading assignments, guest scholars, evening performances of music and dance, and historical movies supplement the site visits. Students create electronic journals of their class experiences in which they integrate readings, discussions, and field trips.

Criteria: Application (deadline May 1); transcript; personal essay; recommendations.

Grade: 10-12.

Cost: $2,750 (Virginia residents); $4,462 (non-Virginia residents). Financial aid is available.

Contact: Carolyn S. Whittenburg, Director
Pre-Collegiate Summer Program in Early American History
The College of William and Mary
National Institute of American History and Democracy
P.O. Box 8795
Williamsburg, VA 23187-8795
(757) 221-7652; Fax: (757)-221-7655
E-mail: precol@wm.edu
Web site: http://www.wm.edu/niahd

Williamsburg

Saturday/Summer Enrichment Programs for Gifted Learners (College of William and Mary)
February 15-March 29 (Spring); July 7-11, July14-25 (Summer)

The Center for Gifted Education at the College of William and Mary has been a learning community for talent development for over ten years. The Center provides a learning laboratory for pre-collegiate learners and those who facilitate their learning. The Saturday/Summer Enrichment Program (SEP) offers a wide variety of enrichment opportunities for gifted and talented students in preschool through tenth grades. Small class size allows rich curriculum offerings and individualized attention in areas of science, mathematics, and the humanities. Course activities are compatible with the expected achievement of talented students at specified grade and age levels. Students apply process skills used in individual fields of inquiry, recognize problems, and approaches to problem solving, understand and appreciate individual differences, and become self-directed learners.

Criteria: Application (and fee); recommendations; test scores.

Grade: PreK-10.

Cost: $195 per course (price subject to change). Need-based scholarships are available.

Contact: Dr. Jeanne M. Struck, Director of Precollegiate Learners
Saturday/Summer Enrichment Programs for Gifted Learners
College of William and Mary Center for Gifted Education
Box 8795
Williamsburg, VA 23187-8795
(757) 221-2362; Fax: (757) 221-2184
E-mail: jmstru@wm.edu or cfge@wm.edu
Web site: http://www.cfge.wm.edu

WASHINGTON

State Director

Gayle Pauley, Director, Title 1, LAP, and Title V
Gifted and Talented Education
Washington Office of Public Instruction
P.O. Box 47200
600 South Washington
Olympia, WA 98504-7200
(360) 725-6100; Fax: (360) 586-3305
E-mail: gpauley@ospi.wednet.edu

State Association

Northwest Gifted Child Association

Northwest Gifted Child Association is a statewide nonprofit organization of people with an interest in meeting the special needs of highly capable children. NWGCA and WAETAG (Washington Association of Talented and Gifted) work together to help meet the informational/support needs of parents and other educators of highly capable students. A newsletter (published three times a year) connects the members of opportunities, developments, and articles of interest to the gifted community, and voice mailbox allows volunteers to respond to questions and provide emotional support over the phone. NWGCA has representation on the Washington Coalition for Gifted Education, the lobbying arm of the gifted community in Washington state.

Northwest Gifted Child Association
Connie Baesman, President
P.O. Box 1226
Bellevue, WA 98009
(206) 528-9240
Web site: http://www.waetag.net

Washington Association for Educators of the Talented and Gifted
Linda Colby, President
P.O. Box 870
Coupeville, WA 98239-0870
(360) 385-3102

Regional Talent Search

Center for Talented Youth (The Johns Hopkins University)
See listing on page 4 for complete information.

Loctions throughout Washington

Adventure Treks
June 15-August 18

See listing on page 8 for complete information.

BELLINGHAM

Youth Programs (Western Washington University)
June 23-August 10 (one-week sessions)

Youth Programs offer academic enrichment for motivated students entering grades 3-12 in an exciting college environment. Since 1982, Youth Programs has featured dynamic workshops—in science, art, leadership development, and college preparation—that engage students in a week of hands-on, applied learning. Fascinating demonstrations, field studies, lab work, lectures, and outdoor activities take student learning to new levels. Optional residential programming enhances social and personal growth and safely previews "college-living." Western Washington faculty or area educators develop and teach workshops. Qualified and trained college students provide supervision in the residence hall. Academic credit is available in some programs.

Criteria: Application; essay; recommendations.

Grade: Rising 3-12.

Cost: $250-$800.

Contact: Debbie Gibbons, Program Manager
Extended Education and Summer Programs
Western Washington University
Mail Stop 5293
Bellingham, WA 98225-5293
(360) 650-6820; Fax: (360) 650-6858
E-mail: Debbie.Gibbons@wwu.edu
Web site: http://www.wwu.edu/~adventur

Walla Walla

College Horizons (Whitman College and Washington University)
June 14-18 (Session 1); June 28-July 2 (Session 2)

College Horizons is a five-day "crash course" in college preparation for 110 Native American high school students. Expert college counselors, teamed with admissions offices from 26 of the nation's best colleges work one-on-one with participants. Students will develop a list of colleges suitable for them and will learn how to apply, how to get admitted, and how to receive financial aid and scholarships. Participating colleges include Barnard College, Brown, the California Institute of Technology, Carleton College, Cornell, Dartmouth, Grinnell College, Guilford College, Harvard, Johns Hopkins, Macalester College, Oberlin College, Occidental College, Princeton, Rice, St. John's College/Santa Fe, St. Lawrence University, Skidmore College, Smith College, Stanford, Union College, University of Denver, Washington University, Westmont College, Whitman College, and Yale.

Criteria:	Application ($10 application fee); transcript; personal essay; recommendations; test scores; GPA (B average); Native American student.
Grade:	10-11.
Cost:	$100.
Contact:	Jan Randall, Co-Director College Horizons 686 Black Hawk Drive NE Albuquerque, NM 87122 (505) 856-7576 E-mail: jan@swcp.com Web site: http://www.whitneylaughlin.com

WEST VIRGINIA

STATE DIRECTOR

Cheryl Allen Keffer, Coordinator-Gifted Programs
West Virginia Department of Education
Capitol Complex, Building 6, Room. 304
Charleston, WV 25305
(304) 558-2696; Fax: (304) 558-3741
E-mail: ckeffer@access.k12.wv.us

STATE ASSOCIATION

West Virginia Association for the Gifted and Talented

WVAGT is an organization that offers the opportunity for professional educators, parents, students, and others interested in issues concerning gifted and talented students opportunities to network and extend their areas of expertise. Membership in WVAGT is open to all who share an interest in quality educational programs for gifted and talented youth. WVAGT promotes the education of the gifted and talented within the state of WV; coordinates the efforts of gifted education within the state of WV; provides a communication network for individuals interested in the education for gifted and talented youth; disseminates gifted education information to the educators, parents, and public officials; and serves as advocates for gifted and talented youth. WVAGT publishes a quarterly newsletter, AEGIS, which features informational articles, opinion pieces, and advice for teachers, parents, and students. WVAGT holds an annual meeting, usually in October, at which numerous sessions and workshops address the needs of the gifted and talented. The range of topics includes research reports, philosophical/theoretical discussions, practical teaching strategies, and legal/political issues.

Tom Berlin, President
HC-66, Box 19
Romney, WV 26757-9402
E-mail: tberlin2@yahoo.com

REGIONAL TALENT SEARCH
Center for Talented Youth (The Johns Hopkins University)
See listing on page 4 for complete information.

BARTOW/CHARLESTON

National Youth Science Camp (National Youth Science Foundation)
June-July (four-week session)

The National Youth Science Camp hosts two top graduating high school seniors from each state for four weeks of intensive study in the eastern mountains of West Virginia. Selected by their respective governors through a competitive process, the delegates attend the unique cross-disciplinary program as guests of the state of West Virginia and private sponsors. More than 40 nationally known experts in science, technology, and other fields lecture at the camp and provide intensive hands-on directed studies workshops on diverse research topics. Delegates may also present seminars about their work. Day and overnight trips (to the Monongahela National Forest, the National Radio Astronomy Observatory, and Washington, D.C.) provide opportunities for delegates to study science topics from astronomy to zoology; to go backpacking, caving, rock climbing, mountain biking, and kayaking; to work closely with scientists; to tour national museums/monuments; and to enjoy a formal luncheon with their senators.

Criteria: Varies by state.

Grade: PG (student who graduates from high school in 2003).

Cost: No cost; all expenses paid by the program.

Contact: National Youth Science Camp
P.O. Box 3387, Department T
Charleston, WV 25333
(304) 342-3326; Fax: (304) 342-8856
E-mail: director@sciencecamp.org
Web site: http://www.sciencecamp.org

BUCKHANNON

Wesleyan Summer Gifted Program (West Virginia Wesleyan College)
June 29-July 12; July13-26

The Wesleyan Summer Gifted Program is a summer residential program for gifted children (rising grades 6-12). Academic classes are taught in mathematics, physics, computer science, creative writing and literature, and world history by college professors who have a special interest in the gifted child. Classes are fast-paced and challenging and involve intensive work in the laboratory. Students live in college dormitories where counselors carefully supervise them. There is a full range of recreational facilities including day field trips in the outdoors. Classes are small (about 15 students per class), and the students get to work closely with their professors and advanced college students who work as assistants in the classes. The college campus is self-contained and located in a safe, small town.

Criteria: Application (and fee); test scores.

Grade: Rising 6-12.

Cost: $875 (grades 6-10); $975 (grades 11-12). Financial aid is available.

Contact: Dr. Joseph E. Wiest, Professor of Physics
Wesleyan Summer Gifted Program
West Virginia Wesleyan College
59 College Avenue
Buckhannon, WV 26201
(304) 473-8072; Fax: (304) 472-2571
E-mail: sgp@wvwc.edu
Web site: http://www.wvwc.edu/wvwc/gifted/giftcamp.html

Capon Bridge

Burgundy Center for Wildlife Studies
August (Junior Program); June-August (Senior Program); July (Adult Weekend)

The summer programs of the Burgundy Center for Wildlife Studies are residential nature study programs for students, age 8-10 (Junior Program; one-week session), students, age 11-15 (Senior Program; two-week sessions), and students, over 21 (Adult Weekend). The program is unique for its small size (the limit is 32 campers to a session) and has a camper-to-staff ratio of 2:1. Located in a secluded 500-acre wildlife sanctuary in the Appalachians of West Virginia, the strongest assets of this program are the caring, knowledgeable, dynamic staff, the quality of the education provided, and the beautiful surroundings. The property comprises a large variety of habitats and has a great abundance of wildlife. Days are filled with workshops, hikes, swimming, games, music, and art. This noncompetitive program encourages individual growth and self-challenge while creating a strong sense of community. For returning Senior Program campers, an Advanced Senior Program is offered.

Criteria: Application; interest in nature study.

Grade: Rising 2-5 (one-week session); rising 5-10 (two-week session).

Cost: $635 (Junior Program); $1,100 (Senior Program); $190 individual or $360 per couple (Adult Weekend). Financial aid is available.

Contact: Lavinia Schoene, Director
Burgundy Center for Wildlife Studies
Burgundy Farm Country Day School
3700 Burgundy Road
Alexandria, VA 22303
(703) 960-3431; Fax: (703) 960-5056
E-mail: bcws2@earthlink.net
Web site: http://camppage.com/bcws

Charleston

West Virginia Governor's Schools
July

West Virginia Governor's Honors Academy is a three-week residential, intensive learning experience held this year at Marshall University. Its purpose is to recognize, encourage, and reward outstanding young people whose academic work demonstrates excellence. Students and teachers who are highly motivated and accomplished are encouraged to apply. Students will enroll in two courses from offerings in the arts, humanities, math, and science. **The Governor's School for the Arts**, hosted this year by West Liberty State College, is a three-week residential program for exceptional arts students. The program provides individual and in-depth instruction in dance, theatre, instrumental music, and theatre and visual arts. To qualify, each applicant participates in a regional and state level audition/portfolio review. **The Governor's School for Math and Science**, consisting of two 2-week sessions of problem-based learning, is held at West Virginia University. Rising eighth graders attend one session; rising ninth graders attend the other session.

Criteria: Application; transcript; personal essay; teacher report; parent statement; recommendations; test scores; GPA; nomination; audition (Arts); portfolio (Arts); West Virginia resident and attend school in West Virginia.

Grade: Rising 12 (Governor's Honors Academy); rising 11 (Governor's School for the Arts); rising 8-9 (Governor's School for Math and Science).

Cost: None (transportation cost is not included).

Contact: Cheryl Keffer, State Coordinator
West Virginia Governor's Schools and Gifted Education
WVDE Building 6, Room 304
1900 Kanawha Blvd. E
Charleston, WV 25305
(304) 558-2696; Fax: (304) 558-3741
E-mail: ckeffer@access.k12.wv.us
Web site: http://www.wvgovschools.org

WHEELING

The Linsly School
Academic Year and Summer

The Linsly School, located in Wheeling, West Virginia, is a coeducational college preparatory day and boarding school enrolling grades 5-12. Linsly offers a diverse range of academic, athletic, fine arts, and extracurricular programs tailored to suit the needs of intellectually gifted students. Unique opportunities available at Linsly include The Linsly Outdoor Center, located in Pennsylvania's Raccoon Creek State Park; Summer Studies; and the newest honors program, The Linsly to Bethany Honors Summer Program. Open to qualifying sophomores, juniors, and seniors from any school, this two-week program is based on a unique alliance with Bethany College. The program is excellent for students looking to challenge themselves academically, while broadening their activities and leadership qualities that are important in the college admissions process. With 100 percent college placement for graduating seniors, Linsly provides a structured, disciplined program that challenges students to reach their highest potential intellectually, physically, socially, and morally in a supportive community environment.

Criteria: Admissions test; transcript; recommendations; personal interview.

Grade: 5-12 (day); 7-12 (boarding).

Cost: $9,700 (day); $19,630 (boarding).

Contact: Mr. James Hawkins, Director of Admissions, or
Chad Barnett, Director of Summer Studies
The Linsly School
60 Knox Lane
Wheeling, WV 26003
(304) 233-1436; Fax: (304) 234-4614
E-mail: admit@linsly.org
Web site: http://www.linsly.org

WISCONSIN

STATE DIRECTOR

Sue Grady, Director
Division for Academic Excellence
Wisconsin Department of Public Instruction
P.O. Box 7841
Madison, WI 53707
(615) 266-2364
E-mail: sue.grady@dpi.state.wi.us

STATE ASSOCIATION

Wisconsin Association for Gifted and Talented
Nancy Woodward, Executive Assistant
1608 West Cloverdale Drive
Appleton, WI 54914
(920) 991-9177; Fax: (920) 991-1225
E-mail: watg@focol.org
Web site: http://www.focal.org/watg

REGIONAL TALENT SEARCH
Center for Talent Development (Northwestern University)
See listing on page 3 for complete information.

BEAVER DAM

Wayland Academy
Academic Year

One of the oldest coeducational boarding schools in the nation, Wayland offers a rigorous college preparatory curriculum and residential experience. Historically, college placement has been 100% annually with graduates attending selective and very selective colleges and universities. Students from 20 states and 13 countries enjoy Wayland's small-city atmosphere, diverse extracurricular activities, Midwestern values, and traditional style of education. The nearby cities of Milwaukee and Madison provide ample cultural, sporting, and entertainment offerings. Now in its 148th year, the Academy continues a long tradition of academic excellence, student-faculty mentor relationships, small classes, and character development.

Criteria: Application; transcript; personal essay; recommendations; SSAT; interview.

Grade: 9-12.

Cost: $24,300 (boarding); $12,800 (day). All costs are for 2002-2003 school year. Merit scholarships and need-based financial aid are available.

Contact: Richard R. Eber, Dean of Admissions
          Wayland Academy
          101 North University Avenue
          Beaver Dam, WI 53916
          (800) 860-7725; Fax: (920) 887-3373
          E-mail: admissions@wayland.org
          Web site: http://www.wayland.org

KENOSHA

SuperCamp® (University of Wisconsin-Parkside)
July-August

See listing on page 13 for complete information.

MILWAUKEE

Developing Dimensions Program and Magellan Day School, EPL (The Wisconsin Center for Gifted Learners—WCGL)
Academic Year, Saturdays, and Summer

The Wisconsin Center for Gifted Learners is a nonprofit corporation that serves gifted learners, their parents, and their teachers. Its purpose is to translate research into quality programs for highly intelligent children. Teachers have expertise in education of gifted learners. The **Magellan Day School, EPL** is a day school program that emphasizes science and technology and integrates mathematics and the arts into a theme related to a scientific question. A different theme is pursued each quarter. Both Latin and Spanish are taught. The **Developing Dimensions Program (DDP)** is a Saturday and summer program that thematically integrates seven disciplines: language arts, informal drama, art, music, Latin, mathematics/science, and physical education. Social cognitive skills are stressed, and opportunities to practice leadership and being of service are provided through mentoring and teacher assistant positions. Additional services for gifted learners include dissemination of information, classes, and counseling for parents and persons in helping professions, teacher training, and library resources.

Criteria: Application (and fee); test scores; interview; parent and student questionnaires; student visit to the program.

Grade: PreK-6.

Cost: $1,500 (per quarter, EPL); $700 (Saturdays); $490 (Summer).

Contact: Sharon K. Gerleman, Executive Director
          The Wisconsin Center for Gifted Learners
          217 West Dunwood Road
          Milwaukee, WI 53217-3108
          (414) 351-4441; Fax: (414) 351-9792
          E-mail: wcgl@execpc.com
          Web site: http://www.execpc.com/~wcgl

WYOMING

STATE DIRECTOR

Kenya Hayes, Gifted and Talented Consultant
Wyoming Department of Education
School Improvement Division
2300 Capitol Avenue
Cheyenne, WY 82002
(307) 777-5217

STATE ASSOCIATION

Wyoming Association for Gifted
P.O. Box 513
Riverton, WY 82501

REGIONAL TALENT SEARCH

Rocky Mountain Talent Search (University of Denver)
See listing on page 5 for complete information.

STUDY ABROAD INDEX
(Listed by Country)

Locations Throughout the World
Academic Study Associates, 274
Advanture Treks, 274
Educational Programs Overseas, 276
European Capitals Program, 276
Excel International Programs, 277
Global Teen, 277
Interlocken Center for Experiential Learning, 278
Language Studies Abroad, 280
Putney Student TravelPrograms, 284
Summer Discovery Pre-College Enrichment Program, 287
The Road Less Traveled, 285
TIP Field Studies, 288

England
Cambridge College Programme, 274
Intern Exchange International, 278
Oxbridge Academic Programs, 281
Oxford Advanced Studies Program, 283
TASIS School and Summer Programs in Europe, 288
Winston Churchill in England, Thomas More in England, 289

France
Barat Foundation Summer Programs in Provence and Paris, 274
Oxbridge Academic Programs, 281
Rassias Programs, 284
Spring Break in Paris, 286

Greece
ITHAKA Semester in Greece, 280

Italy
Precollege Artist Abroad Program, 282
Shakespeare in Italy; Latin in Rome, 285
TASIS Schools and Summer Programs in Europe, 288
The Italian Experience, 279
TIP International Field Studies, 289

Latin America/Mexico
Spanish on the Road Program in the Mexican Central Highlands, 286

Russia
Precollege Research Abroad Program, 283

Spain
Discover Spain and Portugal Program, 275
Rassias Programs, 284
Summer Challenge in Spain, 287
TASIS Schools and Summer Programs in Europe, 288

Switzerland
Summer in Switzerland, 287
TASIS Schools and Summer Programs in Europe, 288

Thailand
GlobalQuest, 278

STUDY ABROAD
(Listed Alphabetically by Program Name)

Academic Study Associates
June-August

See listing on page 7 for complete information.

Adventure Treks
June 15-August 18

See listing on page 8 for complete information.

Barat Foundation Summer Programs in Provence and Paris (Barat Foundation)
June 28-July 25; July 25-August 8

Located in a beautiful country estate in Provence, France, or at a three-star residential hotel in the heart of Paris, the Barat Foundation Summer Programs provide the ideal setting for a French language and culture immersion program. Academics are combined with real-life experience to bring learning alive. Total language and culture learning experience are combined with two to three hours of morning academic study. There are exciting activities and excursions planned throughout Provence and Paris. Up to 15 hours of instruction are provided each week, including French language study combined with enrichment classes in art history, French history, literature, architecture, theater, cinema, music, photography, fashion, and cuisine. Hands-on cooking classes taught by a French chef are an integral part of the curriculum. All classes are taught by young French nationals who have advanced degrees in teaching French as a foreign language and additional degrees in one of the specialized areas of study. All levels of French language experience are accepted from true beginners to fluent speakers.

Criteria:	Application (and fee); transcript; teacher report.
Grade:	Rising 9-12.
Cost:	$2,995-$5,395 (airfare is not included). Limited financial aid is available.
Contact:	Chandri Barat, Executive Director Barat Foundation Summer Programs in Provence and Paris P.O. Box 609 Montville, NJ 07045 (973) 263-1013; Fax: (973) 263-2287 E-mail: info@baratfoundation.org Web site: http://www.baratfoundation.org

Cambridge College Programme, LLC (Cambridge University)
July-August

The Programme is the oldest established teen program at Cambridge University. It is the only program at either Oxford or Cambridge where students are lectured only by British professors and supervised only by graduates of the university. Founded in 1986, the Programme provides a stimulating and rigorous course of study plus sports and cultural activities. Faculty guide students to master skills, to acquire knowledge, and to think critically, creatively, and independently. The Programme's structure fosters close association between staff and students for personal, social, and intellectual development. The director and staff live with the students to supervise and ensure their safety and well-being. Academics are enriched with both field trips and day trips to historic sites, plus trips to London, Bath, Stratford-upon-Avon, and Stonehenge. Cultural enrichment is achieved through visits to London museums, workshops at Shakespeare's Globe Theater, and plays in the West End, such as *Les Miserables*. The program is three weeks long, with an optional week in Paris. SAT prep course is optional.

Criteria: Application; personal essay.

Grade: Rising 8-12.

Cost: $5,295. Financial aid is not available.

Contact: Taryn Edwards, Director
Cambridge College Programme
175 East Delaware Street, Suite 5518
Chicago, IL 60611
(800) 922-3552, (312) 787-7477
Fax: (312) 988-7268

Discover Spain and Portugal Program (Knowledge Exchange Institute)
June-August

The Discover Spain and Portugal Program is an educational travel immersion with a focus on the Spanish language, history, and culture. The curriculum consists of intensive language courses, "on-the-road" projects, field-based activities, sightseeing and cultural excursions in Spain and Portugal. Professors and staff from Moreruela, Escuela de Espanol, teach courses and supervise the group. The program itinerary includes Madrid, Toledo, Aranjuez, Segovia, El Escorial, Zaragoza, Barcelona, Valencia, Sierra de Alcaraz, Granada, Salamanca, Sevilla, Sesimbra, Lisbon, Porto, Bragança, and much more. Cultural activities range from visits to museums, festivals, bullfights, sporting events and Flamenco dancing to sightseeing in cities, villages, and historic sites to camping in the mountains and swimming in the ocean. Program costs include academics, textbooks, six college credits, room and board, pre-departure and on-site support, medical and travel insurance, roundtrip travel, airport and ground transportation, visa support, field trips, sightseeing and cultural excursions in Spain and Portugal.

Criteria: Application (deadline: March 20); $50 application fee; transcript; personal essay; recommendations; interview (by phone or in person).

Grade: 9-12.

Cost: $6,350. Partial financial aid is available.

Contact: Eduard Izraylovsky, Principal Director
Knowledge Exchange Institute
Center for International Studies
111 John Street, Suite 800
New York, NY 10038
(800) 831-5095, (212) 931-9953; Fax: (866) 831-5095, (212) 528-2095
E-mail: cis@knowledgeexchange.org
Web site: http://www.knowledgeexchange.org

Educational Programs Overseas (Center for Study Abroad)
Academic Year and Summer

Since 1990, CSA has been a non-profit organization providing quality opportunities for student and working adults to pursue overseas study. CSA offers programs in several countries, primarily in Europe and Asia. Students can participate in weekly, monthly, quarterly, semester, and academic year programs. College credit is available. CSA also conducts a "group" program in Kobe, Japan every summer. It includes an intensive Japanese language experience, and students live with a Japanese family.

Criteria: Application (and fee).

Grade: 12 (minimum age: 18), college students, and working adults.

Cost: Varies. Financial aid is not available.

Contact: Alima K. Virtue, Program Director
Center for Study Abroad
325 Washington Avenue South, No. 93
Kent, WA 98032
(206) 726-1498; Fax: (206) 850-0454
E-mail: info@centerforstudyabroad.com
Web site: http://www.centerforstudyabroad.com

European Capitals Program (Knowledge Exchange Institute)
June-August

The European Capitals Program is designed for serious students interested in the European Union and language studies. The program emphasizes European business, diplomacy, history, and culture, as well as French, German, Spanish, and Dutch languages. The curriculum consists of formal instruction, cultural excursions, and on-the-road projects. The travel itinerary includes at least eleven of the following cities: Brussels, Paris, Antwerp, London, Bruges, Berlin, Vienna, Amsterdam, Geneva, Zurich, Prague, Luxembourg, Budapest, Madrid, Munich, and more. Faculty and staff from the International Management Institute (IMI) teach the courses and accompany the group on all excursions. Program costs include academics, textbooks, six college credits, living accommodations, pre-departure and on-site support, medical and travel insurance, roundtrip travel, airport and ground transportation, visa support, field trips, sightseeing, and cultural excursions in Europe.

Criteria: Application (deadline: March 20); $50 application fee; transcript; personal essay; recommendations; interview (by phone or in person).

Grade: 9-12.

Cost: $6,350. Partial financial aid is available.

Contact: Eduard Izraylovsky, Principal Director
Knowledge Exchange Institute
Center for International Studies
111 John Street, Suite 800
New York, NY 10038
(800) 831-5095; (212) 931-9953; Fax: (866) 831-5095; (212) 528-2095
E-mail: cis@knowledgeexchange.org
Web site: http://www.knowledgeexchange.org

Excel International Programs (Putney Student Travel)
June-August (Three-, four-, and seven-week programs)

See listing on page 9 for complete information.

Global Teen (Language Liaison)
June-August

Global Teen was created by Language Liaison, Inc. in 1996, in response to requests from members of the American Council on the Teaching of Foreign Languages (ACTFL). Global Teen offers teens ages 13-17 exciting language/cultural learning adventures throughout Europe, Asia, Central and South America with other teens from all over the world. Classes in the target language are taught in the mornings by highly qualified native teachers who are sensitive to the needs of younger learners. Afternoons are filled with supervised cultural, social, and sports activities that provide students an opportunity to practice their newly learned language skills. Accommodations are offered in a school residence or with a friendly host family where students experience support and interaction. Language Liaison strengthens the safety and security of each student through an annual recertification program for every host site. Learning while living in such a diverse multicultural environment is particularly enriching for young adults as they meet other students from around the world.

Criteria:	Application; $175 application fee.
Grade:	Ages 13-17.
Cost:	Varies.
Contact:	Nancy Forman, President Language Liaison Global Teen 4 Burnham Parkway Morristown, NJ 07960 (973) 898-1416; Fax: (973) 898-1710 E-mail: learn@languageliaison.com Web site: http://www.languageliaison.com

GlobalQuest
Mid September-mid December; mid February-mid May

GlobalQuest offers high school seniors and students between high school and college a 12-week experience that is interdisciplinary, international, and serves as a culminating and transitional experience from high school to college. Each group is limited to 12 participants and three teachers. Senior high school students may attend during either semester of their senior year, returning to their school to give a full portfolio report on their experience and to graduate with their class. Students who have graduated from high school may also attend during either semester prior to entering college. Thailand is a fascinating, safe country to visit and study. Students experience city and wilderness settings in Thailand; study Thai language; study and experience Thai history and culture, natural history and environmental studies; complete a significant individual research project; and enjoy a two-week home stay and service project. Credit at the high school level is awarded. College credit may be possible.

Criteria: Transcript; personal essay; recommendations.

Grade: 12, PG.

Cost: $12,000. Need-based financial aid is available.

Contact: Tim Ellis, Executive Director
GlobalQuest
195 Montsweag Road
Woolwich, ME 04579
(207) 443-5451
E-mail: tellis@quest.org
Web site: http://www.gquest.org

Interlocken Center for Experiential Learning
July-August

See listing under Multiple Locations for complete information.

Intern Exchange International, Ltd.
June 26-July 25

For sixteen summers, Intern Exchange International has taken students ages 16 to 18 to London for a monthlong program of internships and travel. In the **Internship Programme**, students get the chance to work side by side with professionals in a career that interests them, from archaeology to strategic studies. Interns work at Sotheby's; Barclays Bank; the famous Lanesborough Hotel; and at Bloomsbury Publishing, the home of the Harry Potter series. They are assigned to prominent British attorneys, work with leading stock brokers, do medical research, and teach autistic students. Other students enroll in **Career Plus-Programmes**, project-based workshops that delve into fields ranging from digital media to photography, from fashion and design to theatre workshops at London's Method Studio. Weekends and evenings are devoted to theatre, concerts, trips to Bath, Stonehenge, Cambridge, Paris, and more. The program enables teens to clarify their career interests, get real work experience, and gain independence.

Criteria: Application; $50 application fee; transcript, personal essay, recommendations.

Grade:	Age 16-18.
Cost:	$5,495.
Contact:	Nina Miller Glickman, M.Ed., Director Intern Exchange International, Ltd. 130 Harold Road Woodmere, NY 11598 (516) 374-3939; Fax (516) 374-2104 E-mail: info@internexchange.com Web site: http://www.internexchange.com

The Italian Experience (The Center for Gifted Studies, Western Kentucky University)
June 1-13

The Italian Experience is an opportunity for gifted eighth graders, high school honor students, and interested adults to learn about the history, culture, pageantry, and people of Italy. This program, sponsored by The Center for Gifted Studies at Western Kentucky University, is designed to provide participants with a carefully structured experience in Italy. Points of interest in Venice, Florence, Rome, and Pompeii will be visited. Twenty-three qualified participants will be accompanied by the program directors.

Criteria:	Application; recommendations; participation in a gifted program or high school honors program.
Grade:	Rising 8-12 and adults.
Cost:	$2,825.
Contact:	Dr. Julia Roberts The Center for Gifted Studies Western Kentucky University 1 Big Red Way Bowling Green, KY 42101-3576 (270) 745-6323; Fax: (270) 745-6279 E-mail: gifted@wku.edu Web site: http://www.wku.edu/gifted/

ITHAKA Semester in Greece (ITHAKA Cultural Study Program in Greece)
February-May (Spring); September-December (Fall)

The ITHAKA Semester combines rigorous academic study with experiential cultural learning in a setting very different from the traditional academic environment. The program offers students the opportunity to immerse themselves in a village setting of a foreign culture. Academic emphasis is on literature, mythology, modern history, Greek language, poetry, archaeology, and writing. Classes are held weekday evenings. Students participate in internships with a Greek family or craftsperson every morning. Weekends are spent on excursions to various historical sites, such as Knossos, or cultural events on the island. Unique aspects of the program lie in the intimate size of the group (12 students), the tutorial nature of the courses, the diversity of the guest professors, and the internships. Strong reading and writing skills are emphasized to create a dynamic learning community. The program offers superb preparation for admission to competitive colleges, fostering vigor and excitement in learning.

Criteria: Application (and fee); transcript; personal essay; recommendations; interview.

Grade: 11-12, PG and college.

Cost: $14,500. Tuition fee includes all expenses except airfare, books, and spending money. Limited need-based financial aid is available.

Contact: Catherine K. Hunter, U.S. Director
ITHAKA Cultural Study Programs in Greece
5500 Prytania Street #102
New Orleans, LA 70115
(504) 269-2303; Fax: (504) 269-2301
E-mail: ithakagr@msn.com
Web site: http://www.ithaka.org

Language Studies Abroad
Year-round

Experience language and total cultural immersion in Austria, Argentina, Belgium, Brazil, Bolivia, Canada, Chile, China, Costa Rica, Cuba, Dominican Republic, Ecuador, France, Germany, Guatemala, Italy, Japan, Mexico, Peru, Portugal, Russia, or Switzerland with flexible programs starting almost any Monday and lasting from one week to a full year. In response to the growing importance of fluency in foreign languages in a global economy, and the top priority placed by leading U.S. universities on student applications with study abroad experience, Language Studies Abroad (LSA) was founded in 1985. LSA is the leader in providing high quality foreign language instruction in small classes throughout the world. Excursions and/or weekend travel to nearby attractions are included to provide a sustained linguistic environment and a glance into the cultural treasures of the foreign country and its people. Host families promote lifelong friendships while substantially reducing travel costs. Residences and other accommodations are also available.

Criteria: Application (and fee).

Grade: 1-12, PG.

Cost: From $990 for 4 weeks; shorter programs are available.

Contact: Language Studies Abroad
1801 Highway 50 East, Suite I
Carson City, NV 89701-3203
(800) 424-5522; Fax: (775) 883-2266
E-mail: info@languagestudiesabroad.com
Web site: http://www.languagestudiesabroad.com

Oxbridge Academic Programs
July (four-week session)

Oxbridge Academic Programs offers three intensive summer study programs for students in grades 10-12: The Oxford Tradition, The Cambridge Tradition and Académie de Paris; and two unique academic enrichment programs for eighth and ninth graders: The Cambridge Prep Experience and Ecole de Paris. Each program is designed to immerse talented, motivated students in two academic subjects or creative arts, many of which are outside the regular high school curriculum, such as law, molecular medicine, broadcast journalism, international relations, architecture, and economics. Similarly, all five programs stress imaginative teaching by superb faculty, active learning, and cultural enrichment heightened by the excitement of living abroad. Taking full advantage of the inimitable resources of the historic cities of Oxford, Cambridge, and Paris, students combine their challenging courses with a broad range of field trips, theater performances, eminent guest speakers, and a full sports and activities schedule. For the right student, there is simply nothing like it.

Criteria: Application (and deposit); transcript; personal essay; recommendations; sample of work (French immersion classes only); GPA.

Grade: 8-9 (The Cambridge Prep Experience, Ecole de Paris); 10-12 (The Oxford Tradition, The Cambridge Tradition, Académie de Paris).

Cost: $4,595-$5,195.

Contact: Simon Pickard, Executive Director
Oxbridge Academic Programs
601 Cathedral Parkway, Suite 7R
New York, NY 10025-2186
(800) 828-8349; Fax: (212) 663-8169
E-mail: info@oxbridgeprograms.com
Web site: http://www.oxbridgeprograms.com

Oxford Advanced Studies Program
July 8-August 2

The Oxford Advanced Studies Program takes place at Magdalen College in Oxford each July, giving high school students a unique taste of life in a medieval college. Students select two or three stimulating academic courses from the wide selection offered. All courses are taught in the Oxbridge tutorial mode with one-to-one teaching and small group seminars. This stimulating approach greatly enhances students' academic maturity, allowing them to discuss their work directly with tutors, who are all well-qualified British university graduates. Academic work is complemented by a range of visits to places such as Stratford (including a Shakespeare play), Warwick Castle (including a medieval banquet), Bath, Stonehenge, Blenheim Palace, and of course, London, thereby broadening students' cultural horizons. Visits to Oxford colleges, galleries, and museums are also part of an extremely enjoyable and enriching program. Enrollment is open to academically able sophomores, juniors, and seniors.

Criteria: Application (and fee); transcript; personal essay; recommendations.

Grade: 10-12.

Cost: $5,950 (plus $300 registration fee).

Contact: Joan Ives, Registrar
Oxford Advanced Studies Program
P.O. Box 2043
Darien, CT 06820
(203) 966-2886; Fax: (203) 972-3083
E-mail: oxedge@aol.com
Web site: http://www.oasp.ac.uk

Precollege Artist Abroad Program (Knowledge Exchange Institute)
June-August

The Precollege Artist Abroad Program at the Scuola Internazionale di Grafica in Venice, Italy is designed for serious students interested in the fine arts, printmaking, book arts, graphic design, Web design, digital photography, and art history studies as well as Italian language, history and culture. Coursework is supplemented with sightseeing and cultural excursions in Venice, Veneto, Milan, Florence, and Rome. The Scuola Internazionale di Grafica is a leading visual arts and graphic design academy in Venice, Italy. Its international faculty consists of renowned artists who lived, studied, worked, and exhibited in countries throughout Europe, Americans, Asia, Africa, and Oceania. The Scuola's central location in Venice is ideal for studying art and design as well as language and culture. Program costs include academic and studio fees, textbooks, nine college credits, room and board, on-site support, medical and travel insurance, roundtrip travel, airport and ground transportation, field trips, sightseeing, and cultural excursions.

Criteria: Application (deadline: March 20); $50 application fee; transcript; personal essay; recommendations; interview (by phone or in person).

Grade: 9-12.

Cost: $5,550. Partial financial aid is available.

Contact: Eduard Izraylovsky, Principal Director
Knowledge Exchange Institute
Center for International Studies
111 John Street, Suite 800
New York, NY 10038
(800) 831-5095, (212) 931-9953; Fax: (866) 831-5095, (212) 528-2095
E-mail: cis@knowledgeexchange.org
Web site: http://www.knowledgeexchange.org

Precollege Research Abroad Program (Knowledge Exchange Institute)
June-August

The Precollege Research Abroad Program at the Pushino Science Center (PSC), Russian Academy of Science is designed for motivated students interested in science, mathematics, and technology. The curriculum includes research internships, under the supervision of senior scientist and preparation for the Intel Science Talent Search and other contests. Over 30 percent of our students advance to the semifinal round of the Intel Science Talent Search, over 5 percent become finalist, and do equally well in other science contests. Research projects are available in medical science, pharmacology, neurology, psychology, microbiology, cell biology, biochemistry, molecular biology, genetic engineering, physics, biophysics, astrophysics, mathematics, signal transduction, analytical chemistry, organic chemistry, soil science, plant biology, zoology, agroscience, environmental science, permafrost, cryogenics, and much more. Research is supplemented with cultural activities, sports, interaction with Russian students, and excursions in Moscow, St. Petersburg, and Serpukhov. Program costs include laboratory fees, six college credits, room and board, on-site support, medical and travel insurance, roundtrip travel, airport and ground transportation, sightseeing, and cultural excursions.

Criteria: Application (deadline: March 20); $50 application fee; transcript; personal essay; recommendations; interview (by phone or in person).

Grade: 9-12.

Cost: $5,250. Partial financial aid is available.

Contact: Eduard Izraylovsky, Principal Director
Knowledge Exchange Institute
Center for International Studies
111 John Street, Suite 800
New York, NY 10038
(800) 831-5095, (212) 931-9953; Fax: (866) 831-5095, (212) 528-2095
E-mail: cis@knowledgeexchange.org
Web site: http://www.knowledgeexchange.org

Putney Student Travel Programs
June-August (four-week programs)

Putney's 52nd summer offers small group Adventure Travel, Language Learning, and Community Service Programs throughout the world. These unique programs emphasize learning by doing—having fun, getting off the beaten track, making friends, and giving something of yourself to others—rather than just touring or sightseeing. Participating actively, working together, meeting new challenges, helping build a sense of community-this is the Putney Way. Adventure Travel programs include a series of extended stays that balance country life with city living, outdoor adventures with cultural activities. Language Learning programs in France, Spain, and Costa Rica combine carefully planned, non-touristy itineraries that allow students to have fun as they learn to communicate effectively through immersion in a variety of natural, everyday living situations. Community Service participants give of themselves to people in need in developing countries and disadvantaged communities. Working in unison with other members of a team, students learn they can help others make a difference by reaching out.

Criteria: Application (and fee); personal essay; recommendations.

Grade: 9-12.

Cost: $4,090-$8,790. Limited need-based financial aid is available.

Contact: Jeffrey D. Shumlin
Putney Student Travel
345 Hickory Ridge Road
Putney, VT 05346
(800) 387-5000; Fax: (802) 387-4276
E-mail: info@goputney.com
Web site: http://www.goputney.com

Rassias Programs (Rassias Language Programs Abroad)
June-July

Rassias offers French and Spanish language immersion, family stays, and travel for currently in ninth, tenth, and eleventh grades. Sessions are for four- and five weeks in France and Spain. Accelerate learning the Spanish or French language, delve into their cultures, laugh and learn, all in the famed Rassias Method®, developed by Dartmouth professor, John Rassias. Not an average classroom;, not an average summer-skilled staff, families selected by local friends, proven teaching method, great travel adventures—all are part of Rassias Language Programs. Applicants must be motivated to speak the target language and have two or more years of academic preparation in that language.

Criteria: Application (deadline: March 31); personal essay; recommendations; interview.

Grade: 9-11.

Cost: $6,200-$6,500.

Contact: Bill Miles, President
Rassias Programs
P.O. Box 5456
Hanover, NH 03755
(603) 643-3007; Fax: (603) 643-4249
E-mail: rassias@sover.net
Web site: http://www.rassias.com

The Road Less Traveled

Summer (one- to six-week sessions)

See listing Multiple Locations for complete information.

Shakespeare in Italy; Latin in Rome
(University of Dallas Summer Programs Abroad for High School Students)

Mid July-early August (Shakespeare in Italy); Late June- mid July (Latin in Rome) (3-week programs)

Like the University's two programs in England, the Italy programs instruct talented students and awaken within them a genuine and abiding interest in the history, politics, literature, theology, art, and architecture. The Shakespeare program focuses on two of the many plays Shakespeare set in Italy. Depicting different epochs—from the early moments of the Roman Republic, through the decline of the Empire, to the artistic heights of Italian Renaissance—these plays provide a vital means to convey the basic outlines of the Western Tradition. Students in the Latin program encounter the writings of Livy, Virgil, and Cicero, each in the original Latin, with other course readings supporting study of the development of Rome from the Republic through the Empire. In both programs, travel will complement the academic focus—the Shakespeare group enjoys travel throughout Rome, Florence, and Assisi, while the Latin group explores Rome and Naples. Successful students earn three transferable college credits.

Criteria: Application; transcript; recommendations; GPA; PSAT or SAT; diagnostic essay; 3 years of high school Latin (for Latin in Rome).

Grade: Rising 11-12.

Cost: $3,650 (plus airfare).

Contact: Aaron Thurow, Summer Programs Coordinator
Rome and Summer Programs Office
University of Dallas
1845 E. Northgate Drive
Irving, TX 75062
(972) 721-5181; Fax: (972) 721-5283
E-mail: udsummer@acad.udallas.edu
Web site: http://www.udallas.edu/udtravel

Spanish on the Road Program in the Mexican Central Highlands (Knowledge Exchange Institute)
June-August

The Spanish on the Road Program in the Mexican Central Highlands is designed for serious students interested in Spanish language, Mexican society, and Latin American culture studies. Students learn the Spanish language in its natural environment and become immersed in the culture and society through travel in large cities, countryside villages, and coastal beaches; conversations with people; visits to indigenous locations and archeological sites; cultural activities and sightseeing; and homestay and peer related activities. The travel itinerary includes the following locations: Mexico City, Teotihuacan (Aztec capital and pyramids), Tepotzolan and Tula, Queretaro, San Miguel de Allende, Guanajuato, Guadalajara, Morella, Patzucuaro Islands of Janitzio, Yunnuen, Tzintzuntzan and Quiroga Lakeside villages, Playa Azul, Uruopan (Volcano of Paricutin), Toluca, Zitacuaro, Metepec, Malinalco Pyramids, and Shrine at Chalma. Students are accompanied by a professor from Alliant International University. Program costs include academics, textbooks, six college credits, room and board, on-site support, medical and travel insurance, roundtrip travel, airport and ground transportation, field trips, and sightseeing, cultural and professional excursions.

Criteria: Application (deadline: March 20); $50 application fee; transcript; personal essay; recommendations; interview (by phone or in person).

Grade: 9-12.

Cost: $4,950. Partial financial aid is available.

Contact: Eduard Izraylovsky, Principal Director
Knowledge Exchange Institute
Center for International Studies
111 John Street, Suite 800
New York, NY 10038
(800) 831-5095; (212) 931-9953; Fax: (866) 831-5095; (212) 528-2095
E-mail: cis@knowledgeexchange.org
Web site: http://www.knowledgeexchange.org

Spring Break in Paris (The Center for Gifted Studies, Western Kentucky University)
April 4-13

Spring Break in Paris is an opportunity for gifted eighth graders, high school honors students, and interested adults to spend spring break learning about the history, culture, pageantry, and people of France. This program, sponsored by The Center for Gifted Studies at Western Kentucky University, is designed to provide participants with a carefully structured experience in Paris and selected points of interest outside Paris. The itinerary in Paris includes visits to the Eiffel Tower, the Musée d'Orsay, Montmartre and the Church of the Sacred Heart, Notre Dame Cathedral, Sainte-Chapelle, the Conciergerie, the Musée Marmottan, the Louvre, the Arc de Triomphe, and the Tuileries Gardens. Points of interest outside of Paris will include Caen and the Normandy beaches, Rouen, Mont Saint Michel, Giverny (Monet's house and gardens), the Palace and gardens at Versailles, Chartres, and the Chateau de Chenonceau. Twenty-three qualified participants will be accompanied by the program directors.

Criteria: Application; recommendations; participation in a gifted program or high school honors program.

Grade: Rising 8-12 and adults.

Cost: $1,875.

Contact: Dr. Julia Roberts
The Center for Gifted Studies
Western Kentucky University
1 Big Red Way
Bowling Green, KY 42101-3576
(270) 745-6323; Fax: (270) 745-6279
E-mail: gifted@wku.edu
Web site: http://www.wku.edu/gifted/

Summer Challenge In Spain (Center for Gifted Studies at Murray State University)
July 6-18

See listing on page 101 for complete information.

Summer Discovery Pre-College Enrichment Programs
June-August (three- to six-week programs)

See listing on page 12 for complete information.

Summer in Switzerland (Leysin American School in Switzerland)
June 28-July 18 (Session 1); July 19-August 8 (Session 2)

Summer in Switzerland (SIS) offers students academics, recreational activities, and cultural excursions. Students enroll in one or two three-week sessions and are grouped by age (9-12, 13-15, 16-19). Students attend morning classes and participate in activities during afternoons and evenings. Courses include foreign languages, mathematics, English, computers, performing and creative arts, photography, SAT prep, and more. A specialized program, **Theater International**, allows students to focus on their theatrical skills in an international setting. An intensive **Leadership Adventure** program shows students how to lead trips which include rock climbing, hiking, paragliding, overnight camping, and whitewater rafting. All students participate in a variety of sports and cultural excursions. Weeklong optional highlight tours to France and Italy are offered to students ages 13-19, prior to the first session and after the second session. SIS is part of the Leysin American School in Switzerland, a coeducational American/International boarding school.

Criteria: Application (deadline: June 1); application fee ($500: applied toward tuition); transcript; recommendations.

Grade: Ages 9-19.

Cost: $3,000 (one session); $5,600 (two sessions). Financial aid is available.

Contact: Paul E. Dyer, U.S. Director of Admissions
Summer in Switzerland
P.O. Box 7154
Portsmouth, NH 03802
(888)642-4142; Fax: (603) 431-1280
E-mail: usadmissions@las.ch
Web site: http://www.las.ch/summer

TASIS Schools and Summer Programs in Europe
Academic Year; Summer (three-, four- and six-week programs)

The TASIS Schools and Summer Programs are two full-year schools and seven summer programs in Europe for students ranging in age from 6-18. TASIS, **The American School in Switzerland**, was founded in 1956 by M. Crist Fleming, one of the leaders in international education, and it is the longest-established American boarding school in Europe. Today it serves 270 boarding and day students (grades 7-12, PG). **The American School in England** is frequently cited as the premier American school in the United Kingdom. Now in its third decade, the school offers an American college preparatory curriculum to 600 day students (grades K-12) and 150 boarders (grades 9-12). Summer Programs are held on both campuses each summer with programs including foreign language study, Architecture and Design, Expository Writing, Photography in Switzerland, math, science, computer graphics, English courses, SAT Review, and theatre programs in England. TASIS also offers an intense French language program in Chateau d'Oex, Switzerland, a Spanish program in Salamanaca, Spain, and the Tuscan Academy of Art and Culture in Tuscany, Italy. All programs include sports and travel.

Criteria: Academic Year: Application (and fee); transcript; personal essay; recommendations; test scores; GPA; PSAT; SAT; ACT; SSAT; Summer Program: application (and fee); teacher recommendation.

Grade: The American School in Switzerland: 7-12, PG; The American School in England: PreK-12; Summer Programs: Age 6-18.

Cost: $29,000 (academic year); $3,550-$5,400 (summer). Financial aid is available for the academic year only.

Contact: Toni Soulé, U.S. Representative
The TASIS Schools and Summer Programs
1640 Wisconsin Avenue, NW
Washington, DC 20007
(202) 965-5800; Fax: (202) 965-5816
E-mail:usadmissions@tasis.com
Web site: http://www.tasis.com

TIP International Field Studies (Duke University Talent Identification Program)
June 15-August 6 (two-week programs)

See listing on page 182 for complete information.

Winston Churchill in England; Thomas More in England (University of Dallas Summer Programs Abroad for High School Students)

Mid July-early August (3-week programs)

Like the University's two programs in Italy, the two England programs strive to avoid thoughtless tourism—indeed, the goal of these unique international programs is to make study and travel mutually enhancing. The two England programs fall under the heading "Case Studies in Leadership," a course series aimed at providing serious students with grounding in the fundamental principles of great leadership. To understand more clearly the challenges of great leadership, students in the More program investigate the life, times, and diverse writings of the brilliant lawyer and statesman, Sir Thomas More. The Churchill program focuses on the figure of Winston Churchill, one of the twentieth century's greatest statesmen. The course introduces students to the importance of historical mindedness and intellectual culture in the shaping of a true leader dedicated to the ideal of human liberty. Both programs complement the academic focus with thoughtful travel throughout London, Oxford, Cambridge, and Canterbury. Successful participants earn three transferable college credits. University of Dallas Summer Abroad also offers a Shakespeare in Italy program and a Latin in Rome program.

Criteria: Application; transcript; recommendations; GPA; PSAT or SAT.

Grade: Rising 11-12.

Cost: $3,650 (plus airfare).

Contact: Aaron Thurow, Summer Programs Coordinator
Rome and Summer Programs Office
University of Dallas
1845 E. Northgate Drive
Irving, TX 75062
(972) 721-5181; Fax: (972) 721-5283
E-mail: udsummer@acad.udallas.edu
Web site: http://www.udallas.edu/udtravel

RESOURCES

The following pages provide a selective sampling of various resources available to anyone interested in gifted education. Parents, educators, and students are encouraged to seek additional resources not listed here.

NATIONAL ASSOCIATIONS FOR THE GIFTED

AMERICAN ASSOCIATION FOR GIFTED CHILDREN AT DUKE UNIVERSITY
Box 90270
Durham, NC 27708-0270
(919) 783-6152
Web site: www.aagc.org/index.html

THE COUNCIL FOR EXCEPTIONAL CHILDREN
ERIC Clearinghouse on Disabilities and Gifted Education
1110 North Glebe Road
Arlington, VA 22201-5704
(800) 328-0272
E-mail: ericec@cec.sped.org
Web site: ericec.org

THE GIFTED CHILD SOCIETY
190 Rock Road
Glen Rock, NJ 07452-1736
(201) 444-6530
E-mail: admin@gifted.org
Web site: www.gifted.org

GIFTED STUDENTS INSTITUTE
Southern Methodist University
P.O. Box 750383
Dallas, TX 75275-0383
(214) 768-5437
Web site: http://www2.smu.edu/continuing_education/gsi

NATIONAL ASSOCIATION FOR GIFTED CHILDREN (NAGC)
1707 L Street, NW, Suite 550
Washington, DC 20036
(202) 785-4268
Web site: www.nagc.org

NATIONAL RESEARCH CENTER ON THE GIFTED AND TALENTED
University of Connecticut
2131 Hillside Road, U-7
Storrs, CT 06269-3007
(860) 486-4676
E-mail: renzulli@uconnvm.uconn.edu
Web site: www.ucc.uconn.edu/~wwwgt/nrcgt.html

SUPPORTING EMOTIONAL NEEDS OF THE GIFTED (SENG)
P.O. Box 6550
Scottsdale, AZ 85261
(602) 399-9090; E-mail: senggifted@attbi.com
Web site: www.SENGifted.org

WORLD COUNCIL FOR GIFTED AND TALENTED CHILDREN, INC.
18401 Hiawatha St.
Northridge, CA 91326
(818) 368-7501; E-mail: worldgt@earthlink.net
Web site: www.worldgifted.org

NATIONAL SCHOLARSHIPS FOR THE GIFTED

Davidson Young Scholars
http:www.davidsoninstitute.org
Recognizes, nurtures, and supports the needs of profoundly gifted, ages 4-18. Applications must be completed by March 28, 2003.

National Gifted Children's Fund
http://www.ngcfcharity.org
Assists profoundly gifted youth with educational materials to enhance their education. Aid is provided to individuals, not organizations, based on financial and academic needs.

Jack Kent Cooke Foundation Young Scholars Program
http://jackkentcookefoundation.org
Provides highly gifted youth, with financial need, individualized educational services thoughout high school. Applications for this scholarship must be completed by May 1, 2003.

Select Readings

A Parent Guide to Talent Development During the Elementary Years. Pfeiffer, S. and Olszewski- Kubilius, P., and Limburg-Weber, L. (Waco, TX: Prufrock Press, 2001).

College Countdown: The Parent's and Student's Survival Kit for the College Admissions Process. VonGruben, J. (New York, NY: McGraw-Hill, 2000).

The Duke Gifted Letter. Duke University Talent Identification Program.

Education of the Gifted and Talented. Davis, G. and Rimm, S. (Needham Heights, MA: Allyn and Bacon, 1997).

Gifted Children: Myths and Realities. Winner, E. (New York, NY: Basic Books, 1997).

Guiding the Gifted Child: A Practical Source for Parents and Teachers. Webb, J., Tolan, S., and Meckstroth, E. (Scottsdale, AZ: Gifted Psychology Press, 1983).

Handbook of Gifted Children. Colangelo, N. and Davis, G. (Needham Heights, MA: Allyn and Bacon, 1996).

Keys to Parenting the Gifted Child. Rimm, S. (Hauppauge, NY: Barron's Educational Series, 2001).

Parents' Guide to Raising a Gifted Child. Alvino, J. (New York, NY: Random House, 1996).

Reforming Gifted Education: Matching the Program to the Child. Rogers, Karen B. (Scotsdale, AZ: Great Potential Press, Inc., 2002).

Smart Girls: A New Psychology of Girls, Women, and Giftedness. Kerr, B. (Scottsdale, AZ: Gifted Psychology Press, 1997).

Some of My Best Friends Are Books: Guiding Gifted Readers from Pre-School to High School. Halsted, J. (Scottsdale, AZ: Gifted Psychology Press, 2002).

The Drama of the Gifted Child: The Search for the True Self. Miller, A. and Ward, R. (New York, NY: HarperCollins Publishers, 1996).

The Gifted Kids' Survival Guide: A Teen Handbook. Galbraith, J. and Delisle, J. (Minneapolis, MN: Free Spirit Publishing, 1997).

The Survival Guide for Parents of Gifted Kids: How to Understand, Live With, and Stick Up for Your Gifted Child. Walker, S. (Minneapolis, MN: Free Spirit Publishing, 2002).

The Teenagers' Guide to School Outside the Box. Greene, R. (Minneapolis, MN: Free Spirit Publishing, 2001).

Young Women of Achievement: a Resource for Girls in Science, Math, and Technology. Karnes, Frances A. and Stephens, Kristen R. (Amherst, NY: Prometheus Books, 2002).

Directories of Educational Programs

Peterson's Private Secondary Schools: The Ultimate Resource for Private School Education. (Peterson's Publishing, 2002).

American and Canadian Boarding Schools and Worldwide Enrichment Programs. (Peterson's Publishing, 2002).

The Directory for Exceptional Children. Porter Sargent Staff and McKeever, Daniel P. (Porter Sargent Publishing, 2001).

A Directory of Educational Programs for the Gifted. Axford, Lavonne B. (Scarecrow Press)

The New 2002 Oxford Guide: An Encyclopedia Directory of Non Traditional College Educational Opportunities Including Non-Residential Programs in the United States. (Wyndham Hall Press, 2001)

Vincent Curtis Educational Register. (Boston: VincentCurtis, 2001).

Internet Resources

General Information

AMERICAN SCHOOL DIRECTORY
http://www.asd.com
A search site containing vital information about public and private schools by city, county, and state.

THE EDUCATION HOUND
http://www.eduhound.com
A search site for educational topics including state standards and student resources.

U.S. DEPARTMENT OF EDUCATION
http://www.ed.gov

Organizations

IDEA PRACTICES
http://www.ideapractices.org/
This Web site specializes in answering questions about the Individuals with Disabilities Education Act and supports efforts for all children to learn, progress, and realize their dreams.

THE ASSOCIATION FOR THE GIFTED
http://education.idbsu.edu/tag/
A division of The Council for Exceptional Children, the Web site includes items of interest for parents and children: information and links on legislative efforts; parenting questions answered on-line; interesting and exciting links for kids.

NATIONAL NETWORK OF FAMILIES WITH GIFTED CHILDREN
http://www.nnfgc.org/
A grassroots cyber organization of families supporting the needs of gifted learners; focuses on legislation and advocacy.

GT WORLD
http://www.gtworld.org/
An on-line support community for parents of gifted and talented children.

FAMILIES OF THE TALENTED AND GIFTED
http://users.erols.com/reking/tagfam.html

TAG FAMILY NETWORK
http://www.teleport.com/~rkaltwas/tag/
An organization dedicated to appropriate education for talented and gifted youth and advocacy. Maintained by and for parents, the group disseminates information, supports parents, and monitors and influences legal issues.

ALL KINDS OF MINDS
http://www.allkindsofminds.org
Undertakes applied research, product development, program design, and professional training to foster the understanding and optimal care of children with differences in learning.

Resource Pages

THE HOAGIE'S GIFTED EDUCATION PAGE
http://www.hoagiesgifted.org
Provides information and resources for gifted children and their parents.

GIFTED DEVELOPMENT CENTER RESOURCE PAGE
http://www.gifteddevelopment.com/TOC/ResourceTOC.html

THE SHODOR FOUNDATION INSITES
http://www.shodor.org/insites/
Provides links to Internet sites related to computational science.

NATIONAL FOUNDATION FOR GIFTED AND CREATIVE CHILDREN
http://www.nfgcc.org
Web site includes a message board, parents and children's chat room, pen pal list, and referral list along with articles, links, especially on controversial medications, etc.

GIFTED RESOURCES HOME PAGE
http://www.eskimo.com/~user/kids.html

SOUTHWESTERN OPPORTUNITIES NETWORK, TALENTED AND GIFTED BIBLIOGRAPHY
http://www.swopnet.com/ed/TAG/TAG_Bibliography.html
List of books and articles for parents of talented and gifted children.

SEE JANE WIN
http://www.seejanewin.com
Sponsored by child psychologist and author Dr. Sylvia Rimm, the site is intended to help daughters and women become successful.

GREAT POTENTIAL PRESS, INC.
http://www.giftedbooks.com
Publishes books for parents and teachers of gifted, talented, and creative children.

HOLLINGWORTH CENTER
http://www.hollingworth.org
A national volunteer resource and support network maintained by the Hollingworth Center for highly gifted children, their families, schools and communities.

INDEPENDENT STUDY OPPORTUNITIES

THE UNIVERSITY OF TEXAS AT AUSTIN DISTANCE EDUCATION CENTER
Phone: (512) 232-5000, (888) 232-4723
E-mail: dec@www.utexas.edu
Web site: www.utexas.edu/cee/dec
Offers on-line middle school and high school courses.

APEX LEARNING
Phone: (800) 453-1454
E-mail: inquiries@apexlearning.com
Web site: www.apex.netu.com
Offers on-line Advanced Placement and foreign language courses.

EDUCATION PROGRAM FOR GIFTED YOUTH
Ventura Hall
Stanford University
Stanford, CA 94305-4115
(800) 372-EPGY
Email: epgy-info@epgy.stanford.edu
Web site: www-epgy.stanford.edu/
Offers elementary, secondary, Advanced Placement, and university-level courses on-line.

DUKE UNIVERSITY TALENT IDENTIFICATION PROGRAM
Independent Study Program
P.O. Box 90747
Durham, NC 27701
Phone: (919) 683-1400
Web site: www.tip.duke.edu
Enrichment courses available in booklet form and on CDs that can be completed by students with the assistance of a mentor.

EXTENSION'S CENTER FOR MEDIA AND INDEPENDENT LEARNING (UNIVERSITY OF CALIFORNIA
Phone: (510) 642-4124
E-mail: askus@ucxonline.berkeley.edu
Web site: www.learn.berkeley.edu
Offers independent study and on-line courses.

THE UNIVERSITY OF NEBRASKA -LINCOLN
Independent Study High School
P.O. Box 839801
Lincoln, NE 68583-9801
Phone: (402) 472-4422; E-mail: unlishs2@unl.edu
Web site: www.unl.edu/ishs/
Offers college preparatory and general high school courses.

KEYSTONE NATIONAL HIGH SCHOOL
School House Station
420 W. 5th St.
Bloomsburg, PA 17815-1564
Phone: 1-800-255-4937 or (570) 784-5220
Web site:w ww.keystonehighschool.com/home.htm
Offers independent study and on-line learning opportunities.

FLORIDA VIRTUAL SCHOOL
Phone: (407) 317-3326; E-mail: info@flvs.net
Web site: www.flvs.net
On-line courses for students in grades 9-12, including Advanced Placement. Free for Florida residents.

ADVANCED ACADEMICS
100 East California Avenue
Suite 200
Oklahoma City, OK 73104
Phone: 1-866-2-eLEARN (1-866-235-3276)
Email: info@advancedacademics.com
Web site: www.advancedacademics.com
Offers on-line courses for grades 6-12.

KENTUCKY VIRTUAL HIGH SCHOOL
Web site: www.kvhs.org
Phone: (866) 432-0008 ,(502) 564-4772
Offers general and Advanced Placement high school courses to Kentucky residents.

CYBERSCHOOL
Phone: 1-877-838-6038
Web site: www.cyberschool.k12.or.us
Offers on-line general and Advanced Placement High School courses.

ILLINOIS VIRTUAL HIGH SCHOOL
Contact: Mr. Matthew Wicks
Director of Virtual Learning
Illinois Math and Science Academy
1500 W. Sullivan Rd.
Aurora, IL 60506
Web site: www.ivhs.org/
Offers general and Advanced Placement high school courses.

NORTH DAKOTA DIVISION OF INDEPENDENT STUDY
Phone: (701) 231-6006
Web site: www.NDISonline.org
Offers middle school, high school, and dual credit on-line courses.

CENTER FOR TALENTED YOUTH
The John Hopkins University
3400 N Charles St
Baltimore, MD 21218
Phone: (410) 516-0277
Email: ctyinfo@jhu.edu
Web site: www.jhu.edu/gifted/cde/
Offers writing and math tutorials.

CENTER FOR TALENT DEVELOPMENT
LetterLinks Program
Northwestern University
2003 Sheridan Road
Evanston, IL 60208
Phone: (847) 491-3782
E-mail ctd@northwestern.edu
Web site: www.ctd.northwestern.edu/index.html
Offers on-line and correspondence courses for students in grades 6-12 (including Advanced Placement).

Academic Competitions and Activities

The competitions, contests, and activities listed in this section have been compiled from a variety of sources. Sponsoring organizations, addresses, and the focus of a contest may change without notice. Some competitions can be entered independently by students, whereas others require support from a teacher or school.

Humanities

AMERICAN HIGH SCHOOL ORATORICAL CONTEST
American Legion
Phone: (317) 630-1200
Web site: www.legion.org
Grade: 9-12

AMERICAN HISTORY ESSAY CONTEST
Phone: (202) 879-3253
Web site: www.dar.org
Grade: 7-8

ANN ARLYS BOWLER POETRY CONTEST
Weekly Reader Corporation
Web site: http://www.weeklyreader.com/teens/read/bowlers_poetry_contest.asp
Grade: 6-12

ANTHOLOGY OF POETRY BY YOUNG AMERICANS
American Academy of Poetry
Phone: (336) 626-7762
Web site: www.anthologyofpoetry.com
Grade: K-12

ARTS RECOGNITION AND TALENT SEARCH (ARTS)
National Foundation for the Advancement of the Arts
Phone: (800) 970-ARTS
Web site: www.nfaa.org
Grade: 12

GERMAN TESTING AND AWARDS PROGRAM
American Association of Teachers of German
Phone: (856) 795-5553
Web site: www.aatg.org
Grade: 9-12

HIGH SCHOOL COMMUNICATION CONTEST
National Federation of Press Women
Phone: (785) 594-3846
Web site: www.nfpw.org
Grade: 9-12

THE INTERNATIONAL THESPIAN SOCIETY
Educational Theatre Association
Phone: (513) 421-3900
eb site: www.edta.org
Age: 12-18

KIDS PHILOSOPHY SLAM
Phone: (507)467-2446
ebsite: www.philosphyslam.org
Grade: 1-12

LETTERS ABOUT LITERATURE
Weekly Reader Corporation
Web site: http://www.weeklyreader.com/teens/read/letters_about_literature.asp
Grade: 4-12

LOUIS/BOURNE STUDENT POETRY AWARD
Poetry Society of America
Phone: (800) USA-POEM
Web site: www.poetrysociety.org
Grade: 9-12

MERLYN'S PEN CONTEST AND CRITIQUE
Phone: (800) 247-2027
Web site: www.merlynspen.com
Grade: 5-12

MUSIC TEACHERS NATIONAL ASSOCIATION CONTESTS
Music Teachers National Association
Phone: (513) 421-1420
Web site: http://www.mtna.org
Grade: 1-12

NATIONAL GEOGRAPHY BEE
National Geographic
Phone: (202) 828-6659
Web site: www.nationalgeographic.com/society/ngo/geobee
Grade: 4-8

NJCL/ACL NATIONAL GREEK/LATIN EXAMS
National Junior Classical League
Phone: (800) 459-9847
Web site: www.vroma.org/~nle
Grade: 9-12

NATIONAL MYTHOLOGY EXAM
American Classical League
Miami University of Ohio
Phone: (513) 529-7741
Web site: www.mythologyexam.org
Grade: 3-9

NATIONAL (LANGUAGE ARTS, SOCIAL STUDIES, SCIENCE, GEOGRAPHY) OLYMPIADS
Phone: (516) 584-2016
Web site: olympiads.win.tue.nl
Grade: 7-12

NATIONAL PEACE ESSAY CONTEST
United States Institute of Peace
Phone: (202) 429-3854
Web site: www.usip.org/ed/npec/index.shtml
Grade: 9-12

HUMANITIES (CONTINUED)

NATIONAL SPEECH TOURNAMENT
National Forensic League
Phone: (414) 748-6206
Web site: debate.uvm.edu/wdi.html
Grade: 9-12

WRITING AND ART CONTEST ON THE OLOCAUST
U.S. Holocaust Memorial Museum
Phone: (202) 488-0400
Web site: www.ushmm.org/education/forstudents
Grade: 7-12

NATIONAL WRITING AND PHOTOGRAPHY CONTEST
Quill and Scroll Society
Phone: (319) 335-5795
Web site: www.uiowa.edu/~quill-sc
Grade: 10-12

NATIONAL WRITTEN AND ILLUSTRATED BY . . . AWARDS CONTEST
Phone: (800) 653-2665
Web site: www.landmarkeditions.com
Grade: K-12

THE RALPH WALDO EMERSON PRIZE
The Concord Review
Phone: (800) 331-5007
Web site: www.tcr.org
Grade: 9-12

PROMISING YOUNG WRITERS PROGRAM
National Council of Teachers of English
Phone: (800) 369-NCTE
Web site: www.ncte.org
Grade: 8

READ WRITING AND ART AWARDS
Read Magazine
Phone: (203) 705-3500
Web site: www.weeklyreader.com
Grade: K-12

SCHOLASTIC ART, PHOTOGRAPHY, AND WRITING AWARDS
Alliance for Young Artists and Writers
Phone: (212) 343-6493
Web site: www.scholastic.com/artandwriting
Grade: 7-12

SCRIPPS HOWARD NATIONAL SPELLING BEE
The E.W. Scripps Company
Phone: (800) NSB-WORD
Web site: www.spellingbee.com
Grade: 1-8

SPANISH: NATIONAL SPANISH EXAMINATION
American Association of Teachers of Spanish and Portuguese
Phone: (303) 278-1021
Grade: 7-12

STONE SOUP (THE MAGAZINE BY CHILDREN)
Children's Art Foundation
Phone: (800) 447-4569
Web site: www.stonesoup.com
Age: 6-13

THE WRITING CONFERENCE CONTESTS
The Writing Conference, Inc.
Phone: (913) 681-8894
eb site: www.writingconference.com
Grade: K-12

YOUNG PLAYWRIGHTS FESTIVAL NATIONAL PLAYWRITING COMPETITION
Phone: (212) 307-1140
Web site: ww.youngplaywrights.org/national/htm
Age: 18 or younger

MULTIDISCIPLINARY

LET'S GET REAL
Contact: Dr. Dan Holt
Website:www.lgreal.org
Grade:6-12

NATIONAL CHESS CHAMPIONSHIPS
U.S. Chess Federation
Phone: (845) 562-8350
Web site: www.uschess.org
Grade: K-12

ODYSSEY OF THE MIND
Creative Competitions, Inc.
Phone: (856) 456-7776
Web site: www.odysseyofthemind.com
Grade: K-12, college

QUIZ BOWL TOURNAMENT OF CHAMPIONS
American Scholastic Competition Network
Phone: (800) 252-4289
Web site: morningside.edu/ascn
Grade: 9-12

U.S. SENATE YOUTH PROGRAM
William Randolph Hearst Foundation
Contact: David Hellwig
Phone: (800) 841-7048
Web site: www.isbe.state.il.us/hearst/
Grade: 11-12

Mathematics

AMERICAN MATHEMATICS COMPETITIONS
University of Nebraska-Lincoln
Phone: (402) 472-6566
Web site: www.unl.edu/amc
Grade: 7-12

CONTINENTAL MATHEMATICS LEAGUE
Phone: (516) 265-4792
Web site: ww.continentalmathleague.hostrack.com
Grade: 2-12

INTERNATIONAL COMPUTER PROBLEM- SOLVING CHALLENGE
Phone: (414) 634-0868
Grade: 4-12

INTERNATIONAL MATH OLYMPICS
Youth Net
Web site: youth.net/math.oly/mo.html
Grade: K-12

INTERNET MATHEMATICS CONTEST
Contact: Douglas Zare
Phone: (818) 395-4366
Web site: www.math.columbia.edu/~zare/ontest.html
Grade: K-12, PG

MANDELBROT COMPETITION
Greater Testing Concepts
Phone: (617) 661-3188
Website: www.mandelbrot.org
Grade: 9-12

MATHCOUNTS FOUNDATION
Phone: (703) 684-2828
Web site: mathcounts.org
Grade: 7-8

MATH LEAGUE CONTESTS
Math League Press
Phone: (201) 568-6328
Web site: www.mathleague.com
Grade: 4-12

MATHMAGIC
MathMagic Foundation
Contact: Alan Hodson
Phone: (800) 756-7823
Web site: mathforum.com/mathmagic
Grade: K-12

MATHEMATICAL OLYMPIADS FOR ELEMENTARY SCHOOLS
Contact: Dr. George Lenchner
Phone: (516) 781-2400
Web site: www.moems.org
Grade: 1-6

USA MATHEMATICAL TALENT SEARCH
Consortium for Mathematics
Phone: (800) 772-6627
Web site: www.comap.com
Grade: 9-12

Sciences

DUPONT CHALLENGE: SCIENCE ESSAY AWARDS
Phone: (847) 205-3000
Web site: www.glcomm.com/dupont
Grade: 7-12

INTEL SCIENCE TALENT SEARCH
Science Service, Inc.
Phone: (202) 785-2255
Web site: www.sciserv.org/sts/
Grade: 12

INTERNATIONAL BRIDGE BUILDING CONTEST
Illinois Institute of Technology
Contact: Carlo Segre
Phone: (312) 567-3498
Web site: www.iit.edu/~hsbridge
Grade: 9-12

INTERNATIONAL PHYSICS OLYMPIAD
American Association of Physics Teachers Science Service, Inc.
Phone: (202) 785-2255
Web site: www.sciserv.org
Grade: 9-12

NATIONAL SCIENCE BOWL
United States Department of Energy
Phone: (202) 586-7231
Web site: www.scied.science.doc.gov/nsb/
Grade: 9-12

PRESIDENT'S ENVIRONMENTAL YOUTH AWARDS
U.S. Environmental Protection Agency
Phone: (202) 260-8749
Web site: www.epa.gov/enviroed/awards.html
Grade: K-12

TESTS OF ENGINEERING APTITUDE, MATHEMATICS, AND SCIENCE
Junior Engineering Technical Society (JETS)
Phone: (703) 548-5387
Web site: www.jets.org/teams.htm
Grade: 9-12

U.S. NATIONAL CHEMISTRY OLYMPIAD
Phone: (202) 872-6328
Web site: www.org/education/student/olympiad/html
Grade: 9-12

INDEX

**Academic Year Private Schools, 298
Summer Programs, 299
Programs That Grant College Credit, 303
Leadership, Law and Politics, Business Programs, 304
Visual and Performing Arts, Creative Writing/Literature/Journalism Programs, 304
Wilderness/Outdoor Adventure Programs, 305
Math, Computer Science, and Engineering Programs, 306
Weekend Programs, 306
Laboratory/Internship Programs
Physical Sciences, Life Sciences, Ecology/Environmental Science Programs, 307**

ACADEMIC YEAR PRIVATE SCHOOLS

Academy at the Lakes, 64
Admiral Farragut Academy, 66
Advanced Academy of Georgia, The, 74
Altamont School, The, 14
Arthur I. Meyer Jewish Academy, 70
Arthur Morgan School, 173
Asheville School, 171
Batten Scholars Program, The, 89
Baylor School, The, 226
Beaufort Academy, 216
Berkeley Preparatory School, 68
Brooks School, 124
Canterbury School (CT), 47
Canterbury School (FL), 61
Cardigan Mountain School, 154
Cate School, 28
Chatham Hall, 256
Christ School, 170
Concord Academy, 118
Cushing Academy, 114
Dana Hall School, 127
Darlington School, 79
Deerfield Academy, 119
Developing Dimensions Program/Magellan Day School, EPL, 271
Educational Programs Overseas, 276
Episcopal High School, 254
Episcopal School of Dallas, 237
Fountain Valley School of Colorado, 39
Foxcroft School, 258
GAMES—Georgia Academy of Mathematics, Engineering, and Science, 75
Genesis Preparatory School, 63
George School, 209
Groton School, 122
Gunnery, The, 49
Hammond School, 218
Hathaway Brown School, 197
Heathwood Hall Episcopal School, 218
Idyllwild Arts Academy, 30
Indian Springs School, 15
Interlocken Center for Experiential Learning, 9
Kent School, 44
Kiski School, The, 212
Lake Highland Preparatory School, 64
Language Studies Abroad, 280
Lawrence Academy, 122
Lee Academy for Gifted Education, 70
Linsly School, The, 269
Loomis Chaffee School, The, 51
Maclay School, 67
Maine Coast Semester, The, 108
McCallie School, The, 228
Mercersburg Academy, 208
Middlesex School, 118
Mirman School for Gifted Children, The, 31
Miss Hall's School, 125
Montgomery Academy, The, 17

INDEX 299

New School of Orlando, 65
Oak Ridge Military Academy, 187
Oldfields School, 110
Peddie School, The, 158
Perkiomen School, 210
Phillips Exeter Academy, 155
Program for the Exceptionally Gifted (Mary Baldwin College), 260
Quest Academy, 86
Rabun Gap-Nacoochee School, 78
Roeper School, The, 131
Saint James School, 110
Saint Mary's Hall, 244
Salem Academy, 191
Santa Catalina School, 32
Seacrest Country Day School, 62
Shattuck-St. Mary's School, 137
Simon's Rock College of Bard, 120
St. Andrew's School, 52
St. Andrew's-Sewanee School, 232
St. Anne's-Belfield School, 254
St. Catherine's School, 259
St. Gregory College Preparatory School, 23
St. Johnsbury Academy, 251
St. Timothy's School, 111
Taft School, The, 50
Tampa Preparatory School, 69
TASIS Schools and Summer Programs in Europe, 288
Thacher School, The, 32
Thomas Jefferson School, 147
Trinity Preparatory School, 71
Unity School, 60
University School, 60
Virginia Episcopal School, 25
Virginia Governor's Schools, 252
Wayland Academy, 270
Webb School, The, 226
Western Reserve Academy, 196
Westminster School, 48
Wilbraham and Monson Academy, 128
Williston Northampton School, The, 120
Wilson Hall, 223
Young Scholars Program (Gould Academy), 106

SUMMER PROGRAMS

Those designated with a **C** *are commuter-only programs. Those designated with an* **R** *provide boarding.*

Academy for Creative Engineering/Academy for Legal Thought and Action, 94 R
Acadia Institute of Oceanography, 107 R
ACES—Access to Careers in the Sciences, 238 R
Ad Astra, 152 R
ADVANCE Program for Young Scholars, The, 102 R
Advanced Academy of Georgia, The, 74 R
Advanced Program in Technology and Science, 139 R
Alabama School of Math and Science, 16 R
All-Arts and Sciences Camp, 186 C, R
Altamont School, The, 14 C
Apogee/Spectrum/Equinox Summer Programs, 3 C, R

INDEX

Appalachian Institute for Creative Learning, 256 R
Arete, 152 R
Arts Alive!, 42 R
Astrocamp, 28 C, R
Astronomy Camps, 22 R
Atlanta Workshop Players—"Destiny" Performing Arts Experience, 73 C, R
Barnard's Summer in New York: A Pre-College Program, 166 C, R
Buck's Rock Performing and Creative Arts Camp, 46 R
Burgundy Center for Wildlife Studies, 268 R
Camp Baylor, 227 R
Camp Broadstone Summer Enrichment Program for Gifted and Talented Youth, 172 R
Camp CAEN, 130 C, R
Capstone Summer Honors Program, 18 R
Catalina Sea Camp, 29 R
CATS SUMMERSTARS: Comprehensive Theatre Workshop, 234 R
Center for Creative Youth, 46 R
Center for Talented Youth, 4 C, R
College Experience (Southern Methodist University), 238 R
College Horizons, 265 R
Concordia Language Villages, 136 R
Congressional Student Leadership Conference, 8 R
Constructing Your College Experience, 177 R
Crow Canyon Archaeological Center, 40 R
Cullowhee Experience, The, 176 R
CY-TAG, 92 R
Darlington School, 79 R
DASH, 84 C
Davidson July Experience, 176 R
Deer Hill Expeditions, 38 R
Developing Dimensions Program/Magellan Day School, EPL, 271 C
Discover Spain and Portugal Program, 275 R
Discovery Hall Summer High School Program, 16 R
Drury Leadership Academy, 149 C, R
Duke Action Science Camp for Young Women, 178 C, R
Duke Creative Writers' Workshop, 178 R
Duke Drama Workshop, The, 179 R
Duke Young Writers' Camp, 180 C, R
ECOES—Exploring Career Options in Engineering and Science, 159 R
Education Unlimited Summer Learning Adventures, 27 C, R
Educational Programs Overseas, 276 R
Engineering, Mathematics, and Computer Sciences Summer Institute, 250 R
Environmental Studies Summer Youth Program, 165 R
European Capitals Program, 276 R
EXCEL Programs, 9 R
Exploration Intermediate Program, 128 C, R
Exploration Junior Program, 126 C, R
Exploration Senior Program, 45 C, R
Explorations in Engineering, 132 R
EXPLORATIONS!, 92 R
Explore-A-College, 90 R
Exploring Your Options, 87 R
Firespark, 76 R
Future Astronaut Training Program, 96 C
Gifted and Talented Lyceum, 200 R
Governor's School of South Carolina, The, 216 R
Governor's Program for Gifted Children (LA), 104 R
Governor's Scholars Program (KY), 99 R
Harvard Secondary School Program, 117 R

INDEX 301

High School Journalism Institute, 88 R
High School Summer Scholars Program (Washington University), 146 R
High School Summer Science Research Fellowship Program (Baylor University), 246 R
Honors Orchestra Program, 133 R
Honors Symposium, 25 R
Horizons Unlimited Gifted and Talented Academy, 200 C, R
Idyllwild Arts Academy, 30 R
InnerSpark, 37 R
Interlochen Center for the Arts, 135 R
Interlocken Center for Experiential Learning, 9 R
Intern Exchange International, Ltd., 278 R
International Aerospace Academy, The, 201 C, R
Johns Hopkins Summer Pre-College Program, 109 C, R
Joseph Baldwin Academy for Eminent Young Scholars, The, 146 R
Junior Statesmen Summer School, The (Georgetown University), 54 R
Junior Statesmen Summer School, The (Northwestern University), 85 R
Junior Statesmen Summer School, The (Princeton University), 160 R
Junior Statesmen Summer School, The (Stanford University), 34 R
Junior Statesmen Summer School, The (Yale University), 46 R
Kidcollege.com Arts Camps, 174 C, R
Kidcollege.com Technology Camps, 175 C, R
Lake Highland Preparatory School, 64 C
Language Studies Abroad, 280 C, R
Leadership Studies Program, 144 R
LEARN to LIVE Together, 74 R
Lone Star Scholars Academy, 246 R
Long Island University Center for Gifted Youth, 164 C
LSU Youth Programs, 103 C, R
Maclay School, 67 C
Marine Science Precollege Summer Program, 260 R
MarineQuest, 189 R
Mathematics-Science-Technology Program, The, 132 R
Math-Science-Computer Camps, 140 R
McCallie School, The, 228 R
Mercersburg Adventure Camps, 208 C, R
Midsummer Macon, 77 R
Missouri Scholars Academy, 145 R
MITE2S, 116 R
MPS Summer Challenge, 43 R
National Computer Camps, 10 C
National Junior Leaders Conference, 10 R
National Scholars Academy, 93 R
National Student Leadership Conference, 55 R
National Youth Science Camp, 266 R
New York State Summer School of the Arts, 163 R
North Carolina School of the Arts, 190 R
Oak Ridge Military Academy, 187 R
Oceanology at Occidental College, 31 C, R
Oregon Museum of Science and Industry Science Camps, 205 R
Oxbridge Academic Programs, 281 R
Oxford Advanced Studies Program, 282 R
P.R.I.M.E., 228 R
PATHWAYS, 213 C, R
Paula Program for Young Female Scholars, 90 C
Phillips Academy Summer Session, 113 C, R
Phillips Exeter Academy Summer School, 156 R
Pre College Program for High School Students (Skidmore College), 168 R
Pre-College Academic Experience in Mathematics & Science (Georgetown College), 100 R

Precollege Artist Abroad Program, 282 R
Pre-College Program (Carnegie Mellon University), 211 R
Pre-College Program (Pratt Institute), 164 C, R
Precollege Research Abroad Program, 283 C
Precollege Summer Academy (Southwest Missouri State University), 148 R, C
Pre-College Summer Enrichment Programs, 195 R
Pre-College Summer Institute (The University of the Arts), 210 C, R
Pre-Collegiate Summer Program in Early American History, 261 R
PROMYS, 115 R
Research Science Institute, 116 R
Rhodes Summer Writing Institute, 229 R
Rocky Mountain Talent Search, 5 C, R
Roeper School, The, 131 C
Ross Mathematics Program, 194 R
Saturday/Summer Enrichment Programs for Gifted Learners, 262 C
SCATS—Summer Camp for Academically Talented Middle School Students, 98 R, C
Science at Sea, 129 R
Science Camp Watonka, 207 R
Science Motivation Program, 230 C
Science: It's a Girl Thing, 242 R
Scientific Discovery Program, 140 R
Sea Camp, 240 R
Seacamp, 57 R
SeaWorld/Busch Gardens Adventure Camps (Busch Gardens Tampa Bay), 68 R
SeaWorld/Busch Gardens Adventure Camps (SeaWorld San Antonio), 244
Shake Hands With Your Future, 243 R, C
Shattuck-St. Mary's School, 137 R
Simon's Rock College of Bard, 120 R
Southwest Texas University Honors Summer Math Camp, 245 R
Spanish on the Road Program in the Mexican Central Highlands, 286 R
SPECTACLES Math and Science Camps for Middle School Girls, 78 R
Stanford Discovery Institutes, 36 C
Student Introduction to Engineering, 19 R
Student Science Training Program, 62 R
Summer Academic Adventures, 172 R
Summer Aviation/Aerospace Programs, 59 R
Summer Challenge Camps, 101 R, C
Summer College (University of Delaware), 53 R
Summer College for High School Students (Stanford University), 35 R, C
Summer College for High School Students (Syracuse University), 169 R
Summer Discovery Pre-College Enrichment Programs, 12 R
Summer Enrichment Program (University of Virginia), 255 R
Summer Gifted Studies Program (The Frances A. Karnes Center for Gifted Studies), 143 R
Summer in Switzerland, 287 R
Summer Intensive Studies, 166 R
Summer Math and Computer Science Camp, 200 C
Summer Math Institute, 239 R
Summer of Excellence, A, 22 R
Summer Program for Academically Talented Youth, 142 R
Summer Program for Research Interns, 222 R, C
Summer Programs for High School Students (University of Chicago), 84 R, C
Summer Regional Governor's Schools (VA), 253 R, C
Summer Residential Governor's Schools (VA), 253 R
Summer Scholar Program (University of Miami), 58 R
Summer Scholars (University of Minnesota), 138 R
Summer Scholars (Washington and Lee University), 257 R
Summer Scholars Program (Furman University), 221 R
Summer Scholars Residential Program (University of Louisiana at Lafayette), 104 R
Summer School for Grades 8-12 (Rice University), 242 C

Summer Science Programs (The Science House), 188 R, C
Summer Science, Engineering, and Architecture Enrichment Program, 217 R
Summer Seminar Program (Marie Walsh Sharpe Art Foundation, The), 40 R
Summer Ventures in Science and Mathematics, 181 R
Summer Writing Program (Carleton College), 138 R
SummerMath, 126 R
SUMMERSCAPE, 148 R, C
SuperCamp, 13 R
TAG—Talented & Gifted Distinguished Achievement Summer Program, 241 R
Talented and Gifted (TAG) (Southern Methodist University), 234 R
Tampa Preparatory School, 69 C
TASIS Schools and Summer Programs in Europe, 288 R
TIP Field Studies Programs, 182 R
TIP Global Dialogues: International Politics & Law, 182 R
TIP Leadership Institute, 184 R
TIP PreCollege Program, 184 R
TIP Summer Studies Programs, 186 R
Tufts Summer Study, 123 C
UConnMentor Connection, 48 R
University for Young People, 248 C
VAMPY—Summer Program for Verbally and Mathematically Precocious Youth, 98 R
Vanderbilt Program for Talented Youth, 230 R
Wesleyan Summer Gifted Program, 267 R
Wilderness Education Institute Programs, 41 R
WISE Academic Camp, 198 R
Women in Engineering Summer Camp, 194 R
Women in Engineering, 134 R
World of Wonder, 86 R
Young Scholars Program (Gould Academy), 106 R, C
Young Writers Workshop, 121 R
Youth Adventure Program , 236 R
Youth Programs (Western Washington University), 264 R, C
Yunasa Summer Institute for the Gifted, 13 R

PROGRAMS THAT GRANT COLLEGE CREDIT

Admiral Farragut Academy, 66
Advanced Academy of Georgia, The, 74
Berkeley Preparatory School, 68
Challenge Program, 204
Educational Programs Overseas, 276
Environmental Studies Summer Youth Program, 165
Episcopal School of Dallas, 237
GAMES—Georgia Academy of Mathematics, Engineering, and Science, 75
Governor's Program for Gifted Children (LA), 104
High School Summer Science Research Fellowship Program (Baylor University), 246
Honors Academy, 235
InnerSpark, 37
Johns Hopkins Summer Pre-College Program, 109
LINK Program, 204
MarineQuest, 189
National Student Leadership Conference, 55
P.R.I.M.E., 228
Pre College Program for High School Students (Skidmore College), 168
Pre-College Program (Pratt Institute), 164
Pre-Collegiate Summer Program in Early American History, 261
Rhodes Summer Writing Institute, 229
Simon's Rock College of Bard, 120
Stanford Discovery Institutes, 36

Summer Art Institute/Summer Theatre Institute, 167
Summer College for High School Students (Stanford University), 35
Summer College for High School Students (Syracuse University), 169
Summer Intensive Studies, 166
Summer Program for Research Interns, 222
Summer Programs for High School Students (University of Chicago), 84
Texas Academy of Leadership in the Humanities, 236

LEADERSHIP, LAW AND POLITICS, BUSINESS PROGRAMS

Those designated with an L offer Leadership Studies; those designated with a P offer Law and Politics Studies; and those programs designated with a B offer Business Studies.

Admiral Farragut Academy, 66 L
Congressional Student Leadership Conference, 8 L, B
Cullowhee Experience, The, 176 L
Deer Hill Expeditions, 38 L
Drury Leadership Academy, 149 L
European Capitals Program, 276 P, B
Honors Symposium, 25 L
Interlocken Center for Experiential Learning, 9 L
Junior Statesmen Summer School, The (Georgetown University), 54 L, P
Junior Statesmen Summer School, The (Northwestern University), 85 L, P
Junior Statesmen Summer School, The (Princeton University), 160 L, P
Junior Statesmen Summer School, The (Stanford University), 34 L, P
Junior Statesmen Summer School, The (Yale University), 46 L, P
Leadership Studies Program, 144 L
National Junior Leaders Conference, 10 L, P, B
National Student Leadership Conference, 55 L, P
Putney Student Travel, 284 L
Road Less Traveled, The, 11 L
SuperCamp, 13 L
TIP Global Dialogues: International Politics and Law, 82 P
TIP Leadership Institute , 84 L
Wilderness Education Institute Programs, 41 L
Winston Churchill in England; Thomas More in England, 289 L
Yunasa Summer Institute for the Gifted, 13 L

VISUAL AND PERFORMING ARTS
CREATIVE WRITING/LITERATURE/JOURNALISM PROGRAMS

Programs designated with a V/P offer Visual and Performing Arts, those designated with a CW offer Creative Writing/Literature/Journalism programs.

Atlanta Workshop Players—"Destiny" Performing Arts Experience, 73 V/P
Arts Alive!, 42 V/P, CW
Buck's Rock Performing and Creative Arts Camp, 46 V/P, CW
CATS SUMMERSTARS: Comprehensive Theatre Workshop, 234 V/P
Center for Creative Youth , 46 V/P, CW
Duke Creative Writers' Workshop, 178 CW
Duke Drama Workshop, The, 179 V/P
Duke Young Writers' Camp, 180 CW
Education Unlimited Summer Learning Adventures, 27 V/P
Firespark, 76 V/P, CW
High School Journalism Institute, 88 CW
Honors Orchestra Program, 133 V/P
Idyllwild Arts Academy, 30 V/P, CW

INDEX 305

InnerSpark, 37 V/P, CW
Interlochen Center for the Arts, 135 V/P
Interlocken Center for Experiential Learning, 9 V/P, CW
ITHAKA Semester in Greece, 280 CW
Midsummer Macon, 77 V/P, CW
New York State Summer School of the Arts, 163 V/P
North Carolina School of the Arts, 190 V/P
Precollege Artist Abroad Program, 282 V/P
Pre-College Program (Pratt Institute), 164 V/P
Pre-College Summer Institute (The University of the Arts), 210 V/P
Rhodes Summer Writing Institute, 229 CW
Sewanee Young Writer's Conference, 231 CW
Shakespeare in Italy; Latin in Rome, 285 CW
Simon's Rock College of Bard, 120 CW
Summer Art Institute, Summer Theatre Institute, 167 V/P
Summer Intensive Studies, 166 V/P
Summer Programs in Provence and Paris, 274 V/P
Summer Seminars Program (Marie Walsh Sharpe Art Foundation, The), 40 V/P
Summer Writing Program (Carleton College), 138 CW
Young Writers Workshop, 121 CW

WILDERNESS/OUTDOOR ADVENTURE PROGRAMS

Adventure Treks, 8
Altamont School, The, 14
Burgundy Center for Wildlife Studies, 268
Camp Broadstone Summer Enrichment Program for Gifted and Talented Youth, 172
Catalina Sea Camp, 29
Cottonwood Gulch Expeditions, 162
Country School Farm, The, 196
Deer Hill Expeditions, 38
Episcopal School of Dallas, 237
Green River Preserve, The, 174
Interlocken Center for Experiential Learning, 9
Mercersburg Academy, 208
Road Less Traveled, The, 11
Science Camp Watonka, 207
Sea Camp, 240
Seacamp, 57
SeaWorld Adventure Camp, 33
SeaWorld/Busch Gardens Adventure Camps (SeaWorld Orlando), 66
SeaWorld/Busch Gardens Adventure Camps (SeaWorld San Antonio), 244
Student Hosteling Program, 12
Summer in Switzerland, 287
Wilderness Education Institute Programs, 41
Young Scholars Program (Gould Academy), 106
Youth Programs (Western Washington University), 264
Yunasa Summer Institute for the Gifted, 13

WEEKEND PROGRAMS

Developing Dimensions Program/Magellan Day School, EPL, 271
Interdisciplinary Creative Problem Solving Conference, 247
Long Island University Center for Gifted Youth, 164
Maine Coast Semester, The, 108
Saturday/Summer Enrichment Programs for Gifted Learners, 262
Sea World/Busch Gardens Adventure Camps (SeaWorld San Antonio), 244
TIP Scholar Weekends, 185

MATH, COMPUTER SCIENCE, AND ENGINEERING PROGRAMS

*Programs designated with a **E** offer Engineering programs, those designated with a **C** offer Computer Science programs, and those designated with an **M** offer Mathematics programs.*

Academy for Creative Engineering/Academy for Legal Thought and Action, 94 E
ACES—Access to Careers in the Sciences, 238 E, C, M
Astronomy Camps, 22 E
Buck's Rock Performing and Creative Arts Camp, 46 C
Camp CAEN, 130 C
DASH, 84 E, C
ECOES—Exploring Career Options in Engineering and Science, 159 E
Education Unlimited Summer Learning Adventures, 27 C
Engineering, Mathematics, and Computer Sciences Summer Institute, 250 E, C, M
Explorations in Engineering, 132 E
Exploring Your Options, 87 E
Illinois Mathematics and Science Academy, 83 M
International Aerospace Academy, The, 201 E
Kidcollege.com Technology Camps, 175 C
MPS Summer Challenge, 43 M
National Computer Camps, 10 C
National Youth Science Camp, 266 C
Pre-College Programs (Carnegie Mellon University), 211 E, C, M
PROMYS, 115 M
Research Science Institute, 116 M
Rocky Mountain Talent Search, 5 E
Ross Mathematics Program, 194 M
Southwest Texas University Honors Summer Math Camp, 245 M
Student Introduction to Engineering, 19 E
Summer Math and Computer Science Camp, 200 C, M
Summer Math Institute, 239 M
Summer Science Programs (The Science House), 188 E, M
Summer Ventures in Science and Mathematics, 181 M
TAG—Talented & Gifted Distinguished Achievement Summer Program, 241 E, C
Women in Engineering Summer Camp, 194 E
Women in Engineering, 134 E
Yunasa Summer Institute for the Gifted, 13 E

LABORATORY/INTERNSHIP PROGRAMS

Interlocken Center for Experiential Learning, 9
Intern Exchange International, Ltd., 278
LSU Youth Programs, 103
Science Motivation Program, 230
Summer Program for Research Interns, 222
Summer Programs for High School Students (University of Chicago), 84
Texas Academy of Leadership in the Humanities, 236

PHYSICAL SCIENCES, LIFE SCIENCES, ECOLOGY/ENVIRONMENTAL SCIENCE PROGRAMS

*Those designated with a **L** offer Life Sciences programs, those designated with a **E** offer Ecology or Environmental Science programs, and those designated with a **P** offer Physical Sciences programs.*

Acadia Institute of Oceanography, 107 L, E, P
ACES—Access to Careers in the Sciences, 238 L, E, P
Adventure Treks, 8 L, E
Astrocamp, 28 P
Astronomy Camps, 22 P
Burgundy Center for Wildlife Studies, 268 L
Catalina Sea Camp, 29 L
DASH, 84 P
Discovery Hall Summer High School Program, 16 E
Duke Action Science Camp for Young Women, 178 L, E , P
ECOES—Exploring Career Options in Engineering and Science, 159P
Explorations in Engineering, 132 P
Future Astronaut Training Program, 96 L, P
Green River Preserve, The, 174 L
Illinois Mathematics and Science Academy, 83 L, P
International Aerospace Academy, The, P
Marine Science Precollege Summer Program, 260 L, E
MarineQuest, 189 L, E
Miss Porter's School Summer Challenge, P
National Youth Science Camp, 266 L, P
Oceanology at Occidental College, 31 L
Oregon Museum of Science and Industry Science Camps, 205 L, P
Research Science Institute, 116 L, P
Science Motivation Program, 230 L
Science: It's a Girl Thing, 242 L, E, P
Sea Camp, 240 L, E
Seacamp, 57 L, E
SeaWorld Adventure Camp, 33 L
SeaWorld/Busch Gardens Adventure Camps (Busch Gardens Tampa Bay), 68 L
SeaWorld/Busch Gardens Adventure Camps (SeaWorld Orlando), 66 L
SeaWorld/Busch Gardens Adventure Camps (SeaWorld San Antonio), 244 L, E
Summer Aviation/Aerospace Programs, 59 P
Summer Scholars (University of Minnesota), 138 L
Summer Science Programs (The Science House), 188 L, E, P
Summer Ventures in Science and Mathematics, 181 L, E
TAG—Talented & Gifted Distinguished Achievement Summer Program, 241 L
Wilderness Education Institute Programs, 41 E
Women in Engineering, 134 P
Yunasa Summer Institute for the Gifted, 13 L

EDUCATIONAL OPPORTUNITY GUIDE
Order the new edition now!

NAME

ADDRESS

CITY　　　　　　　　　　　　STATE　　　　　　ZIP

PHONE

PRICE: $15.00 (INCLUDES SHIPPING AND HANDLING)

NUMBER OF COPIES　　　　　　AMOUNT ENCLOSED

METHOD OF PAYMENT

☐ CHECK OR MONEY ORDER　　　☐ CREDIT CARD (Mastercard and Visa only)

CREDIT CARD #　　　　　　　　　　　　　　EXP. DATE

SIGNATURE (IF PAYING BY CREDIT CARD)

EDITION
(New editions are available in early February)

☐ 2003　　　　　　　　☐ 2004

SEND PAYMENT AND ORDER FORM TO
Educational Opportunity Guide
Duke University Talent Identification Program
1121 West Main Street, Suite 100
Durham, NC 27701
Phone: (919) 683-1400
Fax: (919) 683-1742